The HMO Model and its Application:

Problems with Solutions

Edgar Heilbronner · Hans Bock

The HMO Model and its Application

1
Basis and Manipulation

2
Problems with Solutions

3
Tables of Hückel Molecular Orbitals

Translated by
William Martin
Chemistry Dept., Union College,
Schenectady, N.Y., U.S.A.

Anthony J. Rackstraw
Weinheim, Germany

Edgar Heilbronner · Hans Bock

The HMO Model
and its Application

2
Problems with Solutions

A Wiley–Interscience Publication

John Wiley & Sons, London/New York/Sydney/Toronto

Verlag Chemie, GmbH, Weinheim

First published 1970 © Verlag Chemie, GmbH, Weinheim
under E. Heilbronner and H. Bock, *Das HMO-Modell und seine Anwendung.*

CIP-Kurztitelaufnahme der Deutschen Bibliothek

Heilbronner, Edgar
The HMO model and its application / Edgar Heilbronner; Hans Bock. – London,
New York, Sydney, Toronto: Wiley; Weinheim: Verlag Chemie.
    Einheitssacht.: Das HMO-Modell und seine Anwendung <engl.>.

NE: Bock, Hans:

2. Problems with solutions. – 1976.
    (A Wiley-Interscience publication)
    ISBN 3-527-25655-5 (Verlag Chemie)

English translation © 1976, by Verlag Chemie, GmbH, D-6940 Weinheim.

Library of Congress Cataloging in Publication Data:

Heilbronner, Edgar, 1921–
    The HMO model and its application.

    "A Wiley-Interscience publication."
    Includes index.
    CONTENTS: [1] Basis and manipulation. – 2. Problems with solutions. – 3. Tables
of Hückel molecular orbitals.
    1. Molecular orbitals. I. Bock, Hans, 1928 –   joint author. II. Title.
QD461.H4213   1975   541'.224   75–35539
ISBN 0 471 01473 7 (Wiley)

Composition: Richarz Publikations-Service, D-5205 St. Augustin
Printer: Gebrüder Diesbach, D-6940 Weinheim.
Bookbinder: May & Co., D-6100 Darmstadt
Printed in Germany

lw
9-9-81

Preface

The fundamental considerations presented in the introduction to the first volume led to a tripartite division of this book: Volume 1 contains an introduction to the principles of the HMO method together with all formulae required for practical applications. An integral part of Volume 1 are 250 problems the explicit numerical solutions of which are given in the present Volume 2. They should demonstrate the effectiveness, but also the limitations of HMO models, and prevent the reader, who is strongly urged to at least draft procedures for their solution, from underestimating or overestimating the simplest of all quantum mechanical approximations.

The characteristic HMO data of simple π-electron systems required for solving these problems are listed in Volume 3.

Our thanks are due to all who have assisted in testing the problems and especially to Dr. *H.R. Blattmann*, Dipl.-Phys. *H. Kaiser*, Dipl.-Chem. *W. Schmidt*, and Dr. *P. Seiler*.

E. Heilbronner   E. Bock

Contents

1. Introduction to the Basic Principles of HMO Theory

1.1. The Free Electron

Problem 1.1: Electrons with kinetic energy $E_{kin} \geqq 9.3$ eV are able to ionize benzene molecules:

What wave number $[cm^{-1}]$ must a photon have in order to ionize benzene? Conversely, how many kcal/mol will be released on electron capture by benzene cations?

The ionization potential of benzene is 9.3 eV. The table of conversion factors (Table (1/78), Vol. 1, p. 31) shows a light quantum of energy of 1 eV to exhibit a wave number of 8066 cm^{-1}. Hence 75 000 cm^{-1} ($\lambda = 133$ nm) correspond to 9.3 eV. Moreover, 9.3 eV per molecule or 215 kcal/mol will be liberated on electron capture. $E = -215$ kcal/mol, since the system loses energy .

1.2. The Electron in a 'One-Dimensional Box'

Problem 1.2: Calculate the eigenvalues E_1 to E_6 in eV for an electron in a one-dimensional box of length $L = 12$ Å. (Hint: Use formula (1/6).) How large is the energy difference $E_6 - E_5$ expressed in cm^{-1}?

From the quantum condition $L = n \cdot \Lambda/2$, the periodicity for a length $L = 12$ Å is found to be

$$\Lambda = \frac{2L}{n} = \frac{24}{n} \ [Å].$$

The kinetic energy of the electron in a "one-dimensional box" of length 12 Å follows from formula (1/6) as

$$E_{kin} = \frac{(12.3)^2}{\Lambda^2} = \frac{151}{24^2} \cdot n^2 = E_n.$$

From the general relations

$$E_n = 0.26 \, n^2 \quad [eV]$$
$$E_n = 2100 \, n^2 \quad [cm^{-1}]$$

the following eigenvalues are calculated:

$$E_1 = 0.26 \, eV$$
$$E_2 = 1.0 \ \ eV$$
$$E_3 = 2.3 \ \ eV$$
$$E_4 = 4.2 \ \ eV$$
$$E_5 = 6.5 \ \ eV$$
$$E_6 = 9.4 \ \ eV.$$

The excitation energy from E_5 to E_6 is therefore

$$E_6 - E_5 = 2100 \,(36 - 25) = 23\ 000 \text{ cm}^{-1}.$$

(For comparison, consider decapentaene, 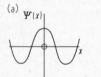 , whose π-system is about $9 \cdot 1.4$ Å $= 12.6$ Å; it has a long wavelength absorption maximum at $30\ 000$ cm^{-1}).

Problem 1.3: One mole of electrons in the systems of Problem 1.2 is in thermal equilibrium with its surroundings at $300°$K. What fraction of the electrons will be found in energy level E_2? (Hint: Neglect populations of higher energy levels and equate the energy difference $E_2 - E_1$ to a free energy change. At $300°$K, changes in the energy difference $E_2 - E_1$ by 1.4 kcal/mol correspond to a 10-fold change in the *Boltzmann* distribution $n_2/n_1 = e^{-(E_2 - E_1)/RT}$.)

According to Problem 1.2, the energy difference between the two eigenvalues is given by $E_n = 0.26\, n^2$ [eV] as

$$E_2 - E_1 = 0.26 \,(4 - 1) = 0.78 \text{ eV} = 18 \text{ kcal/mol}.$$

Since 1.4 kcal/mol at $300\ °$K corresponds to a power of ten in the Boltzmann distribution $n_2/n_1 = \exp[-(E_2 - E_1)/RT]$ the populations of states E_1 and E_2 will differ by $18/1.4 = 13$ powers of ten. This means that at $300\ °$K, only one molecule in $10\ 000\ 000\ 000\ 000$ is in the excited state E_2.

Problem 1.4: Which of the following functions are symmetric and which are antisymmetric with respect to reflection at the origin $x = 0$?

(a) $\Psi(x) = \cos x,$

(b) $\Psi(x) = 1/\sin x,$

(c) $\Psi(x) = (13 + x)(13 - x),$

(d) $\Psi(x) = \sqrt{x},$

(e) $\Psi(x) = e^{-ax^2},$

(f) $\Psi(x) = F(x) \cdot F(-x),$

(g) $\Psi(x) = x^2(4x - 3x^3),$

(h) $\Psi(x) = x^2/\Psi(x).$

(1) The functions (a), (c), (e), and (f) are symmetric:

(f) is a definition of symmetric functions where the symmetry behavior of function $F(x)$ is arbitrary.

(2) Functions (b) and (g) are antisymmetric:

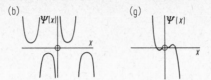

(3) Function (d) is neither symmetric nor antisymmetric:

(4) Function (h) can be either symmetric or antisymmetric; for instance:

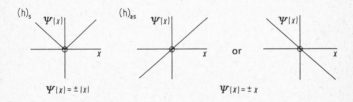

Problem 1.5: The functions below are defined in the interval $x = -a$ and $x = +a$ as follows:

$$F_1(x) = N_1(a^2 - x^2),$$
$$F_2(x) = N_2 x(a^2 - x^2),$$
$$F_3(x) = N_3(a^4 - x^4)$$

and assume the value zero for $x < -a$ and $x > +a$. Calculate the normalization coefficients N_1, N_2, and N_3 for which $\int_{-a}^{+a} F_i^2(x)\, dx = 1$.

(1) $\int_{-\infty}^{+\infty} F_1^2(x)\, dx = \int_{-a}^{+a} N_1^2 (a^2 - x^2)^2\, dx = \int_{-a}^{+a} N_1^2 (a^4 - 2a^2 x^2 + x^4)\, dx$

$$= N_1^2 \left[a^4 x - \frac{2}{3} a^2 x^3 + \frac{1}{5} x^5 \right]_{-a}^{+a}$$

$$= N_1^2\, a^5 \left(2 - \frac{4}{3} + \frac{2}{5} \right) = 1$$

$$N_1 = \sqrt{\frac{15}{16\, a^5}}$$

(2) $\int\limits_{-\infty}^{+\infty} F_2^2\,(x)\,dx = \int\limits_{-a}^{+a} N_2^2\,x^2\,(a^2-x^2)^2\,dx = \int\limits_{-a}^{+a} N_2^2\,(a^4\,x^2 - 2\,a^2\,x^4 + x^6)\,dx$

$\qquad\qquad\qquad\qquad\qquad\qquad = N_2^2\left[\frac{1}{3}a^4\,x^3 - \frac{2}{5}\,a^2\,x^5 + \frac{1}{7}\,x^7\right]_{-a}^{+a}$

$\qquad\qquad\qquad\qquad\qquad\qquad = N_2^2\,a^7\left(\frac{2}{3}-\frac{4}{5}+\frac{2}{7}\right) = 1$

$N_2 = \sqrt{\dfrac{105}{16\,a^7}}$

(3) $\int\limits_{-\infty}^{+\infty} F_3^2\,(x)\,dx = \int\limits_{-a}^{+a} N_3^2\,(a^4-x^4)^2\,dx = \int\limits_{-a}^{+a} N_3^2\,(a^8 - 2\,a^4\,x^4 + x^8)\,dx$

$\qquad\qquad\qquad\qquad\qquad\qquad = N_3^2\left[a^8\,x - \frac{2}{5}\,a^4\,x^5 + \frac{1}{9}\,x^9\right]_{-a}^{+a}$

$\qquad\qquad\qquad\qquad\qquad\qquad = N_3^2\,a^9\left(2-\frac{4}{5}+\frac{2}{9}\right) = 1$

$N_3 = \sqrt{\dfrac{45}{64\,a^9}}$

Problem 1.6: Prove that the functions $F_1(x)$ and $F_2(x)$ of Problem 1.5 are orthogonal.

Substituting functions $F_1(x)$ and $F_2(x)$ in the orthogonality requirement yields:

$\int\limits_{-\infty}^{+\infty} N_1 F_1(x)\cdot N_2 F_2(x)dx = N_1 N_2 \int\limits_{-a}^{+a} (a^2-x^2)\,x\,(a^2-x^2)\,dx$

$\qquad\qquad\qquad\qquad\qquad = N_1 N_2 \int\limits_{-a}^{+a} (a^4 x - 2\,a^2 x^3 + x^5)\,dx$

$\qquad\qquad\qquad\qquad\qquad = N_1 N_2 \left[\frac{1}{2}\,a^4 x^2 - \frac{1}{2}\,a^2 x^4 + \frac{1}{6}\,x^6\right]_{-a}^{+a}$

$\qquad\qquad\qquad\qquad\qquad = N_1 N_2 a^6\left(\frac{1}{2}-\frac{1}{2}+\frac{1}{6}-\frac{1}{2}+\frac{1}{2}-\frac{1}{6}\right) = 0.$

The solution to this problem is trivial, since one can generally show that a symmetric and an antisymmetric eigenfunction are always orthogonal, i.e. the integral

$\int \Psi_s\, F_{as} dx$ is equal to zero.

For this purpose we employ the functions (1/10) and (1/11):

$\qquad\qquad \Psi(x) \quad = \Psi(-x) \qquad\quad \text{(symmetric, } s)$

$\qquad\quad -F(x) \quad = F(-x) \qquad\quad \text{(antisymmetric, } as)$

We find: $\quad \int\limits_{-a}^{+a} \Psi(x)F(x)dx = \int\limits_{-a}^{o} \Psi(x)\,F(x)\,dx + \int\limits_{o}^{+a} \Psi(x)\,F(x)\,dx$

$\qquad\qquad\qquad\qquad\quad = \int\limits_{o}^{+a} \Psi(-x)F(-x)dx + \int\limits_{o}^{+a} \Psi(x)\,F(x)\,dx$

$\qquad\qquad\qquad\qquad\quad = -\int\limits_{o}^{+a} \Psi(x)F(x)dx + \int\limits_{o}^{+a} \Psi(x)\,F(x)\,dx$

$\qquad\qquad\qquad\qquad\quad = 0$

1.3. The Electron in a 'Two-Dimensional Box'

Problem 1.7: An electron is constrained to move in a 'two-dimensional box' of length $L_x = 2L$ and width $L_y = L$. Calculate the orbital energies $E_{n_x n_y}$ in units of $[h^2/32mL^2]$ and draw the energy level diagram for the 10 lowest levels. Formulate the general equation for the orbitals $\Psi_{n_x n_y}(x, y)$ and sketch the functions belonging to the 12 lowest orbital energies in 'two-dimensional boxes' ($L_x = 2L, L_y = L$). Classify the functions with respect to their symmetry behaviour on reflection in the $SE(x)$ and $SE(y)$ planes.

The orbital energies $E_{n_x n_y}$ can be considered to be made up of additive terms E_{n_x} and E_{n_y}:

$$E_{n_x n_y} = E_{n_x} + E_{n_y} = \frac{h^2}{8m(2L)^2} n_x^2 + \frac{h^2}{8m(L)^2} n_y^2$$

$$= \frac{h^2}{32mL^2} (n_x^2 + 4n_y^2) \quad ; \quad (n_x, n_y = 1,2,3, ...)$$

We thus obtain for the 12 lowest orbital energies:

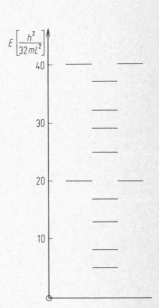

n_x	n_y	$(n_x^2 + 4n_y^2)$	$E_{n_x n_y}$
6	1	40	$E_{23} = E_{61}$
2	3	40	
1	3	37	E_{13}
4	2	32	E_{42}
5	1	29	E_{51}
3	2	25	E_{32}
4	1	20	$E_{22} = E_{41}$
2	2	20	
1	2	17	E_{12}
3	1	13	E_{31}
2	1	8	E_{21}
1	1	5	E_{11}

The set of orbitals of the systems $\Psi_{n_x n_y}(x,y)$ is formed from the orbital sets of the components in the x- and y-directions according to (1/31):

$$\Psi_{n_x n_y}(x,y) = \Psi_{n_x}(x) \cdot \Psi_{n_y}(y) = \sqrt{\frac{1}{L}} \sin\left(\frac{\pi n_x}{2L} x\right) \sqrt{\frac{2}{L}} \sin\left(\frac{\pi n_y}{L} y\right)$$

$$= \frac{\sqrt{2}}{L} \sin\left(\frac{\pi n_x}{2L} x\right) \sin\left(\frac{\pi n_y}{L} y\right)$$

6

The orbitals corresponding to the 12 lowest orbital energies can be classified as follows with respect to reflection in the *SE(x)* and *SE(y)* planes (cf. Chapter I [1.12]):

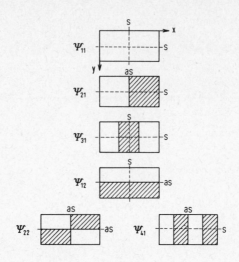

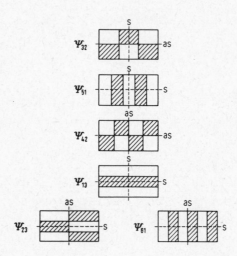

The pairs of functions Ψ_{22}/Ψ_{41} and Ψ_{23}/Ψ_{61} are degenerate, i.e. they correspond to the same orbital energies. In contrast to the model of an electron in a "square box" (Chapter I, [1.13]) it is impossible to interconvert the degenerate functions by symmetry operations. The degeneracy is thus not symmetry conditioned, but accidental, i.e. due to the properties of the model ($L_x = 2L$, $L_y = L$).

Problem 1.8: An electron moves in a cube of edge length L. Calculate the orbital energies $E_{n_x n_y n_z}$ for the five lowest energy levels in units of $[h^2/8mL^2]$ and arrange them in the corresponding energy level diagram. Formulate the general equation for the orbitals $\Psi_{n_x n_y n_z}(x, y, z)$ and sketch the functions belonging to the 11 lowest orbital energies in cubes of edge lengths L. Classify the functions according to their symmetry behaviour on reflection in the $SE(xy)$, $SE(xz)$, and $SE(yz)$ planes.

The orbital energies for motion of an electron in a cube of edge length L follow from the equation:

$$E_{n_x n_y n_z} = \frac{h^2}{8mL^2} \ (n_x^2 + n_y^2 + n_z^2) \ ; \ (n_x, n_y, n_z = 1, 2, 3, \ldots)$$

We obtain for the 11 lowest orbital energies:

$E\left[\dfrac{h^2}{8mL^2}\right]$

n_x	n_y	n_z	$(n_x^2 + n_y^2 + n_z^2)$	$E_{n_x n_y n_z}$
2	2	2	12	E_{222}
3	1	1	11 ⎫	
1	3	1	11 ⎬	$E_{113} = E_{131} = E_{311}$
1	1	3	11 ⎭	
2	2	1	9 ⎫	
2	1	2	9 ⎬	$E_{122} = E_{212} = E_{221}$
1	2	2	9 ⎭	
2	1	1	6 ⎫	
1	2	1	6 ⎬	$E_{122} = E_{121} = E_{211}$
1	1	2	6 ⎭	
1	1	1	3	E_{111}

The associated orbitals are

$$\Psi_{n_x n_y n_z}(x, y, z) = \left(\frac{2}{L}\right)^{\frac{3}{2}} \sin\left(\frac{\pi n_x}{L} x\right) \sin\left(\frac{\pi n_y}{L} y\right) \sin\left(\frac{\pi n_z}{L} z\right)$$

The orbitals belonging to the 11 lowest energies can be classified with respect to reflection in planes $SE(xy)$, $SE(xz)$, and $SE(yz)$ as follows:

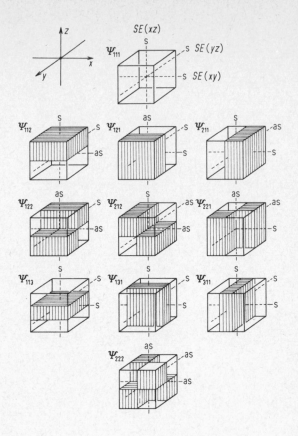

1.4. The Aufbau Principle

Problem 1.9:   Consider the following systems:
(a) 1 free electron,
(b) 8 electrons in a 'one-dimensional box',
(c) 9 electrons in a 'two-dimensional square box',
(d) 10 electrons in a 'two-dimensional box' of length $L_x = 2L$, and $L_y = L$ (Problem 1.7),
(e) 11 electrons in a 'three-dimensional cubic box' of edge length L (Problem 1.8).
Which of these systems has a singlet, and which a multiplet ground state? What are the multiplicities?

(a) 1 free electron corresponds to a doublet state of multiplicity $M = 2$.
(b) through (e) have the following ground states and multiplicities where E is given in units of $[h^2/8mL^2]$:

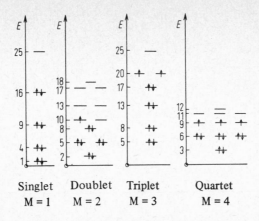

Singlet   Doublet   Triplet   Quartet
M = 1   M = 2   M = 3   M = 4

Problem 1.10: What is the total energy E_G in kcal/mol for a system of 6 electrons in a 'one-dimensional box' of length $L = 8.4\,\text{Å}$ with occupation numbers $b_1 = b_2 = b_3 = 2$?

The total energy E_G is calculated from the individual energies of the electrons according to equation (1/44):

$$E_G = \sum_n b_n E_n = \frac{h^2}{8mL^2}(2\cdot 1 + 2\cdot 4 + 2\cdot 9) = \frac{h^2}{8mL^2}\cdot 28.$$

For calculation in kcal/mol we need the box constant K:

$$K = \frac{h^2}{8mL^2} = \frac{(6.63\cdot 10^{-34})^2}{8\cdot 9.1\cdot 10^{-31}(8.4\cdot 10^{-10})^2} = 8.5\cdot 10^{-20}\ \text{Joule}$$

$$= 12.3\ \text{kcal/mol}$$

(For another calculation of the box constant, see Problem 1.2.) The energy of the 6-electron system in the ground state is therefore given by

$$E_G = 28\,K = 344\ \text{kcal/mol.}$$

The box length of $L = 8.4$ Å was chosen so that the model resembles the hexatriene molecule:

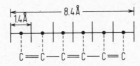

To a first approximation it can generally be shown that the total energy E_G of straight chain systems with many electrons increases linearly with the number of

10

electrons. The demonstration begins by considering a "one-dimensional box" of length $L = N \cdot l$ which contains exactly N electrons in the ground state. According to (1/8) and (1/44) the total energy is then

$$E_G = \sum_n b_n E_n = \sum_n b_n \cdot \frac{h^2}{8m L^2} n^2 \quad ,$$

and thus for the problem at hand:

$$E_G = \sum_{n=1}^{N/2} 2 \cdot \frac{h^2}{8m (N \cdot l)^2} (n)^2$$

$$= \frac{h^2}{4m\, l^2} \cdot \frac{1}{N^2} \left[(1)^2 + (2)^2 + \ldots \left(\frac{N}{2}\right)^2 \right]$$

$$= \frac{h^2}{4m\, l^2} \cdot \frac{1}{N^2} \frac{\frac{N}{2}\left(\frac{N}{2}+1\right)\left(\frac{2N}{2}+1\right)}{6}$$

$$= \frac{h^2}{96m\, l^2} \cdot \frac{(N^2 + 3N + 2)}{N}$$

For large values of N, i.e. in straight chain systems of many electrons, the total energy is directly proportional to N in a first approximation.

$$E_G \propto N$$

Problem 1.11: A compound shows the following electronic spectrum:

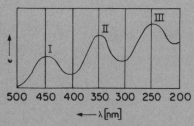

How many eV (and correspondingly, kcal/mol and cm^{-1}) do the excited states corresponding to the bands I, II, and III lie above the ground state? What colour is expected for the compound?

With the aid of Table (1/78), Vol. 1, p. 31, the following table of values can be drawn up:

Absorption	nm	cm^{-1}	Excitation energy eV	kcal/mol
I	450	22 200	2.8	64
II	350	28 600	3.5	82
III	250	40 000	5.0	114

Only the longest wavelength absorption I with its tailing-off into the visible region is responsible for the color. Since the compound absorbs in the violet and blue portion of the visible spectrum, it is predicted to have the complementary color orange.

Problem 1.12: Six electrons occupy the three lowest orbitals ($b_{11} = b_{12} = b_{21} = 2$) of a 'square box' of edge length L. At what positions (x', y') is the total electron density Q a maximum?

The orbital of an electron in a "square box" is

$$\Psi_{n_x n_y}(x,y) = \frac{2}{L} \sin\left(\frac{\pi n_x}{L} x\right) \sin\left(\frac{\pi n_y}{L} y\right) \tag{1/34}$$

The total electron density $Q(x, y)$ for 6 electrons is obtained analogously to (1/49) if the three lowest energy levels are each occupied by two electrons:

$$Q(x, y) = e \cdot \sum_{n_x} \sum_{n_y} b_{n_x} b_{n_y} \Psi^2_{n_x n_y}(x, y)$$

$$= \frac{8e}{L^2}\left[\sin^2\left(\frac{\pi}{L} x\right) \sin^2\left(\frac{\pi}{L} y\right) + \sin^2\left(\frac{2\pi}{L} x\right) \sin^2\left(\frac{\pi}{L} y\right) \right.$$
$$\left. + \sin^2\left(\frac{\pi}{L} x\right) \sin^2\left(\frac{2\pi}{L} y\right) \right]$$

For the total electron density $Q(x, y)$ at points $(x/L, y/L)$, the above equation yields the following table of values (in units of $[-8 \, e/L^2]$):

$\dfrac{x}{L}$	$\dfrac{y}{L}$	$\sin^2\left(\dfrac{\pi}{L}x\right)\cdot\sin^2\left(\dfrac{\pi}{L}y\right)$			$\sin^2\left(\dfrac{2\pi}{L}x\right)\cdot\sin^2\left(\dfrac{\pi}{L}y\right)$			$\sin^2\left(\dfrac{\pi}{L}x\right)\cdot\sin^2\left(\dfrac{2\pi}{L}y\right)$			Σ
0	0	0	$\cdot$ 0	= 0	0	$\cdot$ 0	= 0	0	$\cdot$ 0	= 0	0
0	$\frac{1}{8}$	0		= 0	0		= 0	0	$\cdot\frac{1}{2}$	= 0	0
0	$\frac{1}{4}$	0	$\cdot\frac{1}{2}$	= 0	0	$\cdot\frac{1}{2}$	= 0	0	$\cdot$ 1	= 0	0
0	$\frac{3}{8}$	0		= 0	0		= 0	0	$\cdot\frac{1}{2}$	= 0	0
0	$\frac{1}{2}$	0	$\cdot$ 1	= 0	0	$\cdot$ 1	= 0	0	$\cdot$ 0	= 0	0
$\frac{1}{8}$	$\frac{1}{8}$	0.1465 $\cdot$ 0.1465		= 0.0215	$\frac{1}{2}$ $\cdot$ 0.1465		= 0.0733	0.1465 $\cdot\frac{1}{2}$		= 0.0733	0.1680
$\frac{1}{8}$	$\frac{1}{4}$	0.1465 $\cdot\frac{1}{2}$		= 0.0733	$\frac{1}{2}$ $\cdot\frac{1}{2}$		= 0.25	0.1465 $\cdot$ 1		= 0.1465	0.4698
$\frac{1}{8}$	$\frac{3}{8}$	0.1465 $\cdot$ 0.8536		= 0.1251	$\frac{1}{2}$ $\cdot$ 0.8536		= 0.4268	0.1465 $\cdot\frac{1}{2}$		= 0.0733	0.6252
$\frac{1}{8}$	$\frac{1}{2}$	0.1465 $\cdot$ 1		= 0.1465	$\frac{1}{2}$ $\cdot$ 1		= 0.5	0.1465 $\cdot$ 0		= 0	0.6465
$\frac{1}{4}$	$\frac{1}{8}$	$\frac{1}{2}$ $\cdot$ 0.1465		= 0.0733	1 $\cdot$ 0.1465		= 0.1465	$\frac{1}{2}$ $\cdot\frac{1}{2}$		= 0.25	0.4698
$\frac{1}{4}$	$\frac{1}{4}$	$\frac{1}{2}$ $\cdot\frac{1}{2}$		= 0.25	1 $\cdot\frac{1}{2}$		= 0.5	$\frac{1}{2}$ $\cdot$ 1		= 0.5	1.2500
$\frac{1}{4}$	$\frac{3}{8}$	$\frac{1}{2}$ $\cdot$ 0.8536		= 0.4268	1 $\cdot$ 0.8536		= 0.8536	$\frac{1}{2}$ $\cdot\frac{1}{2}$		= 0.25	1.5304
$\frac{1}{4}$	$\frac{1}{2}$	$\frac{1}{2}$ $\cdot$ 1		= 0.5	1 $\cdot$ 1		= 1	$\frac{1}{2}$ $\cdot$ 0		= 0	1.5000
$\frac{3}{8}$	$\frac{1}{8}$	0.8536 $\cdot$ 0.1465		= 0.1251	$\frac{1}{2}$ $\cdot$ 0.1465		= 0.0733	0.8536 $\cdot\frac{1}{2}$		= 0.4268	0.6252
$\frac{3}{8}$	$\frac{1}{4}$	0.8536 $\cdot\frac{1}{2}$		= 0.4268	$\frac{1}{2}$ $\cdot\frac{1}{2}$		= 0.25	0.8536 $\cdot$ 1		= 0.8536	1.5304
$\frac{3}{8}$	$\frac{3}{8}$	0.8536 $\cdot$ 0.8536		= 0.7286	$\frac{1}{2}$ $\cdot$ 0.8536		= 0.4268	0.8536 $\cdot\frac{1}{2}$		= 0.4268	1.5822
$\frac{3}{8}$	$\frac{1}{2}$	0.8536 $\cdot$ 1		= 0.8536	$\frac{1}{2}$ $\cdot$ 1		= 0.5	0.8536 $\cdot$ 0		= 0	1.3536
$\frac{1}{2}$	$\frac{1}{8}$	1 $\cdot$ 0.1465		= 0.1465	0 $\cdot$ 0.1465		= 0	1 $\cdot\frac{1}{2}$		= 0.5	0.6465
$\frac{1}{2}$	$\frac{1}{4}$	1 $\cdot\frac{1}{2}$		= 0.5	0 $\cdot\frac{1}{2}$		= 0	1 $\cdot$ 1		= 1	1.5000
$\frac{1}{2}$	$\frac{3}{8}$	1 $\cdot$ 0.8536		= 0.8536	0 $\cdot$ 0.8536		= 0	1 $\cdot\frac{1}{2}$		= 0.5	1.3536
$\frac{1}{2}$	$\frac{1}{2}$	1 $\cdot$ 1		= 1	0 $\cdot$ 1		= 0	1 $\cdot$ 0		= 0	1.0000

Plotting the electron densities as a profile parallel to the xz plane shows that the maximum lies close to $x = y = 1/3$:

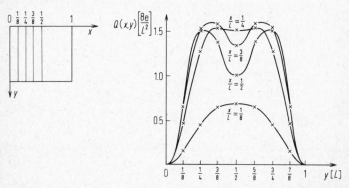

A second solution of this problem consists in analytical determination of the maximum. Since the system has four-fold symmetry, it will suffice to calculate the electron density along the main diagonal. For this purpose we put $x = y$, whereupon $Q(x, y)$ becomes a function of only one parameter:

$$Q(x) = \frac{8e}{L^2} \left[\sin^4 \left(\frac{\pi}{L} x \right) + 4 \sin^2 \left(\frac{\pi}{L} x \right) \cos^2 \left(\frac{\pi}{L} x \right) \sin^2 \left(\frac{\pi}{L} x \right) \right.$$
$$\left. + 4 \sin^2 \left(\frac{\pi}{L} x \right) \sin^2 \left(\frac{\pi}{L} x \right) \cos^2 \left(\frac{\pi}{L} x \right) \right]$$
$$= \frac{8e}{L^2} \left[\sin^4 \left(\frac{\pi}{L} x \right) \cdot \left(1 + 8 \cos^2 \left(\frac{\pi}{L} x \right) \right) \right]$$

Differentiation with respect to x gives:

$$\frac{dQ(x)}{dx} = \frac{8e}{L^2} \left[4 \frac{\pi}{L} \sin^3 \left(\frac{\pi}{L} x \right) \cdot \cos \left(\frac{\pi}{L} x \right) \cdot \left(1 + 8 \cos^2 \left(\frac{\pi}{L} x \right) \right) \right.$$
$$\left. + \sin^4 \left(\frac{\pi}{L} x \right) \cdot 8 \cdot 2 \frac{\pi}{L} \cos \left(\frac{\pi}{L} x \right) \cdot \left(- \sin \left(\frac{\pi}{L} x \right) \right) \right]$$
$$= \frac{96 e \pi}{L^3} \left[\sin^3 \left(\frac{\pi}{L} x \right) \cdot \cos \left(\frac{\pi}{L} x \right) \cdot \left(3 - 4 \sin^2 \left(\frac{\pi}{L} x \right) \right) \right]$$

Equating the derivative to zero affords the maxima and minima:

$$\sin^3 \left(\frac{\pi}{L} x \right) = 0 \quad ; \quad \frac{x}{L} = 0 \text{ and } 1$$
$$\cos \left(\frac{\pi}{L} x \right) = 0 \quad ; \quad \frac{x}{L} = \frac{1}{2}$$
$$3 - 4 \sin^2 \left(\frac{\pi}{L} x \right) = 0 \quad ; \quad \frac{x}{L} = \frac{1}{3} \text{ and } \frac{2}{3}$$

The electron density $Q(x, y)$ thus assumes a maximum value for the following pairs of coordinates (x, y):

$$\left(\frac{1}{3}, \frac{1}{3} \right) ; \left(\frac{1}{3}, \frac{2}{3} \right) ; \left(\frac{2}{3}, \frac{1}{3} \right) ; \left(\frac{2}{3}, \frac{2}{3} \right) .$$

1.5. Box Models with Many Independent Electrons

Electron Distribution in Linear π-Electron Systems

Problem 1.13: Show that in a box model with dimensions $L_x = N \cdot l$ and $L_y = L_z = l$ all orbital energies which belong to the quantum numbers $n_x < \sqrt{3}N$ and $n_y = n_z = 1$ are smaller than all orbital energies with $n_y > 1$ and/or $n_z > 1$. Discuss the consequences for systems of the above geometry which contain N or $2N$ electrons.

It is required that

$$E_{n\,11} \leqslant E_{121} = E_{112}.$$

The orbital energies are (cf. Problem 1.8):

$$E_{n_x n_y n_z} = \frac{h^2}{8m} \left[\left(\frac{n_x}{N \cdot l} \right)^2 + \left(\frac{n_y}{l} \right)^2 + \left(\frac{n_z}{l} \right)^2 \right]$$

Substitution affords:

$$\frac{h^2}{8ml^2} \left[\left(\frac{n_x}{N} \right)^2 + 1 + 1 \right] \leqslant \frac{h^2}{8ml^2} \left[\left(\frac{1}{N} \right)^2 + 4 + 1 \right]$$

$$\frac{n_x{}^2}{N^2} \leqslant \frac{1}{N^2} + 3$$

$$n_x{}^2 \leqslant 1 + 3N^2$$

An approximation for $N \geqslant 2$ is

$$n_x \leqslant N\sqrt{3}.$$

With 1 electron/l^3 (i.e. a total of N electrons) only $N/2$ energy levels are doubly occupied in the ground state, whereas for 2 electrons/l^3 (i.e. a total of $2N$ electrons) the number of filled levels is N. However, since $A < N\sqrt{3}$ energy levels of the system (where A is an integer) are determined solely by the quantum number n_x, it is permissible to use a "one-dimensional model" for the ground state and also for at least the lowest $A - N/2$, or $A - N$ respectively, excited states.

Problem 1.14: Calculate the electron distribution of the hexatriene molecule in its first excited state ($b_1 = b_2 = 2$; $b_3 = b_4 = 1$). What suggestions are forthcoming from the box model with respect to a light-induced *cis-trans* isomerization of hexatriene?

According to (1/49) the total electron density $Q(x)$ is:

$$Q(x) = e \left[2 \cdot \frac{2}{L} \sin^2 \left(\frac{\pi}{L} x \right) + 2 \cdot \frac{2}{L} \sin^2 \left(\frac{2\pi}{L} x \right) + \frac{2}{L} \sin^2 \left(\frac{3\pi}{L} x \right) + \frac{2}{L} \sin^2 \left(\frac{4\pi}{L} x \right) \right]$$

$$= \frac{4e}{L} \left[\sin^2 \left(\frac{\pi}{L} x \right) + \sin^2 \left(\frac{2\pi}{L} x \right) + \frac{1}{2} \sin^2 \left(\frac{3\pi}{L} x \right) + \frac{1}{2} \sin^2 \left(\frac{4\pi}{L} x \right) \right].$$

Hence the following table of values can be drawn up:

x/L	$\sin^2\left(\dfrac{\pi}{L}x\right)$	$\sin^2\left(\dfrac{2\pi}{L}x\right)$	$\dfrac{1}{2}\sin^2\left(\dfrac{3\pi}{L}x\right)$	$\dfrac{1}{2}\sin^2\left(\dfrac{4\pi}{L}x\right)$	Σ
0; 1	0.00	0.00	0.00	0.00	0.00
1/10; 9/10	0.10	0.35	0.33	0.45	1.23
1/6; 5/6	0.25	0.75	0.50	0.38	1.88
1/5; 4/5	0.35	0.90	0.45	0.17	1.87
1/4; 3/4	0.50	1.00	0.25	0.00	1.75
2/7; 5/7	0.61	0.95	0.09	0.09	1.74
1/3; 2/3	0.75	0.75	0.00	0.38	1.88
2/5; 3/5	0.90	0.35	0.17	0.45	1.87
1/2	1.00	0.00	0.50	0.00	1.50

Comparison of the ground state (– – – –) with the excited state (———) reveals that the excited state electron density is lower than that in the ground state in the central double bond (i.e. between positions 3 and 4) of the hexatriene model.

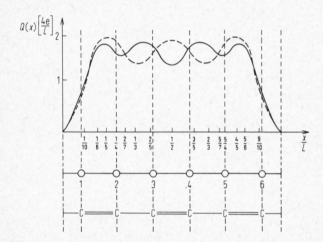

Thus the box model suggests that a cis-trans isomerization should be significantly facilitated in electronically excited hexatriene due to the weakening of the double bond between carbons C_3 and C_4.

Light-induced *cis-trans* isomerizations of polyenes have been demonstrated experimentally.

Differences between Linear and Cyclic π-Electron Systems

Problem 1.15: Calculate the total energy E_G for ring systems of perimeter $L = Z_\pi \cdot l$ with Z_π electrons, in which Z_π obeys the *Hückel* rule. How large is E_G in kcal/mol for $Z_\pi = 6$?

According to (1/44) and (1/54) the total energy of a cyclic π-system is

$$E_G = \sum_n b_n E_n = \frac{h^2}{8mL^2} \sum_n b_n (2n)^2 : (n = 0, \pm 1, \pm 2 \ldots).$$

In the present case, $E_0 = 0$ when $n = 0$, and b_n is always 2. For $|n| \ll N$ we have:

$$E_G = \frac{h^2}{8mL^2} 2 \cdot 2 \cdot 4 \sum_{n=1}^{n=N} n^2$$

$$= \frac{2h^2}{mL^2} \frac{N(N+1)(2N+1)}{6} = \frac{h^2}{3mL^2} N(N+1)(2N+1).$$

In this expression, N obeys the *Hückel* rule $Z_\pi = 2 + 4N$. With $N = (Z_\pi - 2)/4$, the general equation for the total energy of a ring system with Z_π electrons and a circumference of $L = Z_\pi \cdot l$ is:

$$E_G = \frac{h^2}{96ml^2} \frac{(Z_\pi^2 - 4)}{Z_\pi}$$

When $l = 1.4$ Å the value of the constant is

$$\frac{h^2}{96ml^2} = \frac{(6.63 \cdot 10^{-27})^2}{96 \cdot 9.1 \cdot 10^{-28} \cdot (1.4 \cdot 10^{-8})^2} = 0.256 \cdot 10^{-11} \text{ erg}$$

$$= 36.9 \text{ kcal/mol}.$$

and a total energy $E_G = 197$ kcal/mol^{-1} is obtained for a cyclic system of $Z_\pi = 6$ electrons.

Problem 1.16: Compare the localization energies for a pair of electrons in the following 'one-dimensional box' models with $Z_\pi = 6$ in each case:
(a) at the end of a chain of length $L = Z_\pi \cdot l$,
(b) at the centre of the chain,
(c) in a ring of the same circumference.

According to (1/8) and (1/44) the total energy E_K of electrons in a "one-dimensional box" of length $L = Z_\pi \cdot l$ for even values of Z_π is

$$E_K = \frac{h^2}{8ml^2 \, Z_\pi^2} \, \sum_n b_n \, n^2 = \frac{2K}{Z_\pi^2} \, \sum_n n^2 \; ; \quad \left(K = \frac{h^2}{8ml^2} \right) ; (n=1,2,\dots, Z_\pi/2)$$

and for $Z_\pi = 6$

$$E_K \, (6) = \frac{2K}{36} \, (1 + 4 + 9) = 0.777 \, K.$$

The total energy E_R of a corresponding circular model of circumference $L = Z_\pi \cdot l$ in which Z_π obeys the *Hückel* rule is calculated from (1/44) and (1/54) as

$$E_R = \frac{h^2}{8ml^2 \, Z_\pi^2} \, \sum_n b_n \, (2n)^2 = \frac{2K}{Z_\pi^2} \, \sum_n (2n)^2 \, ; (n=0,\pm,1,\dots,\pm(Z_\pi-2)/4)$$

and for $Z_\pi = 6$

$$E_R \, (6) = \frac{2K}{36} \, (0 + 4 + 4) = 0.444 \, K.$$

(a) The total energy $E_K(a)$ for a chain with two electrons localized at its end is obtained as

$$E_K(a) = 2K + \frac{2K}{25} \, (1 + 4) = 2.400 K$$

and the localization energy $E_L(a)$ is thus

$$E_L \, (a) = E_K \, (a) - E_K \, (6) = 1.623 \, K.$$

(b) The total energy $E_K(b)$ for a chain with two electrons localized its middle is approximated by

$$E_K \, (b) = 2K + \frac{2K}{4} \, (1) + \frac{2K}{9} \, (1) = 2.722 \, K$$

and the localization energy is

$$E_L \, (b) = E_K \, (b) - E_K \, (6) = 1.945 \, K.$$

(c) The total energy $E_R(c)$ for a ring with two localized electrons corresponds to the total energy $E_K(a) = 2.400$ K, and the delocalization energy $E_L(c)$ is thus

$$E_L (c) = E_K (a) - E_R (6) = 1.956 \; K.$$

A comparison of localization energies of box models (a), (b), and (c) confirms the observation that electrophilic attack is generally easier for linear π-systems than for cyclic π-systems, and occurs preferentially at the ends of the chains.

Electron Excitation in Linear π-Electron Systems

Problem 1.17: For the series of cyanines and oxonols below, the following absorption maxima have been determined experimentally:

n	$\tilde{v}_m^{exp}(R_2\overset{\oplus}{N}{=}{-}({=})_n{-}NR_2)$	$\tilde{v}_m^{exp}(O{=}{-}({=})_n{-}\overset{\ominus}{O})\,[cm^{-1}]$
1	32 000	37 400
2	24 000	27 600
3	19 300	22 000
4	16 000	18 300

For each one, calculate the correction L_{corr} of the box lengths $L = (N - 1)l + L_{corr}$ (where $l = 1.4$ Å) which yields an optimal fit of the calculated excitation energies (1/63) to the experimental data.

From (1/63) the relation between the excitation energies $\triangle E[cm^{-1}]$ and the length L of the π-system is

$$L^2 = \frac{h^2}{8m} \cdot \frac{Z_\pi + 1}{\triangle E}$$

With $L = N_{corr} \cdot l$, the following relation is found to hold for the 'true' number of centers N_{corr}

$$N_{corr}^2 = \frac{h^2}{8ml^2} \cdot \frac{Z_\pi + 1}{\triangle E} = 1.5477 \cdot 10^5 \, \frac{Z_\pi + 1}{\triangle E} \; ,$$

from which the length correction may be calculated according to (1/66) as:

$$L_{corr} = [N_{corr} - (N - 1)]\, l$$

A considerable correction is needed for the cyanines as shown in the appended table:

n	N	Z_π	N_{corr}	L_{corr}
1	5	6	5.819	$1.819\, l$
2	7	8	7.618	$1.618\, l$
3	9	10	9.392	$1.392\, l$
4	11	12	11.214	$1.214\, l$

The average correction $\bar{L}_{corr} = 1.511\, l$ deviates only slightly from the individual values, and may be used as an approximation for all the cyanines.

The length corrections needed for the oxonols are smaller but show a particularly large systematic change:

n	N	Z_π	N_{corr}	L_{corr}
1	5	6	5.382	$1.382\, l$
2	7	8	7.104	$1.104\, l$
3	9	10	8.797	$0.797\, l$
4	11	12	10.486	$0.486\, l$

The scatter about the average correction $\bar{L}_{corr} = 0.942\, l$ is greater than for the cyanines. The correction applies to both ends in each case, and the calculated values show that the π-system of a linear chain extends beyond the terminal centers by about 1/2 to 2/3 of a bond length

1.6. Correlation Diagrams

Problem. 1.18: For the correlation diagram [1.26], let the deformation parameter be $m = L_x/L_y$ with the restricting condition $L_xL_y = 4l^2$. In addition to the previously determined eigenvalues for $m = 1$ and $m = 4$, calculate those for $m = 2$ and $m = 3$, and sketch the actual shape of the correlation lines.

The eigenvalues of the electrons for the various values of the deformation parameters are:

$$m = 1 : \quad E_{n_x n_y} = \frac{h^2}{32ml^2}\ (n_x^2 + n_y^2)$$

$$m = 2 : \quad E_{n_x n_y} = \frac{h^2}{32ml^2}\ \left(2n_x^2 + \frac{n_y^2}{2}\right)$$

$$m = 3 : \quad E_{n_x n_y} = \frac{h^2}{32ml^2}\ \left(3n_x^2 + \frac{n_y^2}{3}\right)$$

$$m = 4 : \quad E_{n_x n_y} = \frac{h^2}{32ml^2}\ \left(4n_x^2 + \frac{n_y^2}{4}\right)$$

There results the following table of values for $E_{n_x n_y}$ in units of $[h^2/32\,ml^2]$:

n_x	n_y	$m = 1$	$m = 2$	$m = 3$	$m = 4$
5	1	26	50.50	75.33	100.25
1	5	26	14.50	11.33	10.25
4	3	25	36.50	51.00	66.25
3	4	25	26.00	32.33	40.00
4	2	20	34.00	49.33	65.00
2	4	20	16.00	17.33	20.00
3	3	18	22.50	30.00	38.25
4	1	17	32.50	48.33	64.25
1	4	17	10.00	8.33	8.00
3	2	13	20.00	28.33	37.00
2	3	13	12.50	15.00	18.25
3	1	10	18.50	27.33	36.25
1	3	10	6.50	6.00	6.25
2	2	8	10.00	13.33	17.00
2	1	5	8.50	12.33	16.25
1	2	5	4.00	4.33	5.00
1	1	2	2.50	3.33	4.25

Graphic representation of these values yields a correlation diagram:

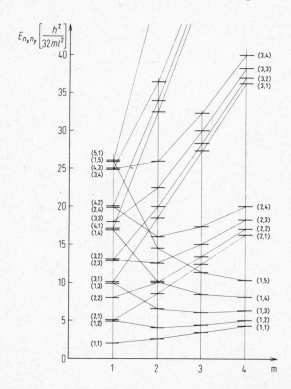

Problem 1.19: Determine the symmetry behaviour of the following configurations:
(a) of the ground state and the first two excited states of 6 electrons in a 'linear box';
(b) of the ground state and the first two excited states of 8 electrons in a 'square box';
(c) of the ground state and the first nine singly excited states of 2 electrons in a 'cube'.

(a) In the energy level diagram of a "one dimensional box", the following energy levels are occupied (E_n in units of $[h^2/8mL^2]$):

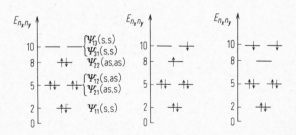

Depending upon the occupation of molecular orbitals, these configurations are found to have the following symmetry types:

$(\Psi_1)^2 \ (\Psi_2)^2 \ (\Psi_3)^2$ \qquad $(\Psi_1)^2 \ (\Psi_2)^2 \ (\Psi_3)^1 \ (\Psi_4)^1$ \qquad $(\Psi_1)^2 \ (\Psi_2)^1 \ (\Psi_3)^2 \ (\Psi_4)^1$

$(s \ \dot\times \ s \ \dot\times \ as \ \dot\times \ as \ \dot\times \ s \ \dot\times \ s) \Rightarrow s$ \qquad $(s \ \dot\times \ s \ \dot\times \ as \ \dot\times \ as \ \dot\times \ s \ \dot\times \ as) \Rightarrow as$ \qquad $(s \ \dot\times \ s \ \dot\times \ as \ \dot\times \ s \ \dot\times \ s \ \dot\times \ as) \Rightarrow s$

(b) In the energy level diagram of the "square box", the following energy levels are occupied ($E_{n_x n_y}$ in units of $[h^2/8mL^2]$):

Depending upon the occupation of the individual molecular orbitals, the ground state configuration and the first and second excited states are found to have the following symmetry types (only the singly occupied orbitals are considered):

$$(\Psi_{11})^2 \ (\Psi_{12})^2 \ (\Psi_{21})^2 \ (\Psi_{22})^2$$
$$(s, s)$$

$$(\Psi_{11})^2 \ (\Psi_{12})^2 \ (\Psi_{21})^2 \ (\Psi_{22})^1 \ (\Psi_{13})^1$$
$$(as \ \dot\times \ s, \ as \ \dot\times \ s) \Rightarrow (as, \ as)$$

$$(\Psi_{11})^2 \ (\Psi_{12})^2 \ (\Psi_{21})^2 \ (\Psi_{13})^1 \ (\Psi_{31})^1$$
$$(s \ \dot\times \ s, \ s \ \dot\times \ s) \Rightarrow (s, \ s)$$

(c) From the energy level diagram of the three dimensional box (with $E_{n_x n_y n_z}$ in units of $[h^2/8mL^2]$)

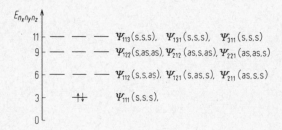

the symmetry type of the ground state results as

$$(\Psi_{111})^2 \ (s, \ s, \ s)$$

Promotion of an electron into the triply degenerate orbitals yields the first nine excited states which exhibit the following symmetry types on occupation:

$$(\Psi_{111})^1 \ (\Psi_{112})^1 \qquad (\Psi_{111})^1 \ (\Psi_{121})^1 \qquad (\Psi_{111})^1 \ (\Psi_{211})^1$$
$$(s, \ s, \ as) \qquad\qquad (s, \ as, \ s) \qquad\qquad (as, \ s, \ s)$$
$$(\Psi_{111})^1 \ (\Psi_{122})^1 \qquad (\Psi_{111})^1 \ (\Psi_{212})^1 \qquad (\Psi_{111})^1 \ (\Psi_{221})^1$$
$$(s, \ as, \ as) \qquad\qquad (as, \ s, \ as) \qquad\qquad (as, \ as, \ s)$$
$$(\Psi_{111})^1 \ (\Psi_{113})^1 \qquad (\Psi_{111})^1 \ (\Psi_{131})^1 \qquad (\Psi_{111})^1 \ (\Psi_{311})^1$$
$$(s, \ s, \ s) \qquad\qquad (s, \ s, \ s) \qquad\qquad (s, \ s, \ s)$$

Problem 1.20: Let a 'square initial system', A, with edge lengths $L_x = L_y = l$ be deformed to a 'rectangular system' E with lengths $L_x = ml$, $L_y = Ml$ ($M > m$):

Assuming two electrons in the system, what values of parameters m and M satisfy the following conditions for the energies of the ground states E_0 and of the first excited states E_* in the initial square and the final rectangular deformed systems

(a) $E_0^A < E_0^E$,   (b) $E_0^A > E_0^E$,   (c) $E_*^A < E_*^E$,   (d) $E_*^A > E_*^E$?

Investigate whether parameters exist for which the ground state and the first excited state are favoured energetically in different systems

(e) $E_0^A < E_0^E$ and $E_*^A > E_*^E$ or $E_0^A > E_0^E$ and $E_*^A < E_*^E$.

On deformation of the system $A \to E$ the edge lengths change as shown. Putting $h^2/8ml^2 = K$ affords the total energies, e.g. for the case of two electrons occupying the energy levels associated with this system:

$$
\begin{aligned}
E_0^A &= 2E_{11}^A &&= 2K \cdot 2 = 4K \\
E_*^A &= E_{11}^A + E_{12}^A &&= K \cdot 2 + K \cdot 5 = 7K \\
E_0^E &= 2E_{11}^E &&= 2K\left(\frac{1}{m^2} + \frac{1}{M^2}\right) \\
E_*^E &= E_{11}^E + E_{12}^E &&= K\left(\frac{1}{m^2} + \frac{1}{M^2}\right) + K\left(\frac{1}{m^2} + \frac{4}{M^2}\right) = K\left(\frac{2}{m^2} + \frac{5}{M^2}\right)
\end{aligned}
$$

Substituting $M = rm$ with $r \geqslant 1$ yields:

$$
\begin{aligned}
E_0^A &= 4K \\
E_0^E &= \frac{2K}{m^2}\left(\frac{r^2+1}{r}\right) \\
E_*^A &= 7K \\
E_*^E &= \frac{K}{m^2}\left(\frac{2r^2+5}{r^2}\right)
\end{aligned}
$$

With respect to questions (a) through (d), we find:

(a), (b) $\quad E_0^A \lessgtr E_0^E$

$$4K \;\leqslant\; \frac{2K}{m^2}\left(\frac{r^2+1}{r^2}\right) \quad\therefore\quad m^2 \;\leqslant\; \frac{1}{2}\left(\frac{r^2+1}{r^2}\right)$$

(c), (d) $\quad E_*^A \lessgtr E_*^E$

$$7K \;\leqslant\; \frac{K}{m^2}\left(\frac{2r^2+5}{r^2}\right) \quad\therefore\quad m^2 \;\leqslant\; \frac{1}{7}\left(\frac{2r^2+5}{r^2}\right)$$

These relations are satisfied for any value of r, where $r \geqslant 1$.

Likewise, with respect to question (e), we find:

(e) $\quad E_0^A < E_0^E$ and $E_*^A > E_*^E$

$$\frac{1}{7}\left(\frac{2r^2+5}{r^2}\right) < m^2 < \frac{1}{2}\left(\frac{r^2+1}{r^2}\right) \quad\therefore\quad \frac{1}{7}\,(2r^2+5) \;<\; \frac{1}{2}\,(r^2+1)$$

$$4r^2+10 \;<\; 7r^2+7$$
$$3 \;<\; 3r^2$$
$$1 \;<\; r^2$$
$$\underline{\;r \;>\; 1\;}$$

Thus for $r = 2$:

$$\frac{1}{7}\left(\frac{4+5}{4}\right) < m^2 < \frac{1}{2}\left(\frac{4+1}{4}\right)$$

$$\frac{9}{28} < m^2 < \frac{5}{8}$$

For the second condition of (e) with inverted inequality signs,

(e) $\quad E_0^A > E_0^E$ and $E_*^A < E_*^E$

$$\frac{1}{7}\left(\frac{2r^2+5}{r^2}\right) > m^2 > \frac{1}{2}\left(\frac{r^2+1}{r^2}\right) \quad\therefore\quad \frac{1}{7}\,(2r^2+5) \;>\; \frac{1}{2}\,(r^2+1)$$

$$1 \;>\; r^2$$
$$\underline{\;r \;<\; 1\;}$$

This result contradicts the assumption $r > 1$, and such an energy relationship therefore cannot occur.

The general case for occupation with many electrons can be solved in a similar manner by inclusion of the relevant terms, while paying attention to the total energy E_G of the individual configurations.

2. Atomic and Bond Orbitals

2.1. Orbitals of Hydrogen-Like Atoms

Problem 2.1: Calculate the position of the first 3 lines as well as the limit of the *Lyman* series in the spectrum for the hydrogen atom $(E_1 \rightarrow E_n)$ in cm^{-1}. Where will these lines and the series limit occur in the spectrum of the deuterium atom, and in that of the He$^\oplus$ ion?

The orbital energies of the hydrogen atom in cm^{-1} are given by (2/1)

$$E_n\,(1) \; = \; -13.60 \cdot 8066 \cdot \frac{1^2}{n^2} \; = \; -109700 \cdot \frac{1}{n^2} \; [cm^{-1}]$$

as

$$
\begin{aligned}
E_1 &= -\;109700 \quad cm^{-1} \\
E_2 &= -\;\;\;27400 \quad cm^{-1} \\
E_3 &= -\;\;\;12200 \quad cm^{-1} \\
E_4 &= -\;\;\;\;\;6900 \quad cm^{-1} \\
E_\infty &= -\;\;\;\;\;\;\;\;\;0 \quad cm^{-1}
\end{aligned}
$$

The wavenumbers of the three short wave lines and the series limit are

$$
\begin{aligned}
\triangle E_{12} &= E_2 - E_1 = \;\;82300 \quad cm^{-1} \\
\triangle E_{13} &= E_3 - E_1 = \;\;97500 \quad cm^{-1} \\
\triangle E_{14} &= E_4 - E_1 = 102800 \quad cm^{-1} \\
\triangle E_{1\infty} &= E_\infty - E_1 = 109700 \quad cm^{-1}
\end{aligned}
$$

Because the same nuclear charge is used in the present calculations these lines lie at the same wavenumbers for the deuterium atom. If the neglected motion of the nucleus having twice the mass is also taken into account, the spectral lines are shifted by about 20–30 cm^{-1} towards shorter wavelengths.

Similarly, for the He$^\oplus$-ion

$$E_n\,(2) \; = \; -\,109700 \cdot \frac{4}{n^2} \; = \; 4\,E_n\,(1) \quad \text{and} \quad \triangle E_{nn'}\,(2) = 4\,\triangle E_{nn'}\,(1),$$

from which the following values result:

$$
\begin{aligned}
\triangle E_{12} &= 329100 \quad cm^{-1} \\
\triangle E_{13} &= 390000 \quad cm^{-1} \\
\triangle E_{14} &= 411400 \quad cm^{-1} \\
\triangle E_{1\infty} &= 438800 \quad cm^{-1}
\end{aligned}
$$

Thus removal of an electron from the field of an n-fold positively charged hydrogen-like ion requires an n^2-fold energy.

Problem 2.2: Show that the angular components of p_x-, p_y-, and p_z-atomic orbitals form an orthonormal set of functions.

For the angular component of the $2p_x$-, $2p_y$-, and $2p_z$-functions ((2/57), Vol. 1, p. 70), the general normalization conditions hold

$$\int_0^\pi d\vartheta \int_0^{2\pi} d\varphi \, \sin \vartheta \, \Theta_{\ell,m}^2 (\vartheta,\varphi) \qquad\qquad = 1 \tag{2/11}$$

$$2p_x : \int_0^\pi d\vartheta \int_0^{2\pi} d\varphi \, \sin \vartheta \left(\frac{\sqrt{3}}{2\sqrt{\pi}} \sin \vartheta \cos \varphi \right)^2 =$$

$$\frac{3}{4\pi} \int_0^\pi \sin^3 \vartheta \, d\vartheta \int_0^{2\pi} \cos^2 \varphi d\varphi \qquad = \frac{3}{4\pi} \cdot \frac{4}{3} \cdot \pi \qquad = 1$$

$$2p_y : \int_0^\pi d\vartheta \int_0^{2\pi} d\varphi \, \sin \vartheta \left(\frac{\sqrt{3}}{2\sqrt{\pi}} \sin \vartheta \sin \varphi \right)^2 =$$

$$\frac{3}{4\pi} \int_0^\pi \sin^3 \vartheta \, d\vartheta \int_0^{2\pi} \sin^2 \varphi \, d\varphi \qquad = \frac{3}{4\pi} \cdot \frac{4}{3} \cdot \pi \qquad = 1$$

$$2p_z : \int_0^\pi d\vartheta \int_0^{2\pi} d\varphi \, \sin\vartheta \left(\frac{\sqrt{3}}{2\sqrt{\pi}} \cos \vartheta \right)^2 =$$

$$\frac{3}{4\pi} \int_0^\pi \sin \vartheta \cos^2 \vartheta \, d\vartheta \int_0^{2\pi} d\varphi \qquad = \frac{3}{4\pi} \cdot \frac{2}{3} \cdot 2\pi \qquad = 1$$

Furthermore, the angular component must satisfy the orthogonality conditions:

$$\int_0^\pi \sin\vartheta d\vartheta \int_0^{2\pi} d\varphi \, \Theta_{\ell,m} \Theta_{\ell',m'} \qquad\qquad = 0 \tag{2/14}$$

$$2p_x \Big| 2p_y : \int_0^\pi \sin\vartheta d\vartheta \int_0^{2\pi} d\varphi \left(\frac{\sqrt{3}}{2\sqrt{\pi}} \sin\vartheta \cos\varphi \right) \left(\frac{\sqrt{3}}{2\sqrt{\pi}} \sin\vartheta \sin\varphi \right) =$$

$$\frac{3}{4\pi} \int_0^\pi \sin^3 \vartheta d\vartheta \int_0^{2\pi} \cos\varphi \sin\varphi d\varphi = \frac{3}{4\pi} \cdot \frac{4}{3} \cdot 0 \qquad = 0$$

$$2p_x \Big| 2p_z : \int_0^\pi \sin\vartheta d\vartheta \int_0^{2\pi} d\varphi \left(\frac{\sqrt{3}}{2\sqrt{\pi}} \sin \vartheta \cos \varphi \right) \left(\frac{\sqrt{3}}{2\sqrt{\pi}} \cos \vartheta \right) =$$

$$\frac{3}{4\pi} \int_0^\pi \sin^2 \vartheta \cos \vartheta d\vartheta \int_0^{2\pi} \cos\varphi d\varphi = \frac{3}{4\pi} \cdot 0 \cdot 0 \qquad = 0$$

$$2p_y \Big| 2p_z : \int_0^\pi \sin\vartheta d\vartheta \int_0^{2\pi} d\varphi \left(\frac{\sqrt{3}}{2\sqrt{\pi}} \sin \vartheta \sin \varphi \right) \left(\frac{\sqrt{3}}{2\sqrt{\pi}} \cos \vartheta \right) =$$

$$\frac{3}{4\pi} \int_0^\pi \sin^2 \vartheta \cos \vartheta d\vartheta \int_0^{2\pi} \sin\varphi d\varphi = \frac{3}{4\pi} \cdot 0 \cdot 0 \qquad = 0$$

Problem 2.3: Draw the section of the yz plane through the indicatrix of the angular component of the d_{z^2} function. The function may be taken from the Table (2.57) in Section 2.5; the required section is characterized by $\varphi = 90°$.

The contributions of the angular part $\Theta_{d_{z^2}} = \dfrac{\sqrt{5}}{4\sqrt{\pi}} (3\cos^2\vartheta - 1)$ are listed in the following table:

ϑ	$\cos\vartheta$	$\Theta_{d_{z^2}}$
0°	1.000	0.631
10°	0.985	0.603
20°	0.940	0.521
30°	0.866	0.394
40°	0.766	0.240
50°	0.643	0.076
60°	0.500	− 0.079
70°	0.342	− 0.205
80°	0.174	− 0.287
85°	0.087	− 0.308
90°	0.000	− 0.315

The indicatrix possesses the following cross section in the yz plane:

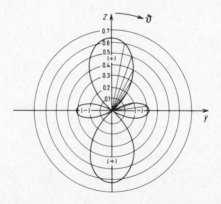

Problem 2.4: Construct the section of the yz plane through that surface which satisfies the condition $|\Phi(2p_z)| = $ constant. (Hint: In direction ϑ, the distance ρ should be chosen such that $\rho \cdot e^{-\rho/2} = K/\cos\vartheta$; $K = 0.1$. The ρ values are obtained from the graphic representation of $\rho \cdot e^{-\rho/2}$; the functions R_{21} and Θ_{1z} are taken from the Tables (2/56) and (2/57) in Section 2.5.)

The $2p_z$ atomic orbital ((2/57), Vol. 1, p. 70) reads:

$$\Phi_{2p_z} = R_{21} \cdot \Theta_{1Z} = \left(\frac{Z}{a_0}\right)^{\frac{3}{2}} \frac{\rho}{2\sqrt{6}} \; e^{-\rho/2} \cdot \frac{\sqrt{3}}{2\sqrt{\pi}} \; \cos\vartheta = \frac{1}{K} \cdot \rho e^{-\rho/2} \cdot \cos\vartheta \, .$$

The ρ-values, which are to be plotted in spherical coordinates in the direction ϑ, are obtained with $K = 0.1$ from the relation

$$\frac{0.1}{\cos\vartheta} = \rho \cdot e^{-\rho/2}$$

To simplity the calculations the function $\rho \cdot e^{-\rho/2}$ is represented graphically:

ρ	$\rho \cdot e^{-\rho/2}$
0.0	0.000
0.5	0.389
1.0	0.607
1.5	0.709
2.0	0.736
2.5	0.716
3.0	0.669
4.0	0.541
5.0	0.410
6.0	0.299
7.0	0.211
8.0	0.147
9.0	0.100
10.0	0.067

The following table contains the values of ϑ, $\cos\vartheta$, and $0.1/\cos\vartheta$ as well as the corresponding ρ-values taken from the above graphic representation.

ϑ	$\cos\vartheta$	$\dfrac{0.1}{\cos\vartheta}$	ρ
0°	1.000	0.100	9.0
10°	0.985	0.102	9.0
20°	0.940	0.106	8.8
30°	0.866	0.115	8.6
40°	0.766	0.131	8.3
50°	0.643	0.156	7.8
60°	0.500	0.200	7.2
70°	0.342	0.292	6.1
80°	0.174	0.575	3.7
90°	0.000		

30

The section of the yz plane through the surface $|\Phi_{2p_z}| = $ constant has the following form:

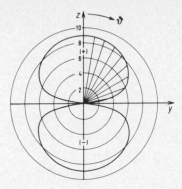

Problem 2.5:   Show that the angular parts of the two normalized $3d$-functions

$$\Theta(d_{z^2-x^2}) = \frac{\sqrt{15}}{4\sqrt{\pi}}(\cos^2 \vartheta - \sin^2 \vartheta \cos^2 \varphi),$$

$$\Theta(d_{y^2-z^2}) = -\frac{\sqrt{15}}{4\sqrt{\pi}}(\cos^2 \vartheta - \sin^2 \vartheta \sin^2 \varphi)$$

are not orthogonal to each other, but that the angular parts of the following two are:

$$\Theta(d_{x^2-y^2}) = \frac{\sqrt{15}}{4\sqrt{\pi}}(\sin^2 \vartheta \cos 2\varphi),$$

$$\Theta(d_{z^2}) = \frac{\sqrt{5}}{4\sqrt{\pi}}(3 \cos^2 \vartheta - 1).$$

The orthogonality condition $\quad \int\limits_0^\pi \sin \vartheta \, d\vartheta \int\limits_0^{2\pi} d\varphi \, \Theta_{l,m} \, \Theta_{l',m'} = 0 \qquad$ (2/14)

gives for the angular components of the $3d_{z^2-x^2}$ and $3d_{y^2-z^2}$ functions:

$$\int\limits_0^\pi \sin \vartheta d\vartheta \int\limits_0^{2\pi} d\varphi \frac{\sqrt{15}}{4\sqrt{\pi}} (\cos^2\vartheta - \sin^2\vartheta \cos^2\varphi) \frac{\sqrt{15}}{4\sqrt{\pi}} (\sin^2\vartheta \sin^2\varphi - \cos^2\vartheta) =$$

$$\frac{15}{16\pi} \int\limits_0^\pi \sin\vartheta d\vartheta \int\limits_0^{2\pi} d\varphi (\cos^2\vartheta \sin^2\vartheta(\sin^2\varphi + \cos^2\varphi) - \cos^4\vartheta - \sin^4\vartheta \cos^2\varphi \sin^2\varphi) =$$

$$\frac{15}{16\pi} \left(\int\limits_0^\pi \sin^3\vartheta \cos^2\vartheta d\vartheta \int\limits_0^{2\pi} d\varphi - \int\limits_0^\pi \sin\vartheta \cos^4\vartheta d\vartheta \int\limits_0^{2\pi} d\varphi - \int\limits_0^\pi \sin^5\vartheta d\vartheta \int\limits_0^{2\pi} \sin^2\varphi \cos^2\varphi d\varphi \right) =$$

$$\frac{15}{16\pi} \left(2\pi \cdot \frac{4}{15} - 2\pi \cdot \frac{2}{5} - \frac{4}{15}\pi \right) = -\frac{1}{2}$$

In contrast, condition (2/14) gives for the angular components of the $3d_{x^2-y^2}$ and $3d_{z^2}$ functions:

$$\int_0^\pi \sin\vartheta\,d\vartheta \int_0^{2\pi} d\varphi\,\frac{\sqrt{15}}{4\sqrt{\pi}}(\sin^2\vartheta\cos 2\varphi)\,\frac{\sqrt{5}}{4\sqrt{\pi}}(3\cos^2\vartheta - 1) =$$

$$\frac{5\sqrt{3}}{16\pi}\int_0^\pi \sin^3\vartheta\,(3\cos^2\vartheta - 1)\,d\vartheta \int_0^{2\pi}\cos 2\varphi\,d\varphi =$$

$$\frac{5\sqrt{3}}{16\pi}\left(3\int_0^\pi \sin^3\vartheta\cos^2\vartheta\,d\vartheta - \int_0^\pi \sin^3\vartheta\,d\vartheta\right)\int_0^{2\pi}\cos 2\varphi\,d\varphi =$$

$$\frac{5\sqrt{3}}{16\pi}\left(3\cdot\frac{4}{15} - \frac{4}{3}\right)\cdot 0 = 0$$

2.2. Many-Electron Atoms: Valence State and Hybridization

Problem 2.6: Show with a graphical representation that for the two electron systems He, $Li^\oplus$, $Be^{2\oplus}$, $B^{3\oplus}$, $C^{4\oplus}$, $N^{5\oplus}$, and $0^{6\oplus}$, the difference between the first and second ionization potentials (Table (2.53) in Section 2.5) is a simple function of the nuclear charge Z. Use this empirical relationship to determine the electron affinity of the hydrogen atom ($H^. + e^- \rightarrow H^\ominus$).

From the Table (2/53), Vol. 1, p. 69, the differences $\triangle$ between the first and second ionization energies are:

	He	$Li^\oplus$	$Be^{2\oplus}$	$B^{3\oplus}$	$C^{4\oplus}$	$N^{5\oplus}$	$0^{6\oplus}$
$\triangle [eV]$	29.8	46.8	63.8	80.8	97.8	114.9	132.0
Increment		17.0	17.0	17.0	17.0	17.1	17.1

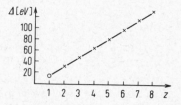

For hydrogen, extrapolation gives: $\triangle = 29.8 - 17.0 = 12.8$ eV, and the ionization energy of the hydrogen anion obtained as $I_{H\ominus} = I_H - \triangle = 13.6 - 12.8 = +0.8$ eV. Removal of an electron from the hydride anion therefore requires expenditure of energy:

$$H \;\; + \ominus \rightarrow H^\ominus ; \;\; E = -0.8\,eV$$

The sign convention widely adopted in the literature for the electron affinity unfortunately contradicts the convention that energy released by a system has a negative sign. The electron affinity of the hydrogen atom is given as $+ 0.8$ eV.

Problem 2.7: Calculate the interaction energy of the two electrons in the K shell for the particles He, $Li^{\oplus}$, $Be^{2\oplus}$, $B^{3\oplus}$, $C^{4\oplus}$, $N^{5\oplus}$ and $0^{6\oplus}$. How large are the effective nuclear charges and the shielding values?

If the interaction between the electrons is neglected then ionization of each of the two electrons would require an energy expenditure corresponding to the second ionization energy I_2. That less energy is actually required for ionization of the first electron is due to the interelectronic interaction:

$$\text{interaction} = I_2 - I_1 = \triangle$$

The interaction thus corresponds to the $\triangle$-value of Problem 2.6. For electrons in hydrogen-like atomic orbitals, the ionization energy is calculated according to (2/1) from the nuclear charge Z and the principal quantum number n of the occupied atomic orbitals. With 2 electrons in the same atomic orbital, the effective nuclear charge Z_{eff} is obtained correspondingly from the average ionization energy $\bar{I}$ (cf. (2/19)):

$$I = 13.6 \, \frac{Z^2}{n^2} \; [\text{eV}]$$

$$\bar{I} = \frac{I_1 + I_2}{2} \; ; \; Z_{eff} = \sqrt{\frac{\bar{I} \cdot n^2}{13.6}} \; [\text{Electronic charge } e]$$

As can be seen from the following table of values, the shielding $A = Z - Z_{eff}$ is independent of the nuclear charge.

	He	$Li^{\oplus}$	$Be^{2\oplus}$	$B^{3\oplus}$	$C^{4\oplus}$	$N^{5\oplus}$	$0^{6\oplus}$
$\bar{I}$ [eV]	39.5	99.0	185.8	299.7	440.9	609.3	805.1
Z_{eff} [e]	1.7	2.7	3.7	4.7	5.7	6.7	7.7
A [e]	0.3	0.3	0.3	0.3	0.3	0.3	0.3

Problem 2.8: Calculate according to the *Slater* rules (2/22) the effective nuclear charges for

$1s$-, $2s$-, $2p$-electrons of the carbon atom,
$1s$-, $2s$-, $2p$-, $3s$-, $3p$-electrons of the silicon atom.

The numerical values of the shielding and the nuclear charge numbers are assembled in the following table:

		ΔA	$\Sigma \Delta A$	Z	Z_{eff}
C	$1s:$	$1 \cdot 0.30$	0.30	6	5.70
	$2s/2p:$	$2 \cdot 0.85 + 3 \cdot 0.35$	2.75		3.25
Si	$1s:$	$1 \cdot 0.30$	0.30	14	13.70
	$2s/2p:$	$2 \cdot 0.85 + 7 \cdot 0.35$	4.15		9.85
	$3s/3p:$	$2 \cdot 1.00 + 8 \cdot 0.85 + 3 \cdot 0.35$	9.85		4.15

Problem 2.9: Prove that the orthonormalization condition for the hybrid orbitals (2/25) is identical with the requirement (2/26)

$$\int_{\mathfrak{R}} h_i h_j \, dv = \delta_{ij} \quad \therefore \quad \sum_k a_{ik} a_{jk} = \delta_{ij}.$$

Show that single electron occupancy of each of the 4 hybrid orbitals, independently of the values of the coefficients a_{ij}, always leads to a spherically symmetrical charge distribution if the conditions for orthonormalization are fulfilled. (Hint: $\sum_k a_{ik} a_{jk} = \delta_{ij} = \sum_k a_{ki} a_{kj}$.)

For the normalization, where $\Phi_{2s} = \Phi_1$, $\Phi_{2p_x} = \Phi_2$, $\Phi_{2p_y} = \Phi_3$ and $\Phi_{2p_z} = \Phi_4$, the following relation holds:

$$
\begin{aligned}
\int_{\mathfrak{R}} h_i^2 \, dv = 1 &= \int_{\mathfrak{R}} (a_{i1}\Phi_1 + a_{i2}\Phi_2 + a_{i3}\Phi_3 + a_{i4}\Phi_4)^2 \, dv \\
&= a_{i1}^2 \int \Phi_1^2 \, dv + 2a_{i1}a_{i2} \int \Phi_1 \Phi_2 \, dv + 2a_{i1}a_{i3} \int \Phi_1 \Phi_3 \, dv + \\
&\quad 2a_{i1}a_{i4} \int \Phi_1 \Phi_4 \, dv + a_{i2}^2 \int \Phi_2^2 \, dv + 2a_{i2}a_{i3} \int \Phi_2 \Phi_3 \, dv + \\
&\quad 2a_{i2}a_{i4} \int \Phi_2 \Phi_4 \, dv + a_{i3}^2 \int \Phi_3^2 \, dv + 2a_{i3}a_{i4} \int \Phi_3 \Phi_4 \, dv + a_{i4}^2 \int \Phi_4^2 \, dv \\
&= a_{i1}^2 + a_{i2}^2 + a_{i3}^2 + a_{i4}^2 = \sum_{k=1}^{4} a_{ik}^2
\end{aligned}
$$

The orthogonality condition reads

$$\int_{\mathfrak{R}} h_i h_j \, dv = 0 = \int_{\mathfrak{R}} (a_{i1}\Phi_1 + a_{i2}\Phi_2 + a_{i3}\Phi_3 + a_{i4}\Phi_4)(a_{j1}\Phi_1 + a_{j2}\Phi_2 + a_{j3}\Phi_3 + a_{j4}\Phi_4) \, dv$$

$$= a_{i_1}a_{j_1} \int \Phi_1^2 \, dv + a_{i_1}a_{j_2} \int \Phi_1 \Phi_2 \, dv + a_{i_1}a_{j_3} \int \Phi_1 \Phi_3 \, dv + a_{i_1}a_{j_4} \int \Phi_1 \Phi_4 \, dv +$$

$$a_{i_2}a_{j_1} \int \Phi_1 \Phi_2 dv + a_{i_2}a_{j_2} \int \Phi_2^2 \, dv + a_{i_2}a_{j_3} \int \Phi_2 \Phi_3 \, dv + a_{i_2}a_{j_4} \int \Phi_2 \Phi_4 \, dv +$$

$$a_{i_3}a_{j_1} \int \Phi_1 \Phi_3 dv + a_{i_3}a_{j_2} \int \Phi_2 \Phi_3 \, dv + a_{i_3}a_{j_3} \int \Phi_3^2 \, dv + a_{i_3}a_{j_4} \int \Phi_3 \Phi_4 \, dv +$$

$$a_{i_4}a_{j_1} \int \Phi_1 \Phi_4 \, dv + a_{i_4}a_{j_2} \int \Phi_2 \Phi_4 \, dv + a_{i_4}a_{j_3} \int \Phi_3 \Phi_4 \, dv + a_{i_4}a_{j_4} \int \Phi_4{}^2 \, dv$$

$$= a_{i_1}a_{j_1} + a_{i_2}a_{j_2} + a_{i_3}a_{j_3} + a_{i_4}a_{j_4} = \sum_{k=1}^{4} a_{ik}a_{jk}$$

Summarizing: $\sum_{k=1}^{4} a_{ik}a_{jk} = \delta_{ij}$

A spherically symmetrical charge distribution is characterized by the probability density of the electron

$$W = \sum_{i=1}^{4} h_i^2 = h_1^2 + h_2^2 + h_3^2 + h_4^2$$

being angularly independent. This is then expanded

e.g. $\quad h_1^2 = (a_{11}\Phi_1 + a_{12}\Phi_2 + a_{13}\Phi_3 + a_{14}\Phi_4)^2$

$$= a_{11}^2 \Phi_1^2 + 2a_{11}a_{12}\Phi_1 \Phi_2 + 2a_{11}a_{13}\Phi_1 \Phi_3 + 2a_{11}a_{14}\Phi_1 \Phi_4 +$$

$$a_{12}^2 \Phi_2^2 + 2a_{12}a_{13}\Phi_2 \Phi_3 + 2a_{12}a_{14}\Phi_2 \Phi_4 + a_{13}^2 \Phi_3^2 +$$

$$2a_{13}a_{14}\Phi_3 \Phi_4 + a_{14}^2 \Phi_4^2$$

$$h_2^2 = \ldots\ldots$$
$$h_3^2 = \ldots\ldots$$
$$h_4^2 = \ldots\ldots$$

From h_1^2, h_2^2, h_3^2, and h_4^2 the following terms are collected:

$$W = \sum_{i=1}^{4} h_i^2 = (a_{11}^2 + a_{21}^2 + a_{31}^2 + a_{41}^2) \, \Phi_1^2 + (a_{12}^2 + a_{22}^2 + a_{32}^2 + a_{42}^2) \, \Phi_2^2 +$$

$$(a_{13}^2 + a_{23}^2 + a_{33}^2 + a_{43}^2) \, \Phi_3^2 + (a_{14}^2 + a_{24}^2 + a_{34}^2 + a_{44}^2) \, \Phi_4^2 +$$

$$(2a_{11}a_{12} + 2a_{21}a_{22} + 2a_{31}a_{32} + 2a_{41}a_{42}) \, \Phi_1 \Phi_2 + (2a_{11}a_{13} + 2a_{21}a_{23} +$$

$$2a_{31}a_{33} + 2a_{41}a_{43}) \, \Phi_1 \Phi_3 + (2a_{11}a_{14} + 2a_{21}a_{24} + 2a_{31}a_{34} + 2a_{41}a_{44}) \, \Phi_1 \Phi_4$$

where

$$\sum_k a_{ki} a_{kj} = \delta_{ij} \text{ , i.e. } \sum_k a_{ik}^2 = 1 \text{ and } \sum_k a_{ki} a_{kj} = 0$$

hence the probability density W is

$$W = \Phi_1^2 + \Phi_2^2 + \Phi_3^2 + \Phi_4^2,$$

which corresponds to a spherically symmetrical charge distribution according to (2/23).
    A more economical proof runs thus:

$$\begin{aligned}
W &= \sum_k h_k^2 \\
&= \sum_k [(\sum_i a_{ki} \Phi_i)(\sum_j a_{kj} \Phi_j)] \\
&= \sum_k \sum_i \sum_j a_{ki} a_{kj} \Phi_i \Phi_j \\
&= \sum_i \sum_j \Phi_i \Phi_j \sum_k a_{ki} a_{kj} \\
&= \sum_i \Phi_i^2
\end{aligned}$$

Supplement: The identity of the summations

$$\sum_k a_{ik} a_{jk} = \sum_k a_{ki} a_{kj}$$

can be established as follows: the matrix product is defined as

$$\mathbf{C} = \mathbf{AB}; \quad c_{ij} = a_{ik} b_{kj}.$$

Let $\mathbf{A} = (a_{ij})$ and $\mathbf{B} = (b_{ij}) = (a_{ji})$ then the following holds:

$$\mathbf{C} = \mathbf{AB}; \quad c_{ij} = \sum_k a_{ik} b_{kj} = \sum_k a_{ik} a_{jk},$$

$$\mathbf{D} = \mathbf{BA}; \quad d_{ij} = \sum_k b_{ik} a_{kj} = \sum_k a_{ki} a_{kj}.$$

For $c_{ij} = \delta_{ij}$, $\mathbf{C}$ is equivalent to the identity matrix $\mathbf{E}$, and it follows that

$$(\mathbf{BA})\mathbf{B} = \mathbf{B}(\mathbf{AB}) = \mathbf{BE} = \mathbf{EB}.$$

Consequently, $\mathbf{D} = \mathbf{BA}$ is always equal to the identity matrix $\mathbf{E}$, i.e. if

$$\sum_k a_{ik} a_{jk} = \delta_{ij} \text{ then } \sum_k a_{ki} a_{kj} = \delta_{ij}.$$

Problem 2.10: Draw the indicatrix for each of the hybrid orbitals te_z, tr_z, and di_z. (Hint: Plot for the angles of the absolute value of $\vartheta_{l,m}$ in units of $1/2\sqrt{\pi}$ along the corresponding directions in spherical coordinates; the negative sign should be denoted separately. Since the functions

$$\Theta_{te_z} = \frac{1}{2\sqrt{\pi}}(\tfrac{1}{2} + \tfrac{3}{2}\cos\vartheta),$$

$$\Theta_{tr_z} = \frac{1}{2\sqrt{\pi}}\left(\frac{1}{\sqrt{3}} + \sqrt{2}\cos\vartheta\right),$$

$$\Theta_{di_z} = \frac{1}{2\sqrt{\pi}}\left(\frac{1}{\sqrt{2}} + \sqrt{\tfrac{3}{2}}\cos\vartheta\right)$$

are rotationally symmetric with respect to the z-axis, the plot in the yz-plane is sufficient to illustrate the indicatrix.)

The values of the angular components Θ_{te_z}, Θ_{tr_z}, Θ_{di_z} in units of $1/2\sqrt{\pi}$ are listed in the following table:

ϑ	$\cos\vartheta$	Θdi_z	Θtr_z	Θte_z
0/360	1.00	1.93	1.99	2.00
30/330	0.87	1.77	1.81	1.81
60/300	0.50	1.32	1.28	1.25
90/270	0	0.71	0.58	0.50
120/240	−0.50	0.09	−0.13	−0.25
150/210	−0.87	−0.36	−0.65	−0.81
180	−1.00	−0.52	−0.84	−1.00

The indicatrices for the hybrid orbitals te_z (sp^3), tr_z (sp^2), and di_z (sp) have the following cross sections in the x,y-plane:

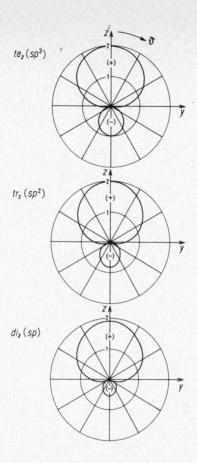

Note: The indicatrix describes the charge distribution over a sphere of given radius ρ. In the s and p functions, the radial and angular components can be separated according to (2/10)

$$\Phi_{n,l,m} = R_{n,l}(\rho) \cdot \Theta_{l,m}(\vartheta,\varphi).$$

Hence in these functions the angular component Θ, and thus also the indicatrix, is independent of the principal quantum number n and the radius ρ of the sphere. No analogous separation can be carried out with the above hybrids since the radius-dependent part differs for s- and p-functions. The pertinent indicatrix thus only gives the charge distribution for the sphere having the radius,

$$\rho = \frac{a_o}{z} \cdot r = \frac{2\sqrt{3}}{1+\sqrt{3}} \cdot \frac{a_o}{z}.$$

2.3. Molecular Orbitals: The Two Center Bond

Problem 2.11: Normalize the LCAO molecular orbitals

$$\Psi_1 = N_1(\Phi_a - \Phi_b);$$

$$\Psi_2 = N_2(\Phi_a + 2\Phi_b + \Phi_c),$$

and calculate the normalization coefficients N_1 and N_2 by taking into account the overlap (S_{ab}, S_{ac}, S_{bc}) between the atomic orbitals Φ_a, Φ_b, Φ_c.

The normalization coefficient N_1 is obtained as follows:

$$
\begin{aligned}
<\psi_1 \mid \psi_1> &= N_1^2 < \Phi_a - \Phi_b \mid \Phi_a - \Phi_b > \\
&= N_1^2 \left(< \Phi_a \mid \Phi_a > + < \Phi_b \mid \Phi_b > - 2 < \Phi_a \mid \Phi_b > \right) \\
&= N_1^2 \left(1 + 1 - 2\, S_{ab} \right) = 1
\end{aligned}
$$

$$N_1 = \frac{1}{\sqrt{2 - 2\, S_{ab}}}$$

The normalization coefficient N_2 is calculated in corresponding manner:

$$
\begin{aligned}
<\psi_2 \mid \psi_2> &= N_2^2 < \Phi_a + 2\Phi_b + \Phi_c \mid \Phi_a + 2\Phi_b + \Phi_c > \\
&= N_2^2 \Big(< \Phi_a \mid \Phi_a > + 2 < \Phi_a \mid 2\Phi_b > + 2 < \Phi_a \mid \Phi_c > \\
&\quad + < 2\Phi_b \mid 2\Phi_b > + 2 < 2\Phi_b \mid \Phi_c > + < \Phi_c \mid \Phi_c > \Big) \\
&= N_2^2 \left(1 + 4\, S_{ab} + 2\, S_{ac} + 4 + 4\, S_{bc} + 1 \right)
\end{aligned}
$$

$$N_2 = \frac{1}{\sqrt{6 + 4 S_{ab} + 2 S_{ac} + 4 S_{bc}}}$$

Problem 2.12: Let the normalized molecular orbital of a homonuclear two centre bond be:

$$\Psi = a\Phi_1 + b\Phi_2,$$

and the overlap integral be:

$$\langle \Phi_1 / \Phi_2 \rangle = S..$$

Then for a given internuclear distance R the following equation

$$\Phi_1(R/2) = \Phi_2(R/2).$$

at the centre of gravity $R/2$ of the system is valid. Determine the ratio $a:b$ for which

The normalized function Ψ can be described by the two mutually independent variables a' and b'

$$\psi = \frac{a'\phi_1 + b'\phi_2}{\sqrt{a'^2 + b'^2 + 2a'b'S}}$$

For a maximum of Ψ at point $R/2$ the following relation must hold:

$$d\psi = \frac{\partial \psi}{\partial a'}\, da' + \frac{\partial \psi}{\partial b'}\, db' = 0$$

Since a' and b' are independent of each other, two further conditions must both be fulfilled: (I) $\dfrac{\partial \Psi}{\partial a'} = 0$, and (II) $\dfrac{\partial \Psi}{\partial b'} = 0$. From condition (I) it follows:

$$\frac{\partial \Psi}{\partial a'} = \frac{\phi_1 \sqrt{a'^2 + b'^2 + 2a'b'S} - (a'\phi_1 + b'\phi_2)\dfrac{1}{2}\dfrac{1}{\sqrt{a'^2 + b'^2 + 2a'b'S}}(2a' + 2b'S)}{(\sqrt{a'^2 + b'^2 + 2a'b'S})^2}$$

$$= \frac{\phi_1 (\sqrt{a'^2 + b'^2 + 2a'b'S})^2 - (a'\phi_1 + b'\phi_2)\cdot(a' + b'S)}{(\sqrt{a'^2 + b'^2 + 2a'b'S})^3} = 0$$

and with $\Phi_1(R/2) = \Phi_2(R/2) = $ constant, we obtain

$$(a'^2 + b'^2 + 2a'b'S) - a'^2 - a'b'S - a'b' - b'^2 S = 0$$
$$b'^2(1 - S) - a'b'(1 - S) = 0$$
$$b'(b' - a') = 0$$

Correspondingly, from condition (II)

$$a'(a' - b') = 0.$$

The conditions (I) and (II) must be fulfilled simultaneously, for which a unique solution $a' : b' = 1$ is obtained. $\Psi(R/2)$ therefore has the maximum value for the coefficients

$$a = b = 1/\sqrt{2(1+S)}.$$

(Note: when $b = 0$, according to (I) a must equal 0 also according to (II), which is physically meaningless.)

Problem 2.13: According to the simplest LCAO-MO model, the total energy $E(R)$ of the $H_2^\oplus$ molecule-ion in the ground state can be approximated by

$$E(R) = \frac{1}{R} + \frac{K + I}{1 + S} \text{ [in atomic units]},$$

where R = internuclear distance in $[a_0]$, and $E(R)$ is measured relative to the energy for a hydrogen atom and an infinitely distant proton. Sketch the curve $E(R)$ from the values for $S(R)$, $K(R)$, and $I(R)$ tabulated in (2/47); read off the equilibrium internuclear distance and the dissociation energy $H_2^\oplus \rightarrow H^. + H^\oplus$. Compare these values with the experimentally determined ones of 1·06 Å for the equilibrium internuclear distance and 2·8 eV for the dissociation energy (corrected for zero point energy).

With the aid of values from (2/47) one obtains the following potential energy curve $E(R)$:

R	$E(R)$
0.5	1.079
1.0	0.212
1.5	0.005
2.0	− 0.054
2.5	− 0.065
3.0	− 0.059
3.5	− 0.048
4.0	− 0.038
4.5	− 0.028
5.0	− 0.019

From the curve, values of $R_O \sim 2.5a_O = 1.3$ Å and $E_D \sim 0.065$ atomic energy units = 41 kcal/mol can be read off at the equilibrium distance. Agreement with the experimental values $R_O = 1.06$ Å and $E_D = 64$ kcal/mol would accordingly appear to be rather modest. However it should be remembered that the potential curve results from differences between large energy values. On a percentage basis the individual values are therefore considerably more accurate, and quite satisfactory in view of the crudeness of the approximation.

Problem 2.14: What would be the consequences of replacing the electron of the $H_2^\oplus$ molecule-ion by a meson having the same charge but two hundred times the mass of an electron? (Hint: The atomic unit of length $a_0 = \hbar^2/me^2$ is defined relative to the mass m of the electron).

Obviously the $1s$ atomic orbital for the motion of a meson about a proton is formally identical with that for the motion of an electron about a proton. The difference is that the *Bohr* radius

$$a_o = \frac{\hbar^2}{m e^2}$$

has to be replaced by the expression

$$A_o = \hbar^2 / m_M e^2$$

upon the introduction of the meson mass $m_M = 200\, m$, and that the unit $[e^2/A_o]$ applies instead of the atomic energy unit $[e^2/a_o]$. If all energy values are now expressed in this 200-fold greater unit and all distances R in the 200-fold smaller unit $[A_o]$, the numerical values listed in Table (2/47) remain unchanged. This means that the minimum of the potential curve will be at a 200-fold smaller distance, and that the dissociation energy must be 200-fold greater.

The above considerations neglect differences in mass between the electron and the meson in so for as the centers A and B are assumed to remain at rest in spite of the strongly reduced mass ratio relative to the proton

$$\frac{m_{H^\oplus}}{m} = 1836 \quad ; \quad \frac{m_{H^\oplus}}{m_M} = 9.18$$

Since this is not permissible, the above discussion has at best a semiquantitative validity.

Problem 2.15: Consider the following situations: an s-, p_x-, p_y-, or p_z-orbital is allowed to approach either a d_{xy}- or a $d_{y^2-z^2}$-orbital [2.7] along the z-axis. Which orbitals will give rise to a σ-bond, and which will form a π-bond? Sketch the dependence of S upon R for each of these cases.

The overlap integral $S(R)$ differs from zero only in the following three cases:

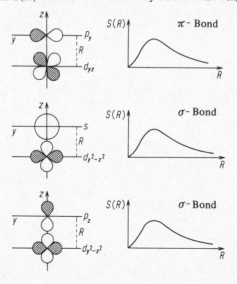

Problem 2.16: Describe the bonds in the molecules ethane, ethylene, acetylene, allene, and benzene, using the symbols $\sigma(\Phi_a, \Phi_b)$ and $\pi_r(\Phi_a, \Phi_b)$, and for hybrid orbitals the abbreviations *te*, *tr*, and *di*.

Ethane:

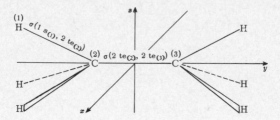

Ethylene:

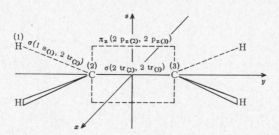

Acetylene:

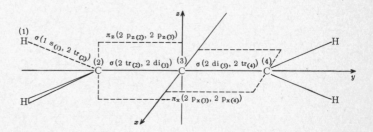

Allene:

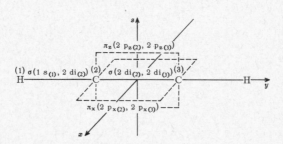

Benzene:

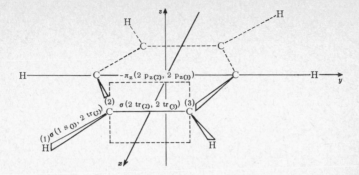

Problem 2.17: Starting from the overlap functions for the 2s- and 2p-atomic orbitals [2.18], construct the corresponding functions for two sp^3- and two sp^2-hybrid orbitals. (Hint: Use equations (2/32) and (2/33).)

The overlap integral between two sp^3 hybrid orbitals can be constructed with (2/32) as follows:

$$S(sp^3, sp^3) = < \frac{1}{2}s + \frac{\sqrt{3}}{2}p \mid \frac{1}{2}s + \frac{\sqrt{3}}{2}p >$$

$$= \frac{1}{4} < s \mid s > + \frac{\sqrt{3}}{2} < s \mid p > + \frac{3}{4} < p \mid p > .$$

With the aid of [2.18] the following values result:

$\dfrac{RZ}{a_o}$	$\dfrac{1}{4} < s\mid s >$	$\dfrac{\sqrt{3}}{2} < s\mid p >$	$\dfrac{3}{4} < p\mid p >$	$< sp^3 \mid sp^3 >$
0	0.25	0.00	− 0.75	− 0.50
2	0.24	0.24	− 0.55	− 0.07
4	0.20	0.40	− 0.17	0.43
6	0.16	0.44	0.11	0.71
8	0.11	0.39	0.24	0.74
10	0.07	0.28	0.24	0.59
12	0.05	0.18	0.19	0.42
14	0.03	0.11	0.12	0.26

Similarly for the overlap integral $S(R)$ between two sp^2 hybrid orbitals, one finds according to (2/33):

$$S(sp^2, sp^2) = < \frac{1}{\sqrt{3}}s + \sqrt{\frac{2}{3}}p \mid \frac{1}{\sqrt{3}}s + \sqrt{\frac{2}{3}}p >$$

$$= \frac{1}{3} < s \mid s > + \frac{2\sqrt{2}}{3} < s \mid p > + \frac{2}{3} < p \mid p > .$$

The tabulated values are obtained with the aid of [2.18]

$\dfrac{RZ}{a_o}$	$\dfrac{1}{3} < s \mid s >$	$\dfrac{2\sqrt{2}}{3} < s \mid p >$	$\dfrac{2}{3} < p \mid p >$	$< sp^2 \mid sp^2 >$
0	0.33	0	− 0.66	− 0.33
2	0.31	0.26	− 0.48	0.09
4	0.26	0.43	− 0.15	0.54
6	0.21	0.48	0.11	0.80
8	0.15	0.42	0.21	0.78
10	0.10	0.30	0.21	0.61
12	0.06	0.20	0.17	0.43
14	0.03	0.12	0.10	0.25

The values obtained are plotted analogously to [2.18].

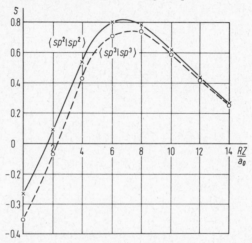

It can be seen that the sp^2 hybrid orbitals overlap better at all distances than the sp^3 hybrid orbitals. Accordingly, a shorter bond length is to be expected for an sp^2/sp^2 bond than for an sp^3/sp^3 bond, as is confirmed by experiment.

Problem 2.18: According to *Bredt's* rule, bicyclic systems with bridgehead double bonds (as for instance, $\Delta^{1,2}$-bicyclo[2.2.1]-heptene) are not capable of existence. This rule has exceptions. An example for a ring system with a double bond at the bridgehead is ($\Delta^{1,9}$-bicyclo-[4.3.1]-decene.)

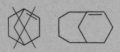

Rationalize *Bredt's* rule, and discuss the conditions under which it is no longer valid.

In ring systems such as that of the hypothetical bicycloheptene, the non-σ-bonded atomic orbitals of centers 1 and 2 would be oriented as in (A):

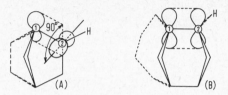

Regardless of whether atomic orbital $\Phi_1 = a\,(2s) + b\,(2p)$ is dominantly sp^3 hybridized ($a = \frac{1}{2}; b = \frac{1}{2}\sqrt{3}$) or a $2p$ orbital ($a = 0; b = 1$), it is orthogonal to the $2p$ atomic arbital at center 2, since neither the $2s$ nor the $2p$ components can overlap. Only if the molecular geometry allows angles which are much smaller than $90°$ between the atomic orbitals at centers 1 and 2 as in (B) can bonding interaction occur, which eventually leads to a more stable π-bond.

Problem 2.19: Prove that the functions Ψ (2/40) and Ψ^* (2/49) are orthogonal.

Substitution of the functions Ψ and Ψ^* into the orthogonality condition

$$\int \psi \psi^* dv = \int \frac{1}{\sqrt{2 + 2S}}(\phi_a + \phi_b)\frac{1}{\sqrt{2 - 2S}}(\phi_a - \phi_b)dv$$

$$= \frac{1}{\sqrt{(2 + 2S)(2 - 2S)}}\left(\int \phi_a^2 dv - \int \phi_b^2 dv\right)$$

$$= \frac{1}{\sqrt{(2 + 2S)(2 - 2S)}}(1 - 1) = 0$$

The solution to this problem is trivial, as has already been shown in Problem 1.6, since the integral of the product of a symmetric and an antisymmetric function always yields the value zero:

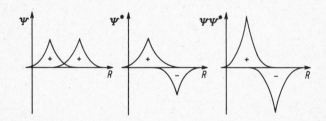

Problem 2.20: As a supplement to Problem 2.13, it can be demonstrated that the energy $E^*(R)$ of state Ψ^* (2/49) in the $H_2^\oplus$ molecule-ion, relative to the energy of a hydrogen atom and an infinitely distant proton, is given by:

$$E^*(R) = \frac{1}{R} + \frac{1-K}{1-S} \text{ [atomic units].}$$

Draw the function $E^*(R)$ using the data from Table (2/47).

With the aid of values from (2/47), one obtains the following potential energy curve $E^*(R)$:

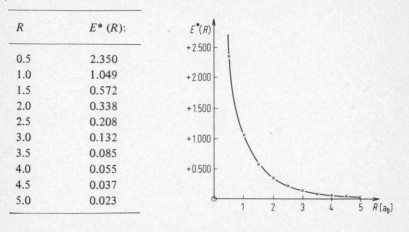

R	E^* (R):
0.5	2.350
1.0	1.049
1.5	0.572
2.0	0.338
2.5	0.208
3.0	0.132
3.5	0.085
4.0	0.055
4.5	0.037
5.0	0.023

Problem 2.21: The dissociation energy of nitric oxide NO is 6·5 eV, whereas that of the nitrosyl cation $NO^\oplus$ is 10·6 eV. Explain this difference using the simple MO scheme for homonuclear diatomic molecules, whose validity is also assumed for NO because of the very small dipole moment of only 0·16 Debye units. Deduce from the MO scheme whether the nitrosyl cation $NO^\oplus$ is paramagnetic like NO, or diamagnetic.

In the approximation of the homonuclear diatomic molecule, the following orbital occupations are valid for nitric oxide and the nitrosyl cation:

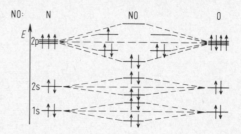

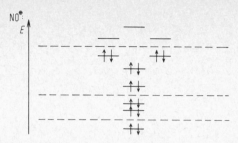

One of the electrons in nitric oxide is seen to occupy an energetically unfavorable antibonding orbital, thus explaining why its dissociation energy is about 4.1 eV lower than that of the nitrosyl cation $NO^\oplus$. The above model for $NO^\oplus$ possesses only paired electrons; the species is therefore expected to be diamagnetic.

Problem 2.22: Which is the preferred conformation of the hydrogen peroxide molecule, H—O—O—H, assuming that it has sp^2-hybridized oxygen atoms? (Hint: Note that antibonding molecular orbitals have their energies raised relative to the energy E of an isolated atomic orbital by an amount (3/40)

$$E + \frac{1 - K}{1 - S}.$$

This value is larger than the corresponding stabilization (3/39)

$$E + \frac{1 + K}{1 + S}$$

in the bonding molecular orbital. I and K are negative stabilization energies.)

The following three conformations are distinguished by their symmetry:

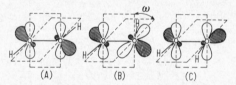

In our discussion of the preferred conformation let us consider the interaction between the free electron pairs of the oxygen atoms in the $2p$ atomic arbitals:

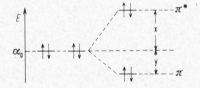

We refer the energies to the level α_0, corresponding to the energy of a lone pair of electrons occupying an oxygen $2p$-atomic orbital, and assume that the antibonding molecular orbital π^* rises above α_0 by an amount x exceeding the amount y by which the bonding molecular orbital sinks below α_0 ($|x| > |y|$). The conformations (A) and (C) (in which an interaction is possible between the $2p$-atomic orbitals each containing two electrons of the oxygen atom) are accordingly at an energetic disadvantage compared to the interaction-free conformation (B). In the same way, the repulsion between the two negative charge clouds Φ^2_{2p} on the oxygen atom also favors the conformation (B), in which the free electron pairs are arranged perpendicular to each other in the $2p$-atomic orbitals.

The above prediction accords with experiment: in H_2O_2 crystals the dihedral angle was determined as $\omega = 93.6°$; the angle OOH amounts to $96.5°$. It is assumed that the hydrogen atoms – which in the crystal form strong $O \ldots H\text{-}O$ hydrogen bonds from one molecule to another – lie on the line joining two oxygen atoms of different molecules.

2.4. Correlation Diagram for One-Electron Molecular Orbitals of Homonuclear Diatomic Molecules

Problem 2.23: Classify the linear combinations shown in 2.16 of pairs of $1s$-, $2s$-, $2p_x$-, $2p_y$-, and $2p_z$-atomic orbitals with respect to their symmetry behavior relative to the inversion centre i.

The following table gives three different designations (I, II and III) of the linear combinations as commonly encountered in the literature.

(2/51)		i	I	II	III
$\sigma(1s/1s)$		g	$1\sigma_g$		$\sigma(1s)_g$
$\sigma^*(1s/1s)$		u	$2\sigma_u$		$\sigma^*(1s)_g$
$\sigma(2s/2s)$		g	$3\sigma_g$	$z\sigma$	$\sigma(2s)_g$
$\sigma^*(2s/2s)$		u	$4\sigma_u$	$y\sigma$	$\sigma^*(2s)_g$
$\sigma(2p_y/2p_y)$		g	$5\sigma_g$	$x\sigma$	$\sigma(2p)_g$
$\sigma^*(2p_y/2p_y)$		u	$6\sigma_u$	$u\sigma$	$\sigma^*(2p)_u$
$\pi(2p_x/2p_x)$		u	$1\pi_x$	$w\pi$	$\pi(2p)_u$
$\pi^*(2p_x/2p_x)$		g	$2\pi_x$	$v\pi$	$\pi^*(2p)_g$
$\pi(2p_z/2p_z)$		u	$1\pi_z$		
$\pi^*(2p_z/2p_z)$		g	$2\pi_z$		

Problem 2.24: Determine the reduced symmetry behaviour of d_{xy}-, d_{yz}-, d_{xz}-, $d_{z^2-x^2}$-, and d_{y^2}-atomic orbitals with respect to the y-axis and the inversion centre i. (Hint: The d_{y^2} orbital is equivalent to the d_{z^2} orbital [2.8] and is represented by linear combination $d_{y^2} = (1/\sqrt{3})(d_{y^2-z^2} - d_{x^2-y^2})$.)

The individual atomic orbitals show the following symmetry behavior with respect to the y-axis and the inversion center i:

Atomic orbital		Symmetry behavior	
		y-**axis**	i
d_{xy}		$\pi_{(x)}$	g
d_{yz}		$\pi_{(z)}$	g
d_{xz}		δ	g
$d_{x^2-z^2}$		δ	g
$d_{y^2-z^2}$		σ	g
$d_{x^2-y^2}$			

3. MO-Theory: An Introduction to Quantum Mechanical Principles for Chemistry

3.1. The *Schrödinger* Equation

Problem 3.1: A system is called a harmonic oscillator if a particle of mass m moves under the influence of potential $V(x) = (k/2)x^2$. If the particle is displaced by an amount x from the equilibrium point $x = 0$, the force $K = -dV(x)/dx = -kx$ acts on it. The intrinsic frequency of the classical oscillator is $v_0 = (1/2\pi)\sqrt{k/m}$. The operator for such a system reads

$$\mathcal{H} = -\frac{h^2}{8\pi^2 m} \cdot \frac{d^2}{dx^2} + \frac{k}{2}x^2.$$

Show that the following functions in which $\alpha = (\pi/h) \cdot \sqrt{mk}$

$$\Psi_0 = N_0 \cdot e^{-\alpha x^2};$$
$$\Psi_1 = N_1 \cdot x \, e^{-\alpha x^2}$$

are eigenfunctions of the operator $\mathcal{H}$. Calculate the corresponding energy eigenvalues E_0 and E_1.

With the function Ψ_0 the *Schrödinger* equation (3/1) yields

$$\mathcal{H}\Psi_0 = E\Psi_0$$

$$= -\frac{h^2}{8\pi^2 m} \cdot \frac{d^2}{dx^2}\left(N_0 e^{-\alpha x^2}\right) + \frac{k}{2}x^2\left(N_0 e^{-\alpha x^2}\right)$$

$$= -\frac{h^2}{8\pi^2 m}\left(N_0 e^{-\alpha x^2}\right)\left(4\alpha^2 x^2 - 2\alpha\right) + \frac{k}{2}x^2\left(N_0 e^{-\alpha x^2}\right)$$

$$= \left(\frac{h^2}{8\pi^2 m}2\alpha + x^2\left(\frac{k}{2} - \frac{h^2}{8\pi^2 m}4\alpha^2\right)\right)\Psi_0$$

Thus the function Ψ_0 is reproduced by the operator $\mathcal{H}$. On substitution of $\alpha = (\pi/h)\sqrt{mk}$ the energy eigenvalue E_0 is found to be

$$E_0 = \frac{h}{4\pi m}\sqrt{mk} + x^2\left(\frac{k}{2} - \frac{k}{2}\right)$$

and with $\sqrt{mk} = 2\pi v_0 m$

$$E_0 = \frac{h v_0}{2}.$$

Correspondingly, substitution of Ψ_1 in the *Schrödinger* equation affords

$$\mathcal{H}\Psi_1 = E_1 \Psi_1$$

$$= -\frac{h^2}{8\pi^2 m}\frac{d^2}{dx^2}\,(N_1\,x\,e^{-\alpha x^2}) + \frac{k}{2}\,x^2\,(N_1\,x\,e^{-\alpha x^2})$$

$$= -\frac{h^2}{8\pi^2 m}\,(N_1\,x\,e^{-\alpha x^2})\,(4\alpha^2 x^2 + 6\alpha) + \frac{k}{2}\,x^2\,(N_1\,x\,e^{-\alpha x^2})$$

$$= (N_1\,x\,e^{-\alpha x^2})\left(\frac{h^2}{8\pi^2 m}\,6\alpha + x^2\left(\frac{k}{2} - \frac{h^2}{8\pi^2 m}\,4\alpha^2\right)\right)$$

$$= \Psi_1\,\frac{h}{4\pi m}\,3\,\sqrt{mk}$$

For the second energy eigenvalue E_1, putting $\sqrt{mk} = 2\pi m v_0$ gives

$$E_1 = \frac{h}{4\pi m}\cdot 2\pi v_0\,m = \frac{3}{2}\,h v_0$$

Supplement: In the above problem we have tested whether the given functions Ψ_0 and Ψ_1 are solutions of the *Schrödinger* equation. However, it remains an open question as to how one finds such functions. A general treatment of this problem will be found in textbooks of quantum mechanics and for the sake of clearer understanding we shall content ourselves with just a brief account of the procedure.

We start from the general expression

$$\Psi = N\cdot H(x)\cdot e^{-Bx^2}$$

in which N is a normalization factor and $H(x)$ represents a polynomial $H(x) = h_0 + h_1 x + h_2 x^2 \dots$

The simplest function of this type is obtained starting from $h_0 \neq 0$, and $h_1 = h_2 \dots = 0$.

$$\Psi_0 = N_0\cdot h_0\cdot e^{-B_0 x^2} = A_0 e^{-B_0 x^2}$$

In order to determine the constants A_0 and B_0, this expression is inserted into the *Schrödinger* equation for the harmonic oscillator

$$\mathcal{H}\Psi_0 = -\frac{h^2}{8\pi^2 m}\frac{d^2\Psi_0}{dx^2} + \frac{k}{2}x^2\Psi_0 = E\Psi_0.$$

With $\dfrac{d\Psi_0}{dx} = -2B_0\,x\cdot A_0\cdot e^{-B_0 x^2} = -2B_0\,x\,\Psi_0$,

$$\frac{d^2\Psi_0}{dx^2} = -2B_0\Psi_0 + 4B_0^2\,x^2\,\Psi_0$$

$$\mathcal{H}\Psi_0 = \frac{h^2 B_0}{4\pi^2 m}\Psi_0 + x^2\left(\frac{k}{2} - \frac{h^2 B_0^2}{2\pi^2 m}\right)\Psi_0 = E\Psi_0$$

The *Schrödinger* equation must of course be valid for all values of the independent variable x, i.e., x may not appear in the right hand side of the equation. This is only fulfilled if the expression in parentheses is equal to zero. Therefore, the value of B_0 is

$$\frac{k}{2} - \frac{h^2 B_0^2}{2\pi^2 m} = 0 \quad \Rightarrow \quad B_0 = \frac{\pi}{h} \sqrt{mk}.$$

With $\sqrt{mk} = 2\pi m\nu_0$, the eigenvalue E_0 becomes

$$E_0 = \frac{h^2 B_0}{4\pi^2 m} = \frac{h^2}{4\pi^2 m} \frac{\pi\sqrt{mk}}{h} = \frac{h\, 2\pi m\nu_0}{4\pi m} = \frac{h\nu_0}{2}$$

The normalization factor A_0, which need not be determined for calculation of E_0, can be obtained from the normalization condition:

$$\langle \Psi_0 | \Psi_0 \rangle = \langle A_0 e^{-B_0 x^2} | A_0 e^{-B_0 x^2} \rangle$$

$$= A_0^2 \int_{-\infty}^{+\infty} e^{-2B_0 x^2}\, dx = 2A_0^2 \int_0^{+\infty} e^{-2B_0 x^2}\, dx = 2A_0^2 \frac{\sqrt{\pi}}{2\sqrt{2B_0}} = 1$$

$$A_0 = \sqrt[4]{\frac{2B_0}{\pi}} = \sqrt[4]{\frac{2\sqrt{mk}}{h}} = \sqrt[4]{\frac{4\pi m\nu_0}{h}}$$

The next higher function Ψ_1 is obtained analogously with $h_1 \neq 0$ and $h_0, h_2, \ldots = 0$:

$$\Psi_1 = N_1 \cdot h_1 x \cdot e^{-B_1 x^2} = A_1 \cdot x \cdot e^{-B_1 x^2}.$$

Thus

$$\mathcal{H}\Psi_1 = \frac{3h^2 B_1}{4\pi^2 m} \Psi_1 + x^2 \left(\frac{k}{2} - \frac{h^2 B_1^2}{2\pi^2 m} \right) \Psi_1 = E\Psi_1$$

$$E_1 = \frac{3h^2 B_1}{4\pi^2 m} = \frac{3h^2}{4\pi^2 m} \cdot \frac{\pi\sqrt{mk}}{h} = \frac{3h \cdot 2\pi m\nu_0}{4\pi m} = \frac{3}{2} h\nu_0$$

$$A_1 = \sqrt[4]{\frac{32 B_1^3}{\pi}}$$

The general solution is obtained in basically the same way by deriving the conditions for the coefficients $h_0, h_1, \ldots h_n$ which render the corresponding function Ψ_n a solution of the *Schrödinger* equation. In so doing it should constantly be borne in mind that Ψ_n must be orthogonal to all the previously calculated functions ψ_0, $\Psi_1, \Psi_2, \ldots \Psi_{n-1}$.

Problem 3.2: Using the operator $\mathcal{H}$,

$$\mathcal{H} = (-h^2/8\pi^2 m).(d^2/dx^2)$$

and the normalized eigenfunctions Ψ_n

$$\Psi_n = (\sqrt{2/L})\sin(\pi n/L)x$$

calculate the eigenvalues (1/8) of the electron in a 'one-dimensional box'.

Introduction of the operator $\mathcal{H}$ and the eigenfunction Ψ_n into equation (3/15) yields

$$E_n = <\Psi_n|\mathcal{H}|\Psi_n>$$

$$= <\sqrt{\frac{2}{L}}\sin\left(\frac{\pi n}{L}\cdot x\right)\left|-\frac{h^2}{8\pi^2 m}\frac{d^2}{dx^2}\right|\sqrt{\frac{2}{L}}\sin\left(\frac{\pi n}{L}\cdot x\right)>$$

$$= <\sqrt{\frac{2}{L}}\sin\left(\frac{\pi n}{L}\cdot x\right)\left|\left(-\frac{h^2}{8\pi^2 m}\right)\left(-\sqrt{\frac{2}{L}}\left(\frac{\pi n}{L}\right)^2\sin\left(\frac{\pi n}{L}x\right)\right)>\right.$$

$$= \frac{h^2}{8\pi^2 m}\left(\frac{\pi n}{L}\right)^2<\sqrt{\frac{2}{L}}\sin\left(\frac{\pi n}{L}x\right)\left|\sqrt{\frac{2}{L}}\sin\left(\frac{\pi n}{L}x\right)>\right. = \frac{h^2}{8mL^2}n^2<\Psi_n|\Psi_n>$$

With the normalization condition $<\Psi_n|\Psi_n>=1$, the energy eigenvalue E_n is found to be

$$E_n = \frac{h^2}{8mL^2}n^2$$

in agreement with (1/8).

Problem 3.3: For the electron in a 'square box', the operator $(V_0 = 0)$ reads

$$\mathcal{H} = (-h^2/8\pi^2 m).(\partial^2/\partial x^2 + \partial^2/\partial y^2).$$

The eigenfunction for the lowest level is

$$\Psi_{11} = \frac{2}{L}\sin\left(\frac{\pi x}{L}\right)\sin\left(\frac{\pi y}{L}\right).$$

Calculate the eigenvalue E_{11}.

Introduction of the operator $\mathcal{H}$ and the eigenfunction Ψ_{11} into equation (3/15) gives

$$E_{11} = <\Psi_{11}|\mathcal{H}|\Psi_{11}>$$

$$= <\frac{2}{L}\sin\left(\frac{\pi}{L}x\right)\sin\left(\frac{\pi}{L}y\right)|-\frac{h^2}{8\pi^2 m}\left(\frac{\partial^2}{\partial x^2}+\frac{\partial^2}{\partial y^2}\right)|\frac{2}{L}\sin\left(\frac{\pi}{L}x\right)\sin\left(\frac{\pi}{L}y\right)>$$

$$= <\frac{2}{L}\sin\left(\frac{\pi}{L}x\right)\sin\left(\frac{\pi}{L}y\right)|\left(-\frac{h^2}{8\pi^2 m}\right)(-2)\left(\frac{\pi}{L}\right)^2\cdot\frac{2}{L}\sin\left(\frac{\pi}{L}x\right)\sin\left(\frac{\pi}{L}y\right)>$$

$$= \frac{h^2}{8\pi^2 m}\cdot 2\left(\frac{\pi}{L}\right)^2<\frac{2}{L}\sin\left(\frac{\pi}{L}x\right)\sin\left(\frac{\pi}{L}y\right)|\frac{2}{L}\sin\left(\frac{\pi}{L}x\right)\sin\left(\frac{\pi}{L}y\right)>$$

With the normalization requirement $<\Psi_{11}|\Psi_{11}>=1$, we obtain

$$E_{11} = \frac{h^2}{8\,m\,L^2}\cdot 2.$$

The general eigenvalue expression for an electron in a "square box"

$$E_{n_x n_y} = \frac{h^2}{8\,m\,L^2}(n_x^2 + n_y^2)$$

leads to the same value for E_{11} with $n_x = n_y = 1$.

3.2. Approximation Functions

Problem 3.4: For the two lowest levels of an electron in a 'one-dimensional box', with the origin of the coordinates in the centre of the box, the eigenvalues and eigenfunctions are:

$$E_1 = \frac{h^2}{8mL^2}; \qquad \Psi_1 = \sqrt{\frac{2}{L}}\cos\left(\frac{\pi}{L}x\right),$$

$$E_2 = \frac{h^2}{8mL^2}\cdot 4; \qquad \Psi_2 = \sqrt{\frac{2}{L}}\sin\left(\frac{2\pi}{L}x\right).$$

Draw the approximation functions

$$F_1 = N_1\left(\frac{L^2}{4} - x^2\right);$$

$$F_2 = N_2 x\left(\frac{L^2}{4} - x^2\right)$$

as well as Ψ_1 and Ψ_2 in units of $\sqrt{2/L}$. Calculate the approximation values ε_1 and ε_2 and compare them with the true eigenvalues E_1 and E_2.

First of all, the normalization factors N_1 and N_2 are to be determined for F_1 and F_2

$$\langle F_1 | F_1 \rangle = N_1^2 \int\limits_{-\frac{L}{2}}^{+\frac{L}{2}} \left(\frac{L^2}{4} - x^2\right)^2 dx = 2N_1^2 \int\limits_{0}^{\frac{L}{2}} \left(\frac{L^2}{4} - x^2\right)^2 dx$$

$$= 2N_1^2 \cdot \frac{L^5}{60} = 1$$

$$N_1 = \sqrt{\frac{30}{L^5}}$$

$$\langle F_1 | F_2 \rangle = N_2^2 \int\limits_{-\frac{L}{2}}^{+\frac{L}{2}} \left(\frac{L^2}{4} x - x^3\right)^2 dx = 2N_2^2 \int\limits_{0}^{\frac{L}{2}} \left(\frac{L^2}{4} x - x^3\right)^2 dx$$

$$= 2N_2^2 \cdot \frac{L^7}{1680} = 1$$

$$N_2 = \sqrt{\frac{840}{L^7}}$$

For the normalized functions

$$F_1 = \sqrt{\frac{2}{L}} \cdot \frac{3.87}{L} \left(\frac{L^2}{4} - x^2\right),$$

$$F_2 = \sqrt{\frac{2}{L}} \cdot \frac{20.5}{L^3} \left(\frac{L^2}{4} x - x^3\right)$$

as well as for Ψ_1 and Ψ_2, it is useful to set up a table of values in units of $\sqrt{2/L}$:

x	F_1	F_2	Ψ_1	Ψ_2
$+ \ L/2$	0.000	0.000	0.000	0.000
$+ 3\,L/8$	0.424	0.841	0.383	0.707
$+ \ L/4$	0.726	0.961	0.707	1.000
$+ \ L/8$	0.908	0.600	0.924	0.707
0	0.968	0.000	1.000	0.000
$- \ L/8$	0.908	-0.600	0.924	-0.707
$- \ L/4$	0.726	-0.961	0.707	-1.000
$-3\,L/8$	0.424	-0.841	0.383	-0.707
$- \ L/2$	0.000	0.000	0.000	0.000

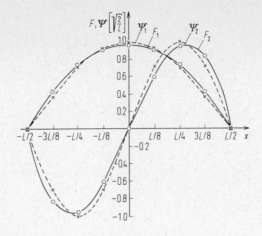

As can be seen, Ψ_1 and Ψ_2 are satisfactorily reproduced by the approximation functions F_1 and F_2.

The approximation value ϵ_1 is expressed as

$$\epsilon_1 = <F_1|\mathcal{H}|F_1>$$

$$= <\sqrt{\frac{30}{L^5}}\left(\frac{L^2}{4} - x^2\right)\left|-\frac{h^2}{8\pi^2 m}\frac{d^2}{dx^2}\right| \sqrt{\frac{30}{L^5}}\left(\frac{L^2}{4} - x^2\right)>$$

$$= <\sqrt{\frac{30}{L^5}}\left(\frac{L^2}{4} - x^2\right)\left|\frac{h^2}{8\pi^2 m}\cdot\sqrt{\frac{30}{L^5}}\cdot 2>\right.$$

$$= \frac{30\,h^2}{4\pi^2 mL^5}\cdot 2\int_0^{\frac{L}{2}}\left(\frac{L^2}{4} - x^2\right)dx$$

$$= \frac{15\,h^2}{\pi^2 mL^5}\left(\frac{L^3}{8} - \frac{L^3}{24}\right) = \frac{h^2}{8mL^2}\cdot\frac{10}{\pi^2} = 1.013\,E_1$$

Correspondingly, for the approximation value ϵ_2, we obtain

$$\epsilon_2 = <F_2|\mathcal{H}|F_2>$$

$$= <\sqrt{\frac{840}{L^7}}\,x\left(\frac{L^2}{4} - x^2\right)\left|-\frac{h^2}{8\pi^2 m}\frac{d^2}{dx^2}\right| \sqrt{\frac{840}{L^7}}\,x\left(\frac{L^2}{4} - x^2\right)>$$

$$= <\sqrt{\frac{840}{L^7}}x\left(\frac{L^2}{4} - x^2\right)\left|\frac{h^2}{8\pi^2 m}\sqrt{\frac{840}{L^7}}\cdot 6x>\right.$$

$$= \frac{840\,h^2}{8\pi^2 mL^7}\cdot 2\cdot\int_0^{\frac{L}{2}}x\left(\frac{L^2}{4} - x^2\right)6x\,dx$$

$$= \frac{210\,h^2}{\pi^2 mL^7}\left(\frac{L^5}{16} - \frac{3L^5}{80}\right) = \frac{h^2}{8mL^2}\cdot 4\cdot\frac{10.5}{\pi^2} = 1.064\,E_2$$

The result $\epsilon_1 > E_1$ and $\epsilon_2 > E_2$ is in agreement with the general principle that the approximation value ϵ always lies higher than the true eigenvalue E. The errors $\epsilon_1 - E_1$ and $\epsilon_2 - E_2$ are small in the present case as is obvious from the graphic representation since the true eigenfunctions Ψ_1 and Ψ_2 are well represented by the approximation functions F_1 and F_2.

3.3. Linear Combinations of Atomic Orbitals

Problem 3.5: Using the data of Table (2/47), show that the total energy E_2 in the first excited state (3/44) of the hydrogen molecule, H_2, satisfies the relation $E'_2 > 2E'_A$ as suggested by [3.2] for all distances R between the two nuclei, if the electronic interaction is taken into account qualitatively.

On introduction of (3/39) and (3/40) into relation (3/44), it follows that

$$E'_2 (R) = E_1 + E_2 + V (R) = \frac{I + K}{1 + S} + \frac{I - K}{1 - S} + \frac{1}{R} + 2 E_A$$

Moreover, the relation

$$E'_2 (R) = E (R) + E^* (R) - \frac{1}{R} + 2 E_A$$

holds, where according to [3.2] $2 E_A$ represents the reference energy of two separate hydrogen atoms. By use of the tables from Problems 2.13 and 2.20, the following table is compiled:

R	$E (R)$	$E^* (R)$	$-\dfrac{1}{R}$	$E'_2 (R)$
0.5	1.079	2.350	-2.000	1.429
1.0	0.212	1.049	-1.000	0.261
1.5	0.005	0.572	-0.667	-0.090
2.0	-0.054	0.338	-0.500	-0.216
2.5	-0.065	0.208	-0.400	-0.257
3.0	-0.059	0.132	-0.333	-0.260
3.5	-0.048	0.085	-0.286	-0.249
4.0	-0.038	0.055	-0.250	-0.233
4.5	-0.028	0.037	-0.222	-0.213
5.0	-0.019	0.023	-0.200	-0.196

Contrary to expectation, $E'_2(R)$ passes through a minimum of 0.26 atomic units at $R = 3a_0$, corresponding to a bond energy of 7.1 eV = 164 kcal/mol. This artefact is to be attributed to the neglected electron interaction, which amounts to 29.8 eV for the distance $R = 0$ (cf. He atom (2/19)). It can be shown that this interaction is considerable even for the distance $R = 2a_0 = 1.06$ Å. The bond energy of the H_2 molecule is 103.2 kcal/mol = 4.5 eV. For an occupation of E_1 by two electrons, a bond energy of +0.61 atomic energy units = 16.6 eV would be calculated, assuming interaction-free electrons, by substitution of the values from (2/47) into (3/43). However, since the bond energy only amounts to 4.5 eV, the difference of 12.1 eV must correspond to the repulsion potential between the electrons. A value of this order of magnitude would have to be added to the tabulated value $E'_2(R = 2a_0) = -0.216$ atomic energy units, which would lead to a total energy of the system $> 2E_A$.

The repulsion between the electrons is therefore an essential factor, which should always be kept in mind, even though the present and future calculations are conducted with interaction-free electrons.

Problem 3.6: Determinants play an important role in HMO theory. It is therefore recommended to do a few exercises. Calculate the values of the determinants:

(a) $\|13\|$

(b) $\begin{Vmatrix} a & b \\ c & d \end{Vmatrix}$

(c) $\begin{Vmatrix} 4 & 3 & 2 \\ -1 & 2 & 1 \\ 1 & 1 & 1 \end{Vmatrix}$

(d) $\begin{Vmatrix} 1 & 2 & 3 & 2 \\ 4 & 0 & -1 & 1 \\ 1 & 2 & 3 & 2 \\ 2 & 0 & -1 & -1 \end{Vmatrix}$

(e) $\begin{Vmatrix} A-x & B-cx \\ B-cx & A-x \end{Vmatrix}$

(f) $\begin{Vmatrix} -x & 1 & 0 & 0 \\ 1 & -x & 1 & 0 \\ 0 & 1 & -x & 1 \\ 0 & 0 & 1 & -x \end{Vmatrix}$

(g) Calculate the coefficients c_1, c_2, and c_3 which satisfy the system of equations

$$c_1 - 2c_2 + c_3 = -1,$$
$$-c_1 - c_2 + 2c_3 = 7,$$
$$2c_1 - 3c_2 - c_3 = -10.$$

(h) For what value of y can the homogeneous system of equations

$$c_1 + c_2 + yc_3 = 0,$$
$$4c_1 + c_2 + 2c_3 = 0,$$
$$yc_1 + 3c_2 - 2c_3 = 0$$

be solved in a non-trivial way? (i.e. different from $c_1 = c_2 = c_3 = 0$)?

a) $\| \ \| = 13$

b) $\| \ \| = ad - bc$

c) $\| \ \| = 8 + 3 - 2 - 4 - 4 + 3 = 4$

d) This determinant yields zero, since the first and third rows are identical.

e) $\| \ \| = (A - x)^2 - (B - cx)^2 = (1 - c^2)x^2 + 2(Bc - A)x + A^2 - B^2$

f) Determinants of order higher than three are best expanded into determinants of order three, which can then be solved.

$$\| \ \| = (-x) \begin{Vmatrix} -x & 1 & 0 \\ 1 & -x & 1 \\ 0 & 1 & -x \end{Vmatrix} - 1 \begin{Vmatrix} 1 & 1 & 0 \\ 0 & -x & 1 \\ 0 & 1 & -x \end{Vmatrix}$$

$$= (-x)(-x^3 + x + x) - (x^2 - 1) = x^4 - 3x^2 + 1$$

g) According to the *Cramer* rule (see appropriate text on matrix algebra):

$$c_1 = \frac{D_1}{D} \quad ; \quad c_2 = \frac{D_2}{D} \quad ; \quad c_3 = \frac{D_3}{D}$$

$$D = \begin{Vmatrix} 1 & -2 & 1 \\ -1 & -1 & 2 \\ 2 & -3 & -1 \end{Vmatrix} = 1 - 8 + 3 + 2 + 6 + 2 = 6$$

$$D_1 = \begin{Vmatrix} -1 & -2 & 1 \\ 7 & -1 & 2 \\ -10 & -3 & -1 \end{Vmatrix} = -1 + 40 - 21 - 10 - 6 - 14 = -12$$

$$D_2 = \begin{Vmatrix} 1 & -1 & 1 \\ -1 & 7 & 2 \\ 2 & -10 & -1 \end{Vmatrix} = -7 - 4 + 10 - 14 + 20 + 1 = 6$$

$$D_3 = \begin{Vmatrix} 1 & -2 & -1 \\ -1 & -1 & 7 \\ 2 & -3 & -10 \end{Vmatrix} = 10 - 28 - 3 - 2 + 21 + 20 = 18$$

$$c_1 = \frac{-12}{6} = -2 \quad ; \quad c_2 = \frac{6}{6} = 1 \quad ; \quad c_3 = \frac{18}{6} = 3$$

h) The system of homogeneous equations admits a non-trival solution if the determinant of the coefficients is identically equal to zero:

$$\begin{vmatrix} 1 & 1 & y \\ 4 & 1 & 2 \\ y & 3 & -2 \end{vmatrix} = -2 + 2y + 12y - y^2 - 6 + 8 = 0$$

$$y^2 - 14y = 0$$

$$y_1 = 0$$

$$y_2 = 14$$

For $y = 0$, substitution in the equations yields

$$c_1 = -c_2 = -\frac{2}{3}c_3 \ .$$

For $y = 14$, substitution in the equations yields

$$c_1 = -\frac{2}{9}c_2 = 4c_3 \ .$$

Problem 3.7: Calculate the coefficients c_A, c_B, and c_C of the linear combination

$$F = c_A\Phi_A + c_B\Phi_B + c_C\Phi_C$$

for the motion of an electron in the field of 3 protons (Φ_A, Φ_B, and Φ_C are $1s$ atomic orbitals of hydrogen), which are centred on the corners of an equilateral triangle of side R. What energy levels are obtained? Show that the molecule-ion $H_3^{\oplus}$ cannot be stable.

In order to simplify the calculation, we introduce the following abbreviations (in analogy to (3/26)):

$$\left. \begin{array}{l} < \Phi_A |\mathcal{H}| \Phi_A > = H_{AA} \\[2mm] < \Phi_B |\mathcal{H}| \Phi_B > = H_{BB} \\[2mm] < \Phi_C |\mathcal{H}| \Phi_C > = H_{CC} \end{array} \right\} = A$$

$$\left. \begin{array}{l} < \Phi_A |\mathcal{H}| \Phi_B > = H_{AB} = H_{BA} \\[2mm] < \Phi_A |\mathcal{H}| \Phi_C > = H_{AC} = H_{CA} \\[2mm] < \Phi_B |\mathcal{H}| \Phi_C > = H_{BC} = H_{CB} \end{array} \right\} = B$$

For the approximation energy value (3/27)

$$
\begin{aligned}
\epsilon(c_A, c_B, c_C) &= \frac{<F|\mathcal{H}|F>}{<F|F>} \\[3mm]
&= \frac{<c_A\Phi_A + c_B\Phi_B + c_C\Phi_C|\mathcal{H}|c_A\Phi_A + c_B\Phi_B + c_C\Phi_C>}{<c_A\Phi_A + c_B\Phi_B + c_C\Phi_C|c_A\Phi_A + c_B\Phi_B + c_C\Phi_C>} \\[3mm]
&= \frac{c_A^2 H_{AA} + c_B^2 H_{BB} + c_C^2 H_{CC} + 2c_A c_B H_{AB} + 2c_A c_C H_{AC} + 2c_B c_C H_{BC}}{c_A^2 + c_B^2 + c_C^2 + 2S(c_A c_B + c_A c_C + c_B c_C)} \\[3mm]
&= \frac{A(c_A^2 + c_B^2 + c_C^2) + 2B(c_A c_B + c_A c_C + c_B c_C)}{c_A^2 + c_B^2 + c_C^2 + 2S(c_A c_B + c_A c_C + c_B c_C)}
\end{aligned}
$$

with $\dfrac{\partial \epsilon}{\partial c_A} = \dfrac{\partial \epsilon}{\partial c_B} = \dfrac{\partial \epsilon}{\partial c_C} = 0$ the secular equations are found to be

$$c_A \,(A - \epsilon) + c_B \,(B - \epsilon S) + c_C \,(B - \epsilon S) = 0$$
$$c_A \,(B - \epsilon S) + c_B \,(A - \epsilon) + c_C \,(B - \epsilon S) = 0$$
$$c_A \,(B - \epsilon S) + c_B \,(B - \epsilon S) + c_C \,(A - \epsilon) = 0$$

Division by $(B - \epsilon S)$ and replacement of $\dfrac{(A - \epsilon)}{(B - \epsilon S)}$ by y gives the following simplified system of equations:

$$c_A \cdot y + c_B \quad + c_C \quad = 0$$
$$c_A \quad + c_B \cdot y + c_C \quad = 0$$
$$c_A \quad + c_B \quad + c_C \cdot y = 0$$

The secular determinant reads:

$$\begin{Vmatrix} y & 1 & 1 \\ 1 & y & 1 \\ 1 & 1 & y \end{Vmatrix} = 0 = \begin{aligned} & y^3 - 3y + 2 \\ & = (y - 1)(y^2 + y - 2) \end{aligned}$$

The resulting polynomial has the solutions

$$y_1 = -2 \quad ; \quad y_2 = y_3 = 1 \ .$$

The approximate energy values y_J are introduced into the simplified secular equations

$$c_{JA} \, y_J + c_{JB} \quad + c_{JC} \quad = 0 \,,$$
$$c_{JA} \quad + c_{JB} \, y_J + c_{JC} \quad = 0 \,,$$
$$c_{JA} \quad + c_{JB} \quad + c_{JC} \, y_J = 0$$

in which c_{JA}, c_{JB}, and c_{JC} are the solutions belonging to y_J. Since these coefficients can clearly only be determined up to an arbitrary factor, as long as we neglect normalization, one can set e.g. $c_{JA} = 1$ without loss of generality and thus obtain for $y_1 = -2$:

$$c_{1A} = 1: \quad -2 + c_{1B} + c_{1C} = 0; \quad c_{1B} + c_{1C} = 2$$
$$1 - 2c_{1B} + c_{1C} = 0; \quad -2c_{1B} + c_{1C} = -1$$
$$c_{1B} = 1$$
$$c_{1C} = 1$$

For the degenerate eigenvalues $y_2 = y_3 = 1$, the coefficients c_{JA}, c_{JB}, and c_{JC} ($J = 2, 3$) are determined only in so far as their sum amounts to 0 according to the secular equations. From among the infinite number of possibilities, we arbitrarily select the following:

$$c_{2A} = 2; c_{2B} = c_{2C} = -1,$$
$$c_{3A} = 0; c_{3B} = -c_{3C} = 1,$$

since these sets belong to two of the possible linear combinations which are orthogonal. Altogether, the linear combinations obtained are

$$\psi_1 = N_1 \left(\Phi_A + \Phi_B + \Phi_C \right)$$

$$\psi_2 = N_2 \left(2\Phi_A - \Phi_B - \Phi_C \right)$$

$$\psi_3 = N_3 \left(\Phi_B - \Phi_C \right)$$

The normalization factors N_J are calculated as follows:

$$\left< \psi_1 \mid \psi_1 \right> = 1 = N_1^2 \left(1+1+1+2S\left(1+1+1\right) \right) = N_1^2 \left(3+6S\right)$$

$$N_1 = \frac{1}{\sqrt{3+6S}}$$

$$\left< \psi_2 \mid \psi_2 \right> = 1 = N_2^2 \left(4+1+1+2S\left(-2-2+1\right) \right) = N_2^2 \left(6-6S\right)$$

$$N_2 = \frac{1}{\sqrt{6-6S}}$$

$$\left< \psi_3 \mid \psi_3 \right> = 1 = N_3^2 \left(1+1+2S\left(-1\right) \right) = N_3^2 \left(2-2S\right)$$

$$N_3 = \frac{1}{\sqrt{2-2S}}$$

The desired coefficients of a possible set of orthogonal functions are therefore:

$$c_{1A} = c_{1B} = c_{1C} = \frac{1}{\sqrt{3+6S}}$$

$$c_{2A} = \frac{2}{\sqrt{6-6S}} \quad ; \quad c_{2B} = c_{2C} = -\frac{1}{\sqrt{6-6S}}$$

$$c_{3A} = 0 \quad ; \quad c_{3B} = -c_{3C} = \frac{1}{\sqrt{2-2S}}$$

The energy level scheme for the cyclic $H_3^{\oplus}$ cation would be occupied with two electrons in the bonding orbital as shown. Nevertheless the system is unstable according to the following calculation. The total energy E_1 of the ground state is made up of twice the energy of the electron in the bonding level ϵ_1 and three times the repulsion potential $V(R)$ between the nuclei:

$$E_1 = 2\epsilon_1 + 3\,V(R).$$

Explicit substitution with $y_1 = -2 = (A - \epsilon)/(B - \epsilon S)$ leads to the expression

$$\epsilon_1 = \frac{A+2B}{1+2S} = \frac{H_{AA}+2H_{AB}}{1+2S} = \frac{(E_A+I)+2(E_A S+K)}{1+2S} = E_A + \frac{I+2K}{1+2S}$$

$$E_1 = 2E_A + 2\left(\frac{I+2K}{1+2S}\right) + 3\,V(K)$$

or, relative to the energy of two hydrogen atoms and a proton separated by an infinite distance from each other:

$$E(R) = 2\left(\frac{I+2K}{1+2S}\right) + 3\,V(R).$$

$E(R)$ can be calculated with the values of Table (2/47).

$R\,[a_o]$	$2\left(\dfrac{I+2K}{1+2S}\right)\left[\dfrac{e^2}{a_o}\right]$	$3\,V(R)\left[\dfrac{e^2}{a_o}\right]$	$E(R)\left[\dfrac{e^2}{a_o}\right]$
0.5	− 1.86	+ 6.00	+ 4.14
1.0	− 1.56	+ 3.00	+ 1.43
2.0	− 1.18	+ 1.50	+ 0.32
3.0	− 0.86	+ 1.00	+ 0.14

Thus the relationship $\left|3\,V(R)\right| > \left|2\,\dfrac{I+2K}{1+2S}\right|$ always applies and the energy does not pass through a minimum corresponding to a bonding state.

As can be shown, the cyclic $H_3^{\oplus}$ cation, is at an energetic disadvantage relative to the linear one in which the repulsion potential between the nuclei amounts to only $2\,V(R)$:

4. The MO-Procedure of *E. Hückel* (HMO)

4.1. General Conventions of HMO Theory

Problem 4.1: Which of the following *Hückel* molecular orbitals are normalized?

(a)
$$\Psi_1 = \frac{1}{\sqrt{2}}(\Phi_1 + \Phi_2),$$

(b)
$$\Psi_2 = \frac{1}{\sqrt{4}}(\Phi_1 - 2\Phi_2 + \Phi_3),$$

(c)
$$\Psi_3 = \frac{1}{\sqrt{3}}(\Phi_1 + \Phi_2 + \Phi_3).$$

Examine whether the following linear combination of the *Hückel* molecular orbitals Ψ_1 and Ψ_3 is normalized

(d)
$$\Psi_4 = \frac{1}{\sqrt{2}}(\Psi_1 - \Psi_3).$$

By substituting in the normalization condition

$$\sum_{\mu=1}^{n} c_\mu^2 = 1 \qquad (4/6)$$

it is found that only the functions Ψ_1 and Ψ_3 are normalized

$$(a) \ \sum_{\mu=1}^{2} c_\mu^2 = 2 \cdot \left(\frac{1}{\sqrt{2}}\right)^2 = 1$$

$$(b) \ \sum_{\mu=1}^{3} c_\mu^2 = 2 \cdot \left(\frac{1}{\sqrt{4}}\right)^2 + \left(\frac{-2}{\sqrt{4}}\right)^2 = \frac{3}{2}$$

The correct normalization factor N_2 in $\Psi_2 = N_2\,(\Phi_1 - 2\Phi_2 + \Phi_3)$ would be

$$\sum_{\mu=1}^{3} c_\mu^2 = (1)^2 + (-2)^2 + (1)^2 = 6 \ ; \ N_2 = \frac{1}{\sqrt{6}} \ .$$

$$(c) \ \sum_{\mu=1}^{3} c_\mu^2 = 3\left(\frac{1}{\sqrt{3}}\right)^2 = \frac{3}{3} = 1$$

(*d*) In this case we obtain

$$(d) \ \psi_4 = \frac{1}{\sqrt{2}}(\psi_1 - \psi_3) = \frac{1}{\sqrt{2}}\left(\frac{1}{\sqrt{2}}(\Phi_1 + \Phi_2) - \frac{1}{\sqrt{3}}(\Phi_1 + \Phi_2 + \Phi_3)\right)$$

$$= \left(\frac{1}{2} - \frac{1}{\sqrt{6}}\right)\Phi_1 + \left(\frac{1}{2} - \frac{1}{\sqrt{6}}\right)\Phi_2 - \frac{1}{\sqrt{6}}\Phi_3$$

$$\sum_{\mu=1}^{3} c_\mu^2 = 2 \cdot \left(\frac{1}{2} - \frac{1}{\sqrt{6}}\right)^2 + \left(-\frac{1}{\sqrt{6}}\right)^2 = \frac{1}{2} - \frac{2}{\sqrt{6}} + \frac{2}{6} + \frac{1}{6} = 1 - \frac{2}{\sqrt{6}}$$

This situation arises because the functions Ψ_1 and Ψ_3 are normalized individually but are not mutually orthogonal.

$$< \Psi_1 | \Psi_3 > = < \frac{1}{\sqrt{2}} \left(\Phi_1 + \Phi_2 \right) | \frac{1}{\sqrt{3}} \left(\Phi_1 + \Phi_2 + \Phi_3 \right) >$$

$$= \frac{1}{\sqrt{6}} \left\{ < \Phi_1 | \Phi_1 > + 2 < \Phi_1 | \Phi_2 > + < \Phi_1 | \Phi_3 > + < \Phi_2 | \Phi_2 > + < \Phi_2 | \Phi_3 > \right\}$$

$$= \frac{2}{\sqrt{6}} \neq 0$$

Problem 4.2: Number the centres of the π-electron systems of compounds (a) through (d) so that the matrices of type (4/13) will differ in as few of the matrix elements as possible:

(a) (b) (c) (d)

Specify the differing matrix elements.

This requirement will be satisfied, for example, by numbering the compounds (a) through (d) in the following way:

(a) (b) (c) (d)

The differing matrix elements are:

	(a)	(b)	(c)	(d)
$H_{1\,10}$	0	$\beta_{1\,10}$	$\beta_{1\,10}$	$\beta_{1\,10}$
H_{56}	0	β_{56}	β_{56}	0
H_{38}	β_{38}	0	β_{38}	β_{38}
H_{39}	0	β_{39}	0	0

4.2. Variational Calculus within the HMO Approximation

Problem 4.3: Write the secular equations for fulvene [4.1] by corresponding substitution of the quantities $H_{\rho\mu}$ by $\beta_{\rho\mu}, \alpha_\mu$, or zero, according to HMO conventions (4/9) through (4/12).

The secular equations for the fulvene molecule in their general form (4/24) read

$$\sum_{\mu=1}^{6} c_\mu (H_{\rho\mu} - \delta_{\rho\mu}\epsilon) = 0 \quad ; \quad \rho = 1,2 \ldots 6$$

We thus obtain:

$$c_1 (H_{11} - \epsilon) + c_2 H_{12} + c_3 H_{13} + c_4 H_{14} + c_5 H_{15} + c_6 H_{16} = 0$$
$$c_1 H_{21} + c_2 (H_{22} - \epsilon) + c_3 H_{23} + c_4 H_{24} + c_5 H_{25} + c_6 H_{26} = 0$$
$$c_1 H_{31} + c_2 H_{32} + c_3 (H_{33} - \epsilon) + c_4 H_{34} + c_5 H_{35} + c_6 H_{36} = 0$$
$$c_1 H_{41} + c_2 H_{42} + c_3 H_{43} + c_4 (H_{44} - \epsilon) + c_5 H_{45} + c_6 H_{46} = 0$$
$$c_1 H_{51} + c_2 H_{52} + c_3 H_{53} + c_4 H_{54} + c_5 (H_{55} - \epsilon) + c_6 H_{56} = 0$$
$$c_1 H_{61} + c_2 H_{62} + c_3 H_{63} + c_4 H_{64} + c_5 H_{65} + c_6 (H_{66} - \epsilon) = 0$$

Substitution affords:

$$c_1 (\alpha - \epsilon) + c_2\beta \qquad\qquad + c_5\beta \qquad = 0$$
$$c_1\beta + c_2 (\alpha - \epsilon) + c_3\beta \qquad\qquad = 0$$
$$c_2\beta + c_3 (\alpha - \epsilon) + c_4\beta \qquad\qquad = 0$$
$$c_3\beta + c_4 (\alpha - \epsilon) + c_5\beta \qquad = 0$$
$$c_1\beta + \qquad\qquad c_4\beta + c_5 (\alpha - \epsilon) + c_6\beta = 0$$
$$c_5\beta + c_6 (\alpha - \epsilon) = 0$$

Problem 4.4: For the π-electron system

$$\mu = \quad \overset{1}{\underset{}{A}} - \overset{2}{\underset{}{B}} - \overset{3}{\underset{}{A}}$$

calculate the orbital energy values ϵ_1, ϵ_2, and ϵ_3. Draw the resulting energy level scheme for increasing values of β_{12}. (Hint: Because of symmetry, $\alpha_1 = \alpha_3$ and $\beta_{12} = \beta_{23}$.)

The secular determinant (4/26) for the system $A - B - A$ is

$$\left\| \begin{array}{ccc} \alpha_1 - \epsilon & \beta_{12} & 0 \\ \beta_{12} & \alpha_2 - \epsilon & \beta_{12} \\ 0 & \beta_{12} & \alpha_1 - \epsilon \end{array} \right\| = 0$$

The resulting polynomial

$$(\alpha_1 - \epsilon)^2 (\alpha_2 - \epsilon) - 2\beta_{12}^2 (\alpha_1 - \epsilon) = 0$$

$$(\alpha_1 - \epsilon)\left[(\alpha_1 - \epsilon)(\alpha_2 - \epsilon) - 2\beta_{12}^2 \right] = 0$$

yields the solutions:

$$\epsilon_1 = \alpha_1$$

$$\epsilon_2 = \frac{\alpha_1 + \alpha_2}{2} + \frac{1}{2}\sqrt{(\alpha_1 - \alpha_2)^2 + 8\beta_{12}^2}$$

$$\epsilon_3 = \frac{\alpha_1 + \alpha_2}{2} - \frac{1}{2}\sqrt{(\alpha_1 - \alpha_2)^2 + 8\beta_{12}^2}$$

The energy level scheme for increasing values of β_{12} has the appearance:

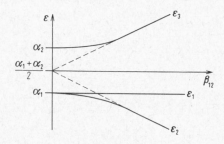

4.3. *Hückel* Determinants for Carbon π-Systems

Problem 4.5: Write the *Hückel* determinants (4/32) for the following carbon π-systems:

(a)   (b)   (c)   (d)   (e)

(f)

The *Hückel* determinants for the individual hydrocarbon π-systems are:

(a)
$$\begin{Vmatrix} -x & 1 & 0 & 0 & 0 & 0 \\ 1 & -x & 1 & 1 & 0 & 0 \\ 0 & 1 & -x & 1 & 0 & 0 \\ 0 & 1 & 1 & -x & 1 & 0 \\ 0 & 0 & 0 & 1 & -x & 1 \\ 0 & 0 & 0 & 0 & 1 & -x \end{Vmatrix} = 0$$

(b)
$$\begin{Vmatrix} -x & 1 & 1 & 1 & 0 & 0 \\ 1 & -x & 1 & 0 & 1 & 0 \\ 1 & 1 & -x & 0 & 0 & 1 \\ 1 & 0 & 0 & -x & 0 & 0 \\ 0 & 1 & 0 & 0 & -x & 0 \\ 0 & 0 & 1 & 0 & 0 & -x \end{Vmatrix} = 0$$

(c)
$$\begin{Vmatrix} -x & 1 & 0 & 0 & 0 & 0 \\ 1 & -x & 1 & 0 & 1 & 0 \\ 0 & 1 & -x & 1 & 0 & 0 \\ 0 & 0 & 1 & -x & 1 & 0 \\ 0 & 1 & 0 & 1 & -x & 1 \\ 0 & 0 & 0 & 0 & 1 & -x \end{Vmatrix} = 0$$

(d)
$$\begin{Vmatrix} -x & 1 & 0 & 0 & 0 & 0 \\ 1 & -x & 1 & 0 & 0 & 0 \\ 0 & 1 & -x & 1 & 0 & 1 \\ 0 & 0 & 1 & -x & 1 & 0 \\ 0 & 0 & 0 & 1 & -x & 1 \\ 0 & 0 & 1 & 0 & 1 & -x \end{Vmatrix} = 0$$

(e)
$$\begin{Vmatrix} -x & 1 & 0 & 0 & 0 & 0 \\ 1 & -x & 1 & 0 & 0 & 0 \\ 0 & 1 & -x & 1 & 1 & 0 \\ 0 & 0 & 1 & -x & 0 & 0 \\ 0 & 0 & 1 & 0 & -x & 1 \\ 0 & 0 & 0 & 0 & 1 & -x \end{Vmatrix} = 0$$

(f)
$$\begin{Vmatrix} -x & 1 & 0 & 0 & 0 & 0 & 0 & 0 & 1 & 0 \\ 1 & -x & 1 & 0 & 0 & 0 & 0 & 0 & 0 & 0 \\ 0 & 1 & -x & 0 & 0 & 0 & 0 & 0 & 0 & 1 \\ 0 & 0 & 0 & -x & 1 & 0 & 0 & 0 & 0 & 1 \\ 0 & 0 & 0 & 1 & -x & 1 & 0 & 0 & 0 & 0 \\ 0 & 0 & 0 & 0 & 1 & -x & 1 & 0 & 0 & 0 \\ 0 & 0 & 0 & 0 & 0 & 1 & -x & 1 & 0 & 0 \\ 0 & 0 & 0 & 0 & 0 & 0 & 1 & -x & 1 & 0 \\ 1 & 0 & 0 & 0 & 0 & 0 & 0 & 1 & -x & 1 \\ 0 & 0 & 1 & 1 & 0 & 0 & 0 & 0 & 1 & -x \end{Vmatrix} = 0$$

Problem 4.6: Draw the carbon π-systems corresponding to the following *Hückel* determinants

(a)
$$\begin{Vmatrix} -x & 0 & 0 & 1 & 1 & 0 \\ 0 & -x & 0 & 0 & 1 & 1 \\ 0 & 0 & -x & 1 & 0 & 1 \\ 1 & 0 & 1 & -x & 0 & 0 \\ 1 & 1 & 0 & 0 & -x & 0 \\ 0 & 1 & 1 & 0 & 0 & -x \end{Vmatrix} = 0;$$

(b)
$$\begin{Vmatrix} -x & 1 & 0 & 0 & 0 & 1 \\ 1 & -x & 0 & 1 & 0 & 0 \\ 0 & 0 & -x & 0 & 1 & 0 \\ 0 & 1 & 0 & -x & 1 & 0 \\ 0 & 0 & 1 & 1 & -x & 1 \\ 1 & 0 & 0 & 0 & 1 & -x \end{Vmatrix} = 0;$$

(c)
$$\begin{Vmatrix} -x & 0 & 0 & 0 & 1 & 1 \\ 0 & -x & 0 & 1 & 0 & 0 \\ 0 & 0 & -x & 1 & 1 & 0 \\ 0 & 1 & 1 & -x & 0 & 1 \\ 1 & 0 & 1 & 0 & -x & 0 \\ 1 & 0 & 0 & 1 & 0 & -x \end{Vmatrix} = 0;$$

(d)
$$\begin{Vmatrix} -x & 1 & 1 & 0 & 0 & 0 & 0 \\ 1 & -x & 1 & 0 & 0 & 0 & 0 \\ 1 & 1 & -x & 1 & 0 & 0 & 0 \\ 0 & 0 & 1 & -x & 1 & 0 & 1 \\ 0 & 0 & 0 & 1 & -x & 1 & 0 \\ 0 & 0 & 0 & 0 & 1 & -x & 1 \\ 0 & 0 & 0 & 1 & 0 & 1 & -x \end{Vmatrix} = 0;$$

(e)
$$\begin{Vmatrix} -x & 0 & 0 & 0 & 0 & 1 & 0 & 0 & 0 & 1 \\ 0 & -x & 0 & 0 & 0 & 1 & 1 & 0 & 0 & 0 \\ 0 & 0 & -x & 0 & 0 & 0 & 1 & 1 & 0 & 1 \\ 0 & 0 & 0 & -x & 0 & 0 & 0 & 1 & 1 & 0 \\ 0 & 0 & 0 & 0 & -x & 0 & 0 & 0 & 1 & 1 \\ 1 & 1 & 0 & 0 & 0 & -x & 0 & 0 & 0 & 0 \\ 0 & 1 & 1 & 0 & 0 & 0 & -x & 0 & 0 & 0 \\ 0 & 0 & 1 & 1 & 0 & 0 & 0 & -x & 0 & 0 \\ 0 & 0 & 0 & 1 & 1 & 0 & 0 & 0 & -x & 0 \\ 1 & 0 & 1 & 0 & 1 & 0 & 0 & 0 & 0 & -x \end{Vmatrix} = 0.$$

Since the number of π-electrons is unknown, only the carbon σ-molecular skeleton will be drawn:

(a)   (b)   (c)   (d)   (f)

The numbering employed is arbitrary and does not reflect the sequence of atomic orbitals in the individual compounds, or the numbering conventions agreed upon in the Ring Index. In general, however, it is convenient to follow the customary chemical numbering, one reason being that the substituent positions then bear the same number as the corresponding centers.

4.4. *Hückel* Molecular Orbitals

Problem 4.7: The following two normalized *Hückel* molecular orbitals of the cyclopropenyl cation

$$\Psi_2 = \frac{1}{\sqrt{2}}(\Phi_1 - \Phi_2),$$

$$\Psi_3 = \frac{1}{\sqrt{2}}(\Phi_1 - \Phi_3)$$

belong to the degenerate *Hückel* eigenvalue $\varepsilon_2 = \varepsilon_3 = \alpha - \beta$ and are demonstrably not mutually orthogonal. By forming a suitable linear combination

$$\Psi_3' = a_2\Psi_2 + a_3\Psi_3,$$

a normalized molecular orbital Ψ_3' may be obtained which is orthogonal to Ψ_2. For what values of coefficients a_2 and a_3 does this hold?

Taking into consideration that $<\Psi_2 \mid \Psi_3> = \frac{1}{2}$, the linear combination Ψ' must satisfy the conditions

$$\begin{aligned}
<\Psi_3'|\Psi_3'> = 1 &= a_2^2 <\Psi_2|\Psi_2> + a_3^2 <\Psi_3|\Psi_3> + 2a_2a_3 <\Psi_2|\Psi_3> \\
&= a_2^2 + a_3^2 + a_2a_3 \\
<\Psi_3'|\Psi_2'> = 0 &= a_2 <\Psi_2|\Psi_2> + a_3 <\Psi_3|\Psi_2> \\
&= a_2 + a_3/2
\end{aligned}$$

Substitution of $a_2 = -a_3/2$ into the above equation gives

$$1 = \frac{a_3^2}{4} + a_3^2 - \frac{a_3^2}{2} = \frac{3}{4}a_3^2$$

$$a_3^2 = \frac{4}{3}; \quad a_3 = \frac{2}{\sqrt{3}}$$

For a_2 we obtain

$$a_2 = -\frac{2}{\sqrt{3}} \cdot \frac{1}{2} = -\frac{1}{\sqrt{3}}.$$

With the coefficients thus found, the normalized linear combination which is orthogonal to Ψ_2 reads

$$\Psi_3' = \frac{2}{\sqrt{3}} \Psi_3 - \frac{1}{\sqrt{3}} \Psi_2 = \frac{1}{\sqrt{3}} \cdot \frac{1}{\sqrt{2}} (2(\Phi_1 - \Phi_3) - (\Phi_1 - \Phi_2))$$

$$= \frac{1}{\sqrt{6}} (\Phi_1 + \Phi_2 - 2\Phi_3).$$

Problem 4.8: On electronic excitation of fulvene an electron is promoted from the molecular orbital Ψ_3 into the molecular orbital Ψ_4. Calculate the charge distribution for this first electronically excited state.

For the first excited state of the fulvene molecule, the occupation numbers are

$$b_1 = b_2 = 2$$
$$b_3 = b_4 = 1$$
$$b_5 = b_6 = 0$$

and the charge orders q_ρ are calculated according to

$$q_\rho = \sum_{J=1}^{n} b_J c_{J\rho} \qquad (4/52)$$

from the coefficients $c_{J\rho}$ given in (4/45) as follows:

$$
\begin{aligned}
q_1 = q_4 &= 2(0.429)^2 && + (\pm 0.602)^2 + (-0.351)^2 = 0.854 \\
q_2 = q_3 &= 2(0.385)^2 + 2(0.500)^2 + (\pm 0.372)^2 + (0.280)^2 = 1.013 \\
q_5 &= 2(0.523)^2 + 2(-0.500)^2 && + (-0.190)^2 = 1.083 \\
q_6 &= 2(0.247)^2 + 2(-0.500)^2 && + (0.749)^2 = 1.183
\end{aligned}
$$

$$\sum_{\rho}^{6} q_\rho = \qquad\qquad 6.000$$

Predictably, the sum of the charge orders $\sum_{\rho}^{6} q_\rho$ corresponds to the number Z_π of π electrons in the overall system (4/54).

Comparison with the charge distribution (4/53) in the ground state of fulvene showns that the transition $\Psi_3 \rightarrow \Psi_4$ in the *Hückel* MO model is accompanied by a marked reorganization of the electronic structure. A pronounced charge transfer takes place from the five-membered ring into the side chain which is, however, overemphasized in the above calculation since the localization of the double bonds in fulvene is largely neglected.

Problem 4.9: Calculate the orbital energies ε_J, the linear combinations Ψ_J, the total π-electron energies E_π, and the charge orders q_ρ for the following carbon π systems:

(a) $[H_2C \cdots CH \cdots CH_2]$ allyl radical,
(b) $[H_2C \cdots CH \cdots CH_2]^{\oplus}$ allyl cation,
(c) $[H_2C \cdots CH \cdots CH_2]^{\ominus}$ allyl anion,
(d) $H_2C = CH - CH = CH_2$ butadiene.

In complete analogy to the calculation carried out explicitly for the pentadienyl cation (cf. (4/56) through (4/73)), we find for the carbon π-systems (a) through (d):

(a) The *Hückel* determinant of a linear three-center π-system leads to the polynomial

$$
\begin{Vmatrix}
-x & 1 & 0 \\
1 & -x & 1 \\
0 & 1 & -x
\end{Vmatrix}
= -x^3 + 2x = 0
$$

The scheme of the solutions x_J of the eigenvalue $\epsilon_J = \alpha + x_J\beta$ corresponding to the polynomial has the form

$$\varepsilon_3 = \alpha - \sqrt{2}\,\beta$$
$$\varepsilon_2 = \alpha$$
$$\varepsilon_1 = \alpha + \sqrt{2}\,\beta$$

The associated linear combinations read

$$
\begin{aligned}
\Psi_1 &= 0.500(\Phi_1 + \Phi_3) + 0.707\,\Phi_2 \\
\Psi_2 &= 0.707(\Phi_1 - \Phi_3) \\
\Psi_3 &= 0.500(\Phi_1 + \Phi_3) - 0.707\,\Phi_2
\end{aligned}
$$

The ground state of the allyl radical is described by the occupation numbers $b_1 = 2, b_2 = 1$, and $b_3 = 0$, and the total π-electron energy E_π is found to be

$$E_\pi = 3\alpha + 2.828\,\beta.$$

The charge orders are

$$
\begin{aligned}
q_1 &= 1.000 \\
q_2 &= 1.000 \\
q_3 &= 1.000
\end{aligned}
$$

$$\sum_\rho q_\rho = 3.000 = Z_\pi$$

(b) In the allyl cation, the occupation numbers simply change to $b_1 = 2, b_2 = b_3 = 0$, the resulting total π-electron energy being

$$E_\pi = 2\alpha + 2.828\,\beta.$$

The charge orders now amount to

$$
\begin{aligned}
q_1 &= 0.500 \\
q_2 &= 1.000 \\
q_3 &= 0.500
\end{aligned}
$$

$$\sum_\rho q_\rho = 2.000 = Z_\pi$$

(c) In the allyl anion, the occupation numbers again merely change to $b_1 = b_2 = 2$ and $b_3 = 0$, and the total π-electron energy for the allyl anion is

$$E_\pi = 4\alpha + 2.828\,\beta.$$

The charge orders for the allyl anion amount to

$$q_1 = 1.500$$
$$q_2 = 1.000$$
$$q_3 = 1.500$$

$$\sum_\rho q_\rho = 4.000 = Z_\pi$$

(d) The *Hückel* determinant of a linear four-center π-system leads to the polynomial

$$\begin{Vmatrix} -x & 1 & 0 & 0 \\ 1 & -x & 1 & 0 \\ 0 & 1 & -x & 1 \\ 0 & 0 & 1 & -x \end{Vmatrix} = x^4 - 3x^2 + 1 = 0.$$

The scheme of orbital energies $\epsilon_J = \alpha + x_J\beta$ corresponding to the solutions x_I of the polynomial has the appearance

$$\epsilon_4 = \alpha - 1.618\,\beta$$
$$\epsilon_3 = \alpha - 0.618\,\beta$$
$$\epsilon_2 = \alpha + 0.618\,\beta$$
$$\epsilon_1 = \alpha + 1.618\,\beta$$

The associated linear combinations read

$$\psi_1 = 0.372\,(\Phi_1 + \Phi_4) + 0.602\,(\Phi_2 + \Phi_3)$$
$$\psi_2 = 0.602\,(\Phi_1 - \Phi_4) + 0.372\,(\Phi_2 - \Phi_3)$$
$$\psi_3 = 0.602\,(\Phi_1 + \Phi_4) - 0.372\,(\Phi_2 + \Phi_3)$$
$$\psi_4 = 0.372\,(\Phi_1 - \Phi_4) - 0.602\,(\Phi_2 - \Phi_3)$$

The ground state of butadiene is described by the occupation numbers $b_1 = b_2 = 2$ and $b_3 = b_4 = 0$, and the total π-electron energy E_π is found to be

$$E_\pi = 4\alpha + 4.472\,\beta.$$

The charge orders amount to

$$q_1 = 1.000$$
$$q_2 = 1.000$$
$$q_3 = 1.000$$
$$q_4 = 1.000$$

$$\sum_{\rho}^{4} q_\rho = 4.000 = Z_\pi$$

4.5. Symmetry Properties of *Hückel* Molecular Orbitals

Problem 4.10: Using the coefficients $c_{j\mu}$ given in the HMO Tables (Vol. 3), draw HMO diagrams analogous to [4.5] for the molecules

(a)   (b)   (c)

[4.10]

Classify the individual molecular orbitals with respect to the different symmetry types of the group C_{2v}.

(a)

Diagram	E	C_{2z}	σ_{xz}	σ_{yz}	Symmetry type
ψ_4	s	s	a	a	A_2
ψ_3	s	a	s	a	B_1
ψ_2	s	s	a	a	A_2
ψ_1	s	a	s	a	B_1

(b)

Diagram	E	C_{2z}	σ_{xz}	σ_{yz}	Symmetry type
ψ_4	s	a	s	a	B_1
ψ_3	s	s	a	a	A_2
ψ_2	s	a	s	a	B_1
ψ_1	s	a	s	a	B_1

(c)

Diagram	E	C_{2z}	σ_{xz}	σ_{yz}	Symmetry type
ψ_{10}	s	s	a	a	A_2
ψ_9	s	a	s	a	B_1
ψ_8	s	a	s	a	B_1
ψ_7	s	s	a	a	A_2

Diagram	E	C_{2z}	σ_{xz}	σ_{yz}	Symmetry type
ψ_6	s	a	s	a	B_1
ψ_5	s	s	a	a	A_2
ψ_4	s	a	s	a	B_1
ψ_3	s	s	a	a	A_2
ψ_2	s	a	s	a	B_1
ψ_1	s	a	s	a	B_1

Problem 4.11: Draw the appropriate HMO diagrams of type [4.5] for (a) and (b) using the coefficients given in the two tables (Vol. 3). Classify the individual molecular orbitals relative to group D_{2h} symmetry types (molecular plane σ_{xy}; x-axis of (a) through centres 3 and 6; x-axis of (b) through centres 7 and 8).

(a)   (b)

(a)

Diagram	E	C_{2z}	C_{2y}	C_{2x}	i	σ_{xy}	σ_{xz}	σ_{yz}	Symmetry type
ψ_6	s	a	s	a	s	a	s	a	B_{2g}
ψ_5	s	s	s	s	a	a	a	a	A_u
ψ_4	s	s	a	a	a	a	s	s	B_{1u}
ψ_3	s	a	s	a	s	a	s	a	B_{2g}
ψ_2	s	a	a	s	s	a	a	s	B_{3g}
ψ_1	s	s	a	a	a	a	s	s	B_{1u}

(b)

Diagram	E	C_{2z}	C_{2y}	C_{2x}	i	σ_{xy}	σ_{xz}	σ_{yz}	Symmetry type
ψ_8	s	a	s	a	s	a	s	a	B_{2g}
ψ_7	s	s	a	a	a	a	s	s	B_{1u}
ψ_6	s	a	a	s	s	a	a	s	B_{3g}

Diagram	E	C_{2z}	C_{2y}	C_{2x}	i	σ_{xy}	σ_{xz}	σ_{yz}	Symmetry type
ψ_5	s	s	s	s	a	a	a	a	A_u
ψ_4	s	s	a	a	a	a	s	s	B_{1u}
ψ_3	s	a	s	a	s	a	s	a	B_{2g}
ψ_2	s	a	a	s	s	a	a	s	B_{3g}
ψ_1	s	s	a	a	a	a	s	s	B_{1u}

Problem 4.12: Show that the two linear combinations for fulvene

$$\Psi = \sum_{\mu=1}^{6} c_\mu \Phi_\mu; \qquad \Psi = \sum_{\kappa=1}^{6} c_\kappa \varphi_\kappa$$

are mutually equivalent, that the functions φ_κ constitute an orthonormal set of functions, and that the matrix elements $\langle \varphi_\kappa | \mathcal{H} | \varphi_\lambda \rangle$ and $\langle \varphi_\kappa | \varphi_\lambda \rangle$ vanish for opposite symmetry behavior of φ_κ and φ_λ.

The symmetry-correct linear combinations φ_κ of fulvene read:

$$\varphi_1 = \frac{1}{\sqrt{2}} (\Phi_1 + \Phi_4) \qquad \varphi_4 = \Phi_6 \tag{4/90}$$

$$\varphi_2 = \frac{1}{\sqrt{2}} (\Phi_2 + \Phi_3) \qquad \varphi_5 = \frac{1}{\sqrt{2}} (\Phi_1 - \Phi_4)$$

$$\varphi_3 = \Phi_5 \qquad \varphi_6 = \frac{1}{\sqrt{2}} (\Phi_2 - \Phi_3)$$

As total linear combination Ψ' we obtain

$$\Psi' = \sum_{\kappa=1}^{6} c'_\kappa \varphi_\kappa = c'_1\varphi_1 + c'_2\varphi_2 + c'_3\varphi_3 + c'_4\varphi_4 + c'_5\varphi_5 + c'_6\varphi_6$$

$$= (c'_1 + c'_5)\frac{1}{\sqrt{2}}\Phi_1 + (c'_2 + c'_6)\frac{1}{\sqrt{2}}\Phi_2 + c'_3\Phi_5 + c'_4\Phi_6 + (c'_1 - c'_5)\frac{1}{\sqrt{2}}\Phi_4 + (c'_2 - c'_6)\frac{1}{\sqrt{2}}\Phi_3$$

If for the linearly independent coefficients we substitute

$$c_1 = (c'_1 + c'_5)\frac{1}{\sqrt{2}} \ ,$$

$$c_2 = (c'_2 + c'_6)\frac{1}{\sqrt{2}} \ ,$$

$$c_3 = (c'_2 - c'_6)\frac{1}{\sqrt{2}} \ ,$$

$$c_4 = (c'_1 - c'_5)\frac{1}{\sqrt{2}} \ ,$$

$$c_5 = c'_3 \ ,$$

$$c_6 = c'_4 \ ,$$

we obtain the identity to be established

$$\Psi' = \sum_{\mu=1}^{6} c_\mu \Phi_\mu = \Psi.$$

The symmetry-correct linear combinations

$$\varphi_\kappa = \frac{1}{\sqrt{2}}(\Phi_\mu \pm \Phi_\nu); \ \varphi_\lambda = \frac{1}{\sqrt{2}}(\Phi_\rho \pm \Phi_\sigma)$$

satisfy the orthonormalization condition

$$\langle \varphi_\kappa | \varphi_\lambda \rangle = \delta_{\kappa\lambda}$$

in the following manner: the normalization condition for φ_κ reads

$$\langle \varphi_\kappa | \varphi_\kappa \rangle = \frac{1}{2}(\langle \Phi_\mu | \Phi_\mu \rangle + \langle \Phi_\nu | \Phi_\nu \rangle \pm 2\langle \Phi_\mu | \Phi_\nu \rangle) = 1$$

The following two cases must be considered with respect to the orthogonality of two linear combinations $\varphi_\kappa, \varphi_\lambda$ ($\kappa \neq \lambda$):

(a) $\mu, \nu \neq \rho, \sigma$: Here all overlap integrals of the type $\langle \Phi_\mu | \Phi_\rho \rangle$ are equal to zero, so that $\langle \varphi_\kappa | \varphi_\lambda \rangle = 0$ is satisfied.

(b) $\mu, \nu = \rho, \sigma$: In this case, because $\varphi_\kappa \neq \varphi_\lambda$, the two linear combinations must differ in signs

$$\varphi_\kappa = \frac{1}{\sqrt{2}}(\Phi_\mu + \Phi_\nu); \quad \varphi_\kappa = \frac{1}{\sqrt{2}}(\Phi_\mu - \Phi_\nu)$$

and one obtains

$$<\varphi_\kappa|\varphi_\lambda> = \frac{1}{2}(<\Phi_\mu|\Phi_\mu> - <\Phi_\nu|\Phi_\nu> + <\Phi_\mu|\Phi_\nu> - <\Phi_\mu|\Phi_\nu>) = 0.$$

For the opposite symmetry behavior of the linear combinations

$$\varphi_\kappa = \frac{1}{\sqrt{2}}(\Phi_\mu + \Phi_\nu); \quad \varphi_\lambda = \frac{1}{\sqrt{2}}(\Phi_\rho - \Phi_\sigma)$$

the matrix elements disappear

$$< \varphi_\kappa|\mathcal{H}|\varphi_\lambda > = < \frac{1}{\sqrt{2}}(\Phi_\mu + \Phi_\sigma|\mathcal{H}|\frac{1}{\sqrt{2}}(\Phi_\rho - \Phi_\sigma) >$$

$$= \frac{1}{2}\left\{ < \Phi_\mu|\mathcal{H}|\Phi_\rho > - <\Phi_\mu|\mathcal{H}|\Phi_\nu> + <\Phi_\nu|\mathcal{H}|\Phi_\rho> - <\Phi_\nu|\mathcal{H}|\Phi_\sigma> \right. = 0,$$

$$<\varphi_\kappa|\varphi_\lambda> = < \frac{1}{\sqrt{2}}(\Phi_\mu + \Phi_\nu)|\frac{1}{\sqrt{2}}(\Phi_\rho - \Phi_\sigma)>$$

$$= \frac{1}{2}\left\{ <\Phi_\mu|\Phi_\rho> - <\Phi_\mu|\Phi_\sigma> + <\Phi_\nu|\Phi_\rho> - <\Phi_\nu|\Phi_\sigma> \right. = 0,$$

since, for the transformation $\mu \to \nu$ and $\rho \to \sigma$ by a symmetry operation, the relationship holds:

$$<\Phi_\mu|\mathcal{H}|\Phi_\rho> = <\Phi_\nu|\mathcal{H}|\Phi_\sigma> \; ; \; <\Phi_\nu|\mathcal{H}|\Phi_\rho> = <\Phi_\mu|\mathcal{H}|\Phi_\sigma>$$

$$<\Phi_\mu|\Phi_\rho> = <\Phi_\nu|\Phi_\sigma> \; ; \; <\Phi_\nu|\Phi_\rho> = <\Phi_\mu|\Phi_\sigma>$$

The symmetry-correct linear combinations φ_κ therefore constitute a set of orthonormal functions, whose linear combination Ψ is equivalent to that of the atomic orbitals in a *Hückel* approach. However, they have the advantage that the matrix elements between two symmetry-correct linear combinations φ_κ and φ_λ behaving differently with respect to a given symmetry operation, i.e. belonging to different irreducible representations, become equal to zero.

Problem 4.13: Factorize the *Hückel* determinant of the benzyl radical using

the symmetry plane σ_{yz}.

According to the procedure (4/98), factorization of the *Hückel* determinant of the benzyl radical entails the following steps:

(1) On reflection on the x-axis, the following centers are transformed into each other:

$$
\begin{array}{ll}
1 & \circlearrowright \\
2 & \circlearrowright \\
3 & \rightleftarrows 7 \\
4 & \rightleftarrows 6 \\
5 & \circlearrowright
\end{array}
$$

(2) Corresponding addition and subtraction of the rows affords:

$$
\begin{vmatrix}
-x & 1 & & & & \\
1 & -x & 1 & & & & 1 \\
& 1 & -x & 1 & & \\
& & 1 & -x & 1 & \\
& & & 1 & -x & 1 \\
& 1 & & & 1 & -x
\end{vmatrix}
\begin{matrix}
(3+7) \\
(4+6) \\
(1) \\
(2) \\
(5) \\
(3-7) \\
(4-6)
\end{matrix}
\Rightarrow
\begin{vmatrix}
& 2 & -x & 1 & & 1 & -x \\
& & 1 & -x & 2 & -x & 1 \\
-x & 1 & & & & \\
1 & -x & 1 & & & & 1 \\
& & 1 & -x & 1 & \\
& -x & 1 & & -1 & x \\
& 1 & -x & & x & -1
\end{vmatrix}
$$

(3) Repetition of the operations with respect to the columns gives

$$
\begin{vmatrix}
\begin{array}{ccc|}
-2x & 2 & 2 \\
2 & -2x & & 2 \\
& & -x & 1 \\
2 & & 1 & -x \\
2 & & & -x \\
\hline
& & & -2x & 2 \\
& & & 2 & -2x
\end{array}
\end{vmatrix}
$$

The *Hückel* determinant of the benzyl radical thus can be written as the product of the two subdeterminants normalized according to (4)

$$\begin{Vmatrix} -x & 1 & & & \sqrt{2} \\ 1 & -x & & & \sqrt{2} \\ & & -x & 1 & \\ \sqrt{2} & & 1 & -x & \\ & \sqrt{2} & & & -x \end{Vmatrix} \times \begin{Vmatrix} -x & 1 \\ 1 & -x \end{Vmatrix} = 0 \; .$$

Problem 4.14: Factorize the *Hückel* determinants of bicylohexatriene and pentalene

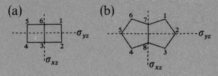

(a)   (b)

using symmetry planes σ_{xz} and σ_{yz}.

By analogy with the factorization of the *Hückel* determinant of naphthalene (4/100) and (4/101), the symmetry operations of procedure (4/98): (1) through (4) are first performed with respect to the symmetry plane σ_{xz} and then with respect to the symmetry plane σ_{yz}.

Bicyclohexatriene:

(x/1)

1 ⇄ 5
2 ⇄ 4
3 ↻
6 ↻

(x/2)

$$\left\| \begin{array}{cccccc} -x & 1 & & & & 1 \\ 1 & -x & 1 & & & \\ & 1 & -x & 1 & & 1 \\ & & 1 & -x & 1 & \\ & & & 1 & -x & 1 \\ 1 & & 1 & & 1 & -x \end{array} \right\|$$

$$\begin{array}{c} (1+5) \\ (2+4) \\ (3) \\ \Longrightarrow \\ (6) \\ (1-5) \\ (2-4) \end{array}$$

$$\left\| \begin{array}{cccccc} -x & 1 & & 1 & -x & 2 \\ 1 & -x & 2 & -x & 1 & \\ & 1 & -x & 1 & & 1 \\ 1 & & 1 & & 1 & -x \\ -x & 1 & & -1 & x & \\ 1 & -x & & x & -1 & \end{array} \right\|$$

(x/3) $\Big\Downarrow$

$$\left\| \begin{array}{ccc} -x & 1 & \sqrt{2} \\ 1 & -x & \sqrt{2} \\ & \sqrt{2} & -x & 1 \\ \sqrt{2} & & 1 & -x \end{array} \right\| \quad \times \quad \left\| \begin{array}{cc} -x & 1 \\ 1 & -x \end{array} \right\|$$

$$\xleftarrow{\ (x/4)\ }$$

$$\left\| \begin{array}{ccc|cc} -2x & 2 & & 2 & \\ 2 & -2x & 2 & & \\ & 2 & -x & 1 & \\ 2 & & 1 & -x & \\ \hline & & & -2x & 2 \\ & & & 2 & 2-2x \end{array} \right\|$$

$$\underset{A}{} \qquad \underset{B}{}$$

(y/1)

$$1 \rightleftharpoons 2$$
$$3 \rightleftharpoons 6$$
$$4 \rightleftharpoons 5$$

The following additions and subtractions are to be performed in the subdeterminants A and B:

$$[(1+5) + (2+4)]$$
$$[(3) + (6)] \qquad\qquad [(1-5) + (2-4)]$$
$$[(1+5) - (2+4)] \qquad [(1.-5) - (2-4)]$$
$$[(3) - (6)]$$

(y/2)

$$\left\| \begin{array}{cccc} 1-x & 1-x & \sqrt{2} & \sqrt{2} \\ \sqrt{2} & \sqrt{2} & 1-x & 1-x \\ -x-1 & 1+x & -\sqrt{2} & \sqrt{2} \\ -\sqrt{2} & \sqrt{2} & -x-1 & 1+x \end{array} \right\| \times \left\| \begin{array}{cc} 1-x & 1-x \\ -1-x & 1+x \end{array} \right\|$$

(y/3)

$$\left\| \begin{array}{cc|cc} 2-2x & 2\sqrt{2} & & \\ 2\sqrt{2} & 2-2x & & \\ \hline & & -2-2x & -2\sqrt{2} \\ & & -2\sqrt{2} & -2-2x \end{array} \right\| \times \left\| \begin{array}{c|c} 2-2x & \\ \hline & -2-2x \end{array} \right\|$$

(y/4)

$$\left\|\begin{matrix} 1-x & \sqrt{2} \\ \sqrt{2} & 1-x \end{matrix}\right\| \times \left\|\begin{matrix} -1-x & -\sqrt{2} \\ -\sqrt{2} & -1-x \end{matrix}\right\| \times \left\| 1-x \right\| \times \left\| -1-x \right\|$$

The subdeterminants obtained belong to the following irreducible representations:

$$B_{1u} \qquad B_{2g} \qquad B_{3g} \qquad A_u$$

Pentalene:

(x/1)

$$
\begin{aligned}
1 &\rightleftarrows 6 \\
2 &\rightleftarrows 5 \\
3 &\rightleftarrows 4 \\
7 &\circlearrowleft \\
8 &\circlearrowleft
\end{aligned}
$$

(x/2)

$$
\left\|\begin{matrix}
-x & 1 & & & & & & 1 \\
1 & -x & 1 & & & & & \\
 & 1 & -x & & & & & 1 \\
 & & & -x & 1 & & & 1 \\
 & & & 1 & -x & 1 & & \\
 & & & & 1 & -x & 1 & \\
1 & & & & & 1 & -x & 1 \\
 & 1 & 1 & & & & 1 & -x
\end{matrix}\right\|
\qquad
\begin{matrix}
(1+6) \\
(2+5) \\
(3+4) \\
(7) \\
\Longrightarrow \\
(8) \\
(1-6) \\
(2-5) \\
(3-4)
\end{matrix}
\qquad
\left\|\begin{matrix}
-x & 1 & & & 1 & -x & 2 \\
1 & -x & 1 & 1 & -x & 1 & \\
 & 1 & -x & -x & 1 & & 2 \\
1 & & & & 1 & -x & 1 \\
 & 1 & 1 & & & 1 & -x \\
-x & 1 & & -1 & x & & \\
1 & -x & 1 & -1 & x & -1 & \\
 & 1 & -x & x & -1 & &
\end{matrix}\right\|
$$

(x/3)

$$\Downarrow$$

$$
\left\|\begin{matrix}
-x & 1 & \sqrt{2} & \\
1 & -x & 1 & \\
 & 1 & -x & \sqrt{2} \\
\sqrt{2} & & -x & 1 \\
 & & \sqrt{2} & 1-x
\end{matrix}\right\|
\times
\left\|\begin{matrix}
-x & 1 & \\
1 & -x & 1 \\
 & 1 & -x
\end{matrix}\right\|
\qquad
\xleftarrow{(x/4)}
\qquad
\left|\begin{matrix}
-2x & 2 & & 2 & \\
2 & -2x & 2 & & \\
 & 2 & -2x & & 2 \\
2 & & & -x & 1 \\
\hline
 & & 2 & 1 & -x \\
\hline
 & & & & & -2x & 2 \\
 & & & & & 2 & -2x & 2 \\
 & & & & & & 2 & -2x
\end{matrix}\right|
$$

$$\qquad\quad A \qquad\qquad\qquad B$$

$(y/1)$

$$1 \rightleftarrows 3$$
$$4 \rightleftarrows 6$$
$$7 \rightleftarrows 8$$
$$2 \circlearrowright$$
$$5 \circlearrowright$$

The following additions and subtractions are to be performed in the subdeterminants A and B:

$$[(1 + 6) + (3 + 4)]$$
$$[(7) + (8)]$$
$$[(2 + 5)]$$
$$[(1 + 6) - (3 + 4)]$$
$$[(7) - (8)]$$

$$[(1 - 6) + (3 - 4)]$$
$$[(2 - 5)]$$
$$[(1 - 6) - (3 - 4)]$$

$(y/2)$

$$
\begin{Vmatrix}
-x & 2 & -x & \sqrt{2} & \sqrt{2} \\
\sqrt{2} & & \sqrt{2} & 1-x & 1-x \\
1 & -x & 1 & & \\
-x & & -x & \sqrt{2} & -\sqrt{2} \\
\sqrt{2} & & -\sqrt{2} & -1-x & 1+x
\end{Vmatrix}
\times
\begin{Vmatrix}
-x & 2 & -x \\
1 & -x & 1 \\
-x & & x
\end{Vmatrix}
$$

$(y/3)$

$$
\begin{Vmatrix}
-2x & 2\sqrt{2} & 2 & & \\
2\sqrt{2} & 2-2x & & & \\
2 & & -x & & \\
& & & -2x & 2\sqrt{2} \\
& & & 2\sqrt{2} & -2-2x
\end{Vmatrix}
\times
\begin{Vmatrix}
-2x & 2 & \\
2 & -x & \\
& & -2x
\end{Vmatrix}
$$

$(y/4)$

$$
\begin{Vmatrix}
-x & \sqrt{2} & \sqrt{2} \\
\sqrt{2} & 1-x & \\
\sqrt{2} & & -x
\end{Vmatrix}
\times
\begin{Vmatrix}
-x & \sqrt{2} \\
\sqrt{2} & 1-x
\end{Vmatrix}
\times
\begin{Vmatrix}
-x & \sqrt{2} \\
\sqrt{2} & -x
\end{Vmatrix}
\times
\begin{Vmatrix} -x \end{Vmatrix}
$$

The resulting subdeterminants belong to the following irreducible representations:

$$B_{1u} \qquad B_{2g} \qquad B_{3g} \qquad A_u$$

5. Some Special π-Electron Systems

5.10. Unbranched Linear π-Electron Systems

Problem 5.1: Calculate in closed form the total π-electron energy E_π of unbranched chains with an even number n of centres. Verify the formula obtained for $n = 2, 4$, and 6 by comparing values with those from HMO Tables K_2, K_4, and K_6 (Volume 3). How large is the total π-electron energy per double bond in each case, and what is the limiting value expected for an infinitely long chain?

For an unbranched linear chain with $n = 2N$ centers, the coefficient X_π of the total π-electron energy E_π is obtained from the general formula for the orbital energies

$$x_J = 2 \cos \left(\frac{\pi}{n+1} J \right)$$

and from the occupation numbers $b_J = 2; J = 1, 2, 3, \ldots N$ as follows:

$$X_\pi = \sum_{J=1}^{N} b_J x_J = \sum_{J=1}^{N} 2 \cdot 2 \cos \left(\frac{\pi}{n+1} J \right)$$

With the aid of the relation

$$\sum_{J=0}^{n} \cos \left(aJ \right) = \frac{\cos \left(\frac{n}{2} a \right) \sin \left(\frac{n+1}{2} a \right)}{\sin \left(\frac{a}{2} \right)}$$

one obtains

$$X_\pi = 4 \left(\frac{\cos \left(\frac{N}{2} \cdot \frac{\pi}{n+1} \right) \cdot \sin \left(\frac{N+1}{2} \cdot \frac{\pi}{n+1} \right)}{\sin \left(\frac{\pi}{2(n+1)} \right)} - 1 \right) = 4 \left(\frac{\cos \left(\frac{n}{n+1} \cdot \frac{\pi}{4} \right) \cdot \sin \left(\frac{n+2}{n+1} \cdot \frac{\pi}{4} \right)}{\sin \left(\frac{1}{n+1} \cdot \frac{\pi}{2} \right)} - 1 \right)$$

According to

$$2 \sin ac \cdot \cos bc = \sin (a - b)c + \sin (a + b)c$$

the cosine sum can be simplified in the following manner:

$$X_\pi = 2 \left(\frac{\sin \left(\frac{2}{n+1} \cdot \frac{\pi}{4} \right) + \sin \left(\frac{2n+2}{n+1} \cdot \frac{\pi}{4} \right)}{\sin \left(\frac{1}{n+1} \cdot \frac{\pi}{2} \right)} - 2 \right) = 2 \left(1 + \frac{\sin \left(\frac{\pi}{2} \right)}{\sin \left(\frac{1}{n+1} \cdot \frac{\pi}{2} \right)} - 2 \right)$$

$$= \frac{2}{\sin \left(\frac{\pi}{2(n+1)} \right)} - 2$$

For chains with $n = 2, 4, 6$, in agreement with the tabulated values (Vol. 3), the total π-electron energies are:

$$n = 2: \quad X_\pi = \frac{2}{\sin\left(\dfrac{\pi}{2\,(2+1)}\right)} - 2 = \frac{2}{\sin 30°} \quad -2 = 4 - 2 \qquad = 2$$

$$n = 4: \quad X_\pi = \frac{2}{\sin\left(\dfrac{\pi}{2\,(4+1)}\right)} - 2 = \frac{2}{\sin 18°} \quad -2 = 6.47 - 2 \qquad = 4.47$$

$$n = 6: \quad X_\pi = \frac{2}{\sin\left(\dfrac{\pi}{2\,(6+1)}\right)} - 2 = \frac{2}{\sin 12°\,51'} - 2 = 9.00 - 2 \qquad = 7.00$$

The total π-electron energy per double bond is therefore:

$$n = 2: \quad 2.000$$
$$n = 4: \quad 2.235$$
$$n = 6: \quad 2.333$$

For infinitely long chains this value approaches 2.546, as can be derived in the following manner:

$$\frac{X_\pi}{\dfrac{n}{2}} = \frac{2\,X_\pi}{n} = \frac{4\left(1 - \sin\left(\dfrac{\pi}{2\,(n+1)}\right)\right)}{n \cdot \sin\left(\dfrac{\pi}{2\,(n+1)}\right)}$$

For $n \to \infty$, i.e. $\dfrac{\pi}{2\,(n+1)} \ll 1$

$$\sin\left(\frac{\pi}{2\,(n+1)}\right) \approx \frac{\pi}{2\,(n+1)} \approx \frac{\pi}{2n}.$$

Substitution affords

$$\frac{2\,X_\pi}{n} = \frac{4\left(1 - \dfrac{\pi}{2n}\right)}{n \cdot \dfrac{\pi}{2n}}.$$

For $n \to \infty$ we obtain

$$\frac{2\,X_\pi}{n} = \frac{4\,(1 - 0)}{\dfrac{\pi}{2}} = \frac{8}{\pi} = 2.546.$$

Problem 5.2: Calculate in closed form the total π-electron energy for unbranched chains with an uneven number n of centres. Verify the formula obtained for $n = 3$ and for $n = 5$ by comparing with values from the HMO Tables $K_3^\bullet$ and $K_5^\bullet$ (Volume 3). How large are the total π-energies for the corresponding cations and anions?

The solution is analogous to that of Problem 5.1, except that summation is performed only from $J = 1$ through $J = \dfrac{n-1}{2}$ because of the nonbonding molecular orbital

$$X_\pi = \sum_{J=1}^{(n-1)/2} 2 \cdot 2 \cos\left(\frac{\pi}{n+1} J\right).$$

With

$$\sum_{J=0}^{n} \cos(xJ) = \frac{\cos\left(\dfrac{nx}{2}\right) \sin\left(\dfrac{n+1}{2} x\right)}{\sin\left(\dfrac{x}{2}\right)}$$

we obtain

$$X_\pi = 4\left(\frac{\cos\left(\dfrac{1}{2} \cdot \dfrac{n-1}{2} \cdot \dfrac{\pi}{n+1}\right) \cdot \sin\left(\dfrac{1}{2} \cdot \left(\dfrac{n-1}{2} + 1\right) \dfrac{\pi}{n+1}\right)}{\sin\left(\dfrac{1}{2} \cdot \dfrac{\pi}{n+1}\right)} - 1\right)$$

$$= 4\left(\frac{\cos\left(\dfrac{n-1}{n+1} \cdot \dfrac{\pi}{4}\right) \cdot \sin\left(\dfrac{\pi}{4}\right)}{\sin\left(\dfrac{1}{n+1} \cdot \dfrac{\pi}{2}\right)} - 1\right)$$

Using

$$2\sin(ax)\cos(bx) = \sin((a-b)x) + \sin((a+b)x)$$

the cosine sum can be simplified as follows:

$$X_\pi = 2\left(\frac{\sin\left(\left(1 - \dfrac{n-1}{n+1}\right) \dfrac{\pi}{4}\right) + \sin\left(\left(1 + \dfrac{n-1}{n+1}\right) \dfrac{\pi}{4}\right)}{\sin\left(\dfrac{1}{n+1} \cdot \dfrac{\pi}{2}\right)} - 2\right)$$

$$= 2\left(1 + \frac{\sin\left(\dfrac{n}{n+1} \cdot \dfrac{\pi}{2}\right)}{\sin\left(\dfrac{1}{n+1} \cdot \dfrac{\pi}{2}\right)} - 2\right)$$

$$= \frac{2\sin\left(\dfrac{n}{n+1} \cdot \dfrac{\pi}{2}\right)}{\sin\left(\dfrac{1}{n+1} \cdot \dfrac{\pi}{2}\right)} - 2.$$

In agreement with the tabulated values (Vol. 3) the total π-electron energies for the chains with $n = 3, 5, 7$ centers are obtained as

$$n = 3: \quad X_\pi \quad \frac{2 \sin \left(\frac{3}{8} \pi \right)}{\sin \left(\frac{1}{8} \pi \right)} - 2 = \frac{2 \cdot 0.924}{0.383} - 2 = 2.83$$

$$n = 5: \quad X_\pi \quad \frac{2 \sin \left(\frac{5}{12} \pi \right)}{\sin \left(\frac{1}{12} \pi \right)} - 2 = \frac{2 \cdot 0.966}{0.259} - 2 = 5.46$$

$$n = 7: \quad X_\pi \quad \frac{2 \sin \left(\frac{7}{16} \pi \right)}{\sin \left(\frac{1}{16} \pi \right)} - 2 = \frac{2 \cdot 0.981}{0.195} - 2 = 8.05$$

On going to the associated cations or anions, the total π-electron energies only change by α corresponding to occupation of a nonbinding molecular orbital.

	$E_{\pi(\text{Cation})}$	$E_{\pi(\text{Radical})}$	$E_{\pi(\text{Anion})}$
$n = 3$	$2\alpha + 2.83\beta$	$3\alpha + 2.83\beta$	$4\alpha + 2.83\beta$
$n = 5$	$4\alpha + 5.46\beta$	$5\alpha + 5.46\beta$	$6\alpha + 5.46\beta$
$n = 7$	$6\alpha + 8.05\beta$	$7\alpha + 8.05\beta$	$8\alpha + 8.05\beta$

Problem 5.3: Addition of an electrophilic reagent $X^\oplus$ (e.g. $Br^\oplus$) to the end carbon atom of a polyene

yields a system in which $(n - 2)$ electrons are delocalized over the remaining $n - 1$ atomic orbitals of the $2p_z$-type. The difference in the total π-electron energies of the two systems contributes to the potential barrier for the reaction. Using the answers to Problems 5.1 and 5.2, show how this difference depends on the chain length n.

The general relationship for the difference in the total π-electron energies ΔE_π between even-numbered polyenes with n centers and the polyene cations with $n-1$ centers formed therefrom on addition, is obtained with the aid of the expressions derived in Problems 5.1 and 5.2:

$$\Delta E_\pi = E_{\pi(\text{Polyene})} - E_{\pi(\text{Cation})}$$

$$= \left[n\alpha + \left(\frac{2}{\sin\left(\frac{1}{n+1} \cdot \frac{\pi}{2}\right)} - 2 \right)\beta \right] - \left[(n-2)\alpha + \left(\frac{2\sin\left(\frac{n-1}{n} \cdot \frac{\pi}{2}\right)}{\sin\left(\frac{1}{n} \cdot \frac{\pi}{2}\right)} - 2 \right)\beta \right]$$

$$= 2\alpha + \left(\frac{2}{\sin\left(\frac{1}{n+1} \cdot \frac{\pi}{2}\right)} - \frac{2\sin\left(\frac{n-1}{n} \cdot \frac{\pi}{2}\right)}{\sin\left(\frac{1}{n} \cdot \frac{\pi}{2}\right)} \right)\beta.$$

We obtain for

$n = 2$:

$$\Delta E_\pi = 2\alpha + \left(\frac{2}{\sin\left(\frac{\pi}{6}\right)} - \frac{2\sin\left(\frac{\pi}{4}\right)}{\sin\left(\frac{\pi}{4}\right)} \right)\beta = 2\alpha + (4-2)\beta = 2\alpha + 2\beta$$

$n = 4$:

$$\Delta E_\pi = 2\alpha + \left(\frac{2}{\sin\left(\frac{\pi}{10}\right)} - \frac{2\sin\left(\frac{3}{8}\pi\right)}{\sin\left(\frac{\pi}{8}\right)} \right)\beta = 2\alpha + (6.47 - 4.83)\beta = 2\alpha + 1.64\beta$$

$n = 6$:

$$\Delta E_\pi = 2\alpha + \left(\frac{2}{\sin\left(\frac{\pi}{14}\right)} - \frac{2\sin\left(\frac{5}{12}\pi\right)}{\sin\left(\frac{\pi}{12}\right)} \right)\beta = 2\alpha + (8.97 - 7.46)\beta = 2\alpha + 1.51\beta$$

$n = 8$:

$$\Delta E_\pi = 2\alpha + \left(\frac{2}{\sin\left(\frac{\pi}{18}\right)} - \frac{2\sin\left(\frac{7}{16}\pi\right)}{\sin\left(\frac{\pi}{16}\right)} \right)\beta = 2\alpha + (11.52 - 10.05)\beta = 2\alpha + 1.47$$

As can be seen, ΔE_π decreases with increasing chain length n, i.e. substitution becomes increasingly easier with respect to the E_π contribution to the potential barrier. As can readily be confirmed the limiting value for infinite chain length $n \to \infty$ is

$$\Delta E_\pi = 2\alpha + \left(\frac{2}{\frac{\pi}{2n}} - \frac{2 \cdot 1}{\frac{\pi}{2n}} \right) \beta = 2\alpha.$$

Problem 5.4: Verify with the aid of the expression

$$c_{J\mu} = \sqrt{\frac{2}{n+1}} \, \sin \left(\frac{\pi}{n+1} J\mu \right), \tag{5/6}$$

that the charge orders in unbranched linear π-electron systems are $q_\mu = 1$ if all bonding molecular orbitals are doubly occupied.

Substitution of (5/6) in the formula (4/52) previously derived for the charge density affords

$$q_\mu = \sum_{J=1}^{n} b_J c_{J\mu}^2 = 2 \sum_{J=1}^{n/2} c_{J\mu}^2 = \left(\frac{4}{n+1} \right) \sum_{J=1}^{n/2} \sin^2 \left(\frac{\pi}{n+1} J\mu \right).$$

With

$$\sum_{k=1}^{n} \sin^2 (kx) = \frac{n}{2} - \frac{\cos((n+1)x) \cdot \sin(nx)}{2 \sin x}$$

we obtain

$$q_\mu = \left(\frac{4}{n+1} \right) \left(\frac{n}{4} - \frac{\cos \left(\frac{n+2}{n+1} \cdot \frac{\pi}{2} \right) \cdot \sin \left(\frac{n}{n+1} \cdot \frac{\pi}{2} \right)}{2 \sin \left(\frac{\pi}{n+1} \right)} \right).$$

Using

$$2 \sin(ax) \cos(bx) = \sin((a - b)x) + \sin((a + b)x)$$

the $\sin^2$ sum can be simplified as follows:

$$q_\mu = \left(\frac{1}{n+1}\right)\left(n - \frac{\sin\left(\left(\frac{n}{n+1} - \frac{n+2}{n+1}\right)\frac{\pi}{2}\right) + \sin\left(\left(\frac{n}{n+1} + \frac{n+2}{n+1}\right)\frac{\pi}{2}\right)}{\sin\left(\frac{\pi}{n+1}\right)}\right)$$

$$= \left(\frac{1}{n+1}\right)\left(n - \frac{\sin\left(-\frac{\pi}{n+1}\right) + \sin\pi}{\sin\left(\frac{\pi}{n+1}\right)}\right)$$

$$= \left(\frac{1}{n+1}\right)\left(n + \frac{\sin\left(\frac{\pi}{n+1}\right) + 0}{\sin\left(\frac{\pi}{n+1}\right)}\right)$$

$$= \frac{n+1}{n+1} = 1$$

5.2. Unbranched Cyclic π-Electron Systems

Problem 5.5:   Prove relationship (5/10).

In analogy to the formula for linear unbranched chains (5/3) the polynomial $R_n(x)$ for unbranched cyclic π-systems is also obtained by development of the associated determinant

$$\begin{vmatrix} -x & 1 & & & & 1 \\ 1 & -x & 1 & & & \\ & 1 & -x & 1 & & \\ & & 1 & & & \\ & & & & & 1 \\ 1 & & & & 1 & -x \end{vmatrix} = 0. \qquad (5/9)$$

Expansion according to the first row gives the subdeterminants

$$= -x\begin{vmatrix} -x & 1 & & \\ 1 & -x & 1 & \\ & 1 & & \\ & & & 1 \\ & & 1 & -x \end{vmatrix} -1\begin{vmatrix} 1 & 1 & & \\ & -x & 1 & \\ & 1 & & \\ & & & 1 \\ 1 & & 1 & -x \end{vmatrix} -(-1)^n\begin{vmatrix} 1 & -x & 1 & \\ & 1 & -x & 1 \\ & & 1 & \\ 1 & & & 1 \end{vmatrix}$$

$$\qquad (A) \qquad\qquad (B) \qquad\qquad (C)$$

The sign of determinant (C) depends on the order n of the determinant (5/9). Even values of n give -1, odd ones give $+1$. Further expansion of the determinants (B) and (C) according to the first column yields

$$(B) = \begin{Vmatrix} -x & 1 & & \\ 1 & & & \\ & & & 1 \\ & & 1 & -x \end{Vmatrix} \quad -(-1)^{n-1} \begin{Vmatrix} 1 & & & \\ -x & 1 & & \\ 1 & & & \\ & & & 1 \end{Vmatrix}$$

$$(D) \qquad\qquad\qquad (I)$$

$$(C) = \begin{Vmatrix} 1 & -x & 1 & \\ & 1 & & \\ & & & \\ & & & 1 \end{Vmatrix} \quad -(-1)^{n-1} \begin{Vmatrix} -x & 1 & & \\ 1 & -x & 1 & \\ & 1 & & \end{Vmatrix}$$

$$(I) \qquad\qquad\qquad (D)$$

The value of the subdeterminants designated (I), which has only unit elements along the main diagonal is unity, as can easily be demonstrated. The result can be summarized as follows:

$$R_n(x) = -x\,(A) - [(D) - (-1)^{n-1}\cdot 1] - (-1)^n[1 - (-1)^{n-1}(D)]$$
$$= -x\,(A) - (D) + (-1)^{n-1} - (-1)^n + (-1)^n(-1)^{n-1}(D).$$

With

$$(-1)^{n-1} = -(-1)^n$$

and

$$(-1)^n(-1)^{n-1} = (-1)^{2n-1} = -1$$

it can be established that

$$R_n(x) = -x\,(A) - 2\,(D) - 2\,(-1)^n.$$

Now since

$$(A) = K_{n-1}(x)$$
$$(D) = K_{n-2}(x)$$

and according to (5/3)

$$-x\,K_{n-1}(x) - K_{n-2}(x) = K_n(x)$$

the polynomial $R_n(x)$ of an unbranched cyclic π-electron system is

$$R_n(x) = K_n(x) - K_{n-2}(x) - 2\,(-1)^n.$$

Problem 5.6: Calculate, for cyclic π-electron systems having $(2 + 4R)$ π-electrons, the total π-electron energy in closed form. Compare the results with those of the corresponding linear π-electron systems obtained by opening the rings, i.e. by severing one bond. Discuss the differences.

For π-electron systems obeying the *Hückel* rule $n = 4R + 2$, the total π-electron energy can be derived in closed form in the following way:

$$E_\pi = \sum_{J=0}^{n} b_J \epsilon_J = 2\epsilon_0 + 2 \sum_{J=1}^{R} b_J \epsilon_J$$

$$= 2(\alpha + 2\beta) + 4 \sum_{J=1}^{R} (\alpha + x_J \beta)$$

$$= (2 + 4R)\alpha + \left(4 + 4 \sum_{J=1}^{R} 2 \cos\left(\frac{2\pi}{n} J\right)\right)\beta.$$

With

$$\sum_{k=1}^{n} \cos(kx) = \frac{\cos\left(\frac{n}{2}x\right) \sin\left(\frac{n+1}{2}x\right)}{\sin\left(\frac{x}{2}\right)} - 1$$

we obtain

$$E_\pi = (2 + 4R)\alpha + \left[4 + 8\left(\frac{\cos\left(\frac{R}{2} \cdot \frac{2\pi}{n}\right) \cdot \sin\left(\frac{R+1}{2} \cdot \frac{2\pi}{n}\right)}{\sin\left(\frac{\pi}{n}\right)} - 1\right)\right]\beta.$$

Simplification with the aid of

$$2 \sin(ax) \cos(bx) = \sin((a - b)x) + \sin((a + b)x)$$

and substitution of $n = 4R + 2$ affords

$$E_\pi = (2 + 4R)\alpha + 4\left(\frac{\sin\left(\frac{\pi}{2 + 4R}\right) + \sin\left(\frac{1 + 2R}{2 + 4R} \cdot \pi\right)}{\sin\left(\frac{\pi}{2 + 4R}\right)} - 1\right)\beta$$

$$= (2 + 4R)\alpha + 4\left(1 + \frac{\sin\left(\frac{\pi}{2}\right)}{\sin\left(\frac{\pi}{2 + 4R}\right)} - 1\right)\beta$$

$$= (2 + 4R)\,\alpha + \frac{4}{\sin\left(\frac{\pi}{2 + 4R}\right)}\,\beta.$$

For $R = 1, 2, 3$ the total π-electron energy is obtained as

$R = 1$:
$$E_{\pi,R} = 6\alpha + \frac{4}{\sin\left(\frac{\pi}{6}\right)}\beta = 6\alpha + 8\beta$$

$R = 2$:
$$E_{\pi,R} = 10\alpha + \frac{4}{\sin\left(\frac{\pi}{10}\right)}\beta = 10\alpha + 12.94\beta$$

$R = 3$:
$$E_{\pi,R} = 14\alpha + \frac{4}{\sin\left(\frac{\pi}{14}\right)}\beta = 14\alpha + 17.94\beta$$

For linear π-electron systems having the same number of centers n, the total π-electron energy (cf. Problem 5.1) is:

$$
\begin{array}{lll}
n = \ \ 6: & E_{\pi,K} = \ \ 6\alpha + \ \ 7\beta & \Delta E_\pi = E_{\pi,R} - E_{\pi,K} = 1\beta \\
n = 10: & E_{\pi,K} = 10\alpha + 12.07\beta & = 0.87\beta \\
n = 14: & E_{\pi,K} = 14\alpha + 17.14\beta & = 0.84\beta
\end{array}
$$

The difference in the total π-electron energies reveals that cyclic π-electron systems obeying the *Hückel* rule are energetically favored relative to linear π-electron systems having the same number of centers n. For infinite values of n, the following limiting value is obtained:

$$\Delta X_\pi = X_{\pi,R} - X_{\pi,K}$$

$$= \frac{4}{\sin\left(\frac{\pi}{n}\right)} - \left(\frac{2}{\sin\left(\frac{\pi}{2n+2}\right)} - 2\right) = \frac{4}{\sin\left(\frac{\pi}{n}\right)} - 2\left(\frac{1 - \sin\left(\frac{\pi}{2n+2}\right)}{\sin\left(\frac{\pi}{2n+2}\right)}\right)$$

$n \to \infty$:

$$\Delta X_\pi = \frac{4}{\frac{\pi}{n}} - 2\left(\frac{1 - \frac{\pi}{2n+2}}{\frac{\pi}{2n+2}}\right) = \frac{4n}{\pi} - \frac{4n}{\pi} - \frac{4}{\pi} + 2 = 2\left(1 - \frac{2}{\pi}\right)$$

$$= 0.727$$

Problem 5.7: Factorize the *Hückel* determinant of a cyclic π-electron system of $n = 2N + 2$ centres with respect to a symmetry plane passing through atomic orbitals Φ_0 and $\Phi_{n/2}$. Show that the antisymmetric solutions are identical with those for a linear π-electron system consisting of N centres.

The *Hückel* determinant of a cyclic π-electron system with $n = 2N + 2$ centers can be factorized according to procedure (4/98) as follows:

(1)

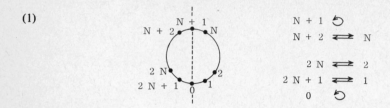

(2)

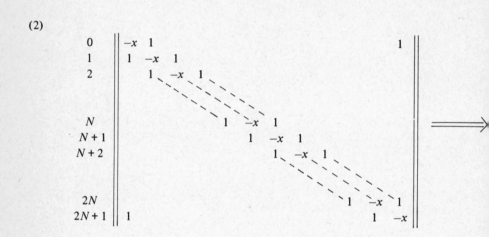

(3) and (4)

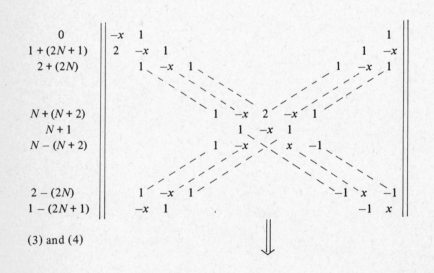

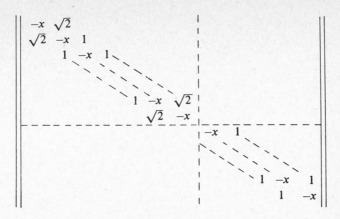

Thus, as can be seen, the subdeterminant of the antisymmetric linear combination is identical with that for a linear chain with n centers.

5.3. Alternant and Nonalternant π-Electron Systems

Problem 5.8: Which of the following π-electron systems are alternant, and which nonalternant?

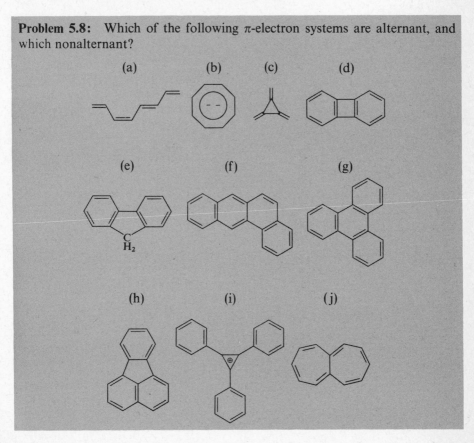

Alternant systems are: (a), (b), (d), (e), (f), (g).
Nonalternant ones are: (c), (h), (i), (j).

Problem 5.9: How many nonbonding molecular orbitals has each of the following π-electron systems?

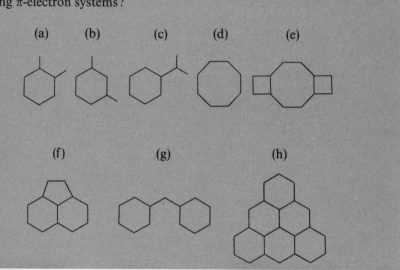

(a)   (b)   (c)   (d)   (e)

(f)   (g)   (h)

In alternant π-electron systems, the number of the nonbonding levels is at least $|n^* - n^0|$ and hence in compounds (a) through (h):

(a)	$|4 - 4| = 0$	(e)	$|6 - 6| = 0$
(b)	$|5 - 3| = 2$	(f)	nonalternant (0)
(c)	$|5 - 4| = 1$	(g)	$|7 - 6| = 1$
(d)	$|4 - 4| = 0$ (2)	(h)	$|12 - 10| = 2$

The hypothetical planar π-electron system of cyclooctatetraene (d) possesses a doubly degenerate nonbonding level according to [5.5] which in this case, however, is to be attributed to the symmetry of the cyclic system.

Problem 5.10: Calculate the nonbonding linear combinations Ψ_{nb} of the π-electron systems

(a)   (b)   (c)

In each case, the calculation should start with the centre indicated by an arrow, setting its coefficient equal to ξ.

According to the rules given in (5/29) through (5/33), the nonbonding linear combinations of the π-electron systems (a) through (c) read as follows:

(a)

$$\sum_\mu c_{nb\,\mu}^2 = 4\,\xi^2 = 1; \quad \xi = \frac{1}{2}$$

$$\Psi_{nb} = \frac{1}{2}(\Phi_1 - \Phi_3 + \Phi_5 - \Phi_7)$$

(b)

$$\sum_\mu c_{nb\,\mu}^2 = 20\,\xi^2 = 1; \xi = \frac{1}{\sqrt{20}}$$

$$\Psi_{nb} = \frac{1}{\sqrt{20}}(-2\,\Phi_2 + 2\,\Phi_4 - \Phi_5 + \Phi_7 - \Phi_9 + 3\,\Phi_{11})$$

(c)

$$\sum_\mu c_{nb\,\mu}^2 = 34\,\xi^2 = 1; \quad \xi = \frac{1}{\sqrt{34}}$$

$$\Psi_{nb} = \frac{1}{\sqrt{34}}(-3\,\Phi_1 - \Phi_3 + \Phi_6 - \Phi_8 + 2\,\Phi_9 - \Phi_{11} + \Phi_{14} + 4\,\Phi_{15})$$

Problem 5.11: Calculate the nonbonding linear combinations Ψ_{nb} of the π-electron systems

(a)   (b)

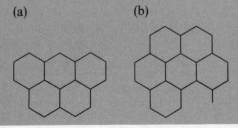

According to the rules given in (5/29) through (5/36), the nonbonding linear combinations of the π-electron systems (a) and (b) read as follows:

(a)

With respect to the circled center, the following holds:

$$-3\eta - 2\eta - \xi - \eta - \xi = 0; \quad \eta = -\frac{1}{3}\xi$$

whence it follows:

$$\sum_\mu c_{nb\,\mu}^2 = \frac{66}{9}\xi^2 = 1; \quad \xi = \frac{3}{\sqrt{66}}$$

$$\Psi_{nb} = \frac{1}{\sqrt{66}}(3\Phi_1 - 3\Phi_2 + 4\Phi_3 - 3\Phi_4 + 3\Phi_5 - 2\Phi_6 + 2\Phi_7 - 2\Phi_8 - \Phi_9 - \Phi_{10})$$

(b)

With respect to the circled center, we find

$$-\eta - \xi - 2\eta - \xi - 3\eta = 0; \quad \eta = -\frac{1}{3}\xi$$

whence it follows

$$\sum_\mu c_{nb\,\mu}^2 = \frac{124}{9}\xi^2 = 1; \quad \xi = \frac{3}{\sqrt{124}}$$

$$\Psi_{nb} = \frac{1}{\sqrt{124}}(3\Phi_1 - 3\Phi_2 + 3\Phi_3 + 4\Phi_4 - 3\Phi_5 + 3\Phi_6 - 2\Phi_7 + 2\Phi_8 - 2\Phi_9 - \Phi_{10} - \Phi_{11} - 7\Phi_{12})$$

Problem 5.12: Calculate the nonbonding linear combinations $\Psi_{nb,1}$, $\Psi_{nb,2}$, and $\Psi_{nb,3}$ of the π-electron system:

(Hint: Let $\Psi_{nb,1}$ be symmetric with respect to rotation about the threefold axis, and let $\Psi_{nb,2}$ be symmetric, $\Psi_{nb,3}$ antisymmetric with respect to reflection in the σ_{xz}-plane. Observe the orthogonality relations.)

According to the usual starring procedure, beginning at center 1, a total of three auxiliary values is required.

Of the three nonbonding molecular orbitals, $\Psi_{nb,1}$ and $\Psi_{nb,3}$ are easily determined:
(1) $\Psi_{nb,1}$ behaves symmetrically on rotation about the three-fold axis of symmetry, whence it follows:

$$\xi = \zeta = \xi + 2\eta + \zeta$$
$$\xi = 2\xi + 2\eta; \; \eta = -\frac{1}{2}\xi$$

(2) $\Psi_{nb,3}$ should be antisymmetric on reflection in σ_{xz}. This requirement leads to

$$\xi = -\zeta; \; \eta = 0$$

As may readily be demonstrated, $\Psi_{nb,1}$ and $\Psi_{nb,3}$ are mutually orthogonal.
(3) The function $\Psi_{nb,2}$ yet to be accounted for should behave symmetrically on reflection in σ_{xz}, from which it merely follows

$$\xi = \zeta$$

$$
\begin{array}{c}
2\xi + 2\eta \\[2pt]
-\xi-\eta \quad\quad -\xi-\eta \\[2pt]
\xi \qquad \eta \qquad \xi
\end{array}
$$

The values of the coefficients therefore have to be determined with the aid of the orthogonality condition. The orthogonality of $\Psi_{nb,2}$ and $\Psi_{nb,3}$ is trivial since the two functions have opposite symmetry behavior with respect to σ_{xz}. However, the orthogonality condition for $\Psi_{nb,1}$ and $\Psi_{nb,2}$ provides the desired answer:

$$\langle \Psi_{nb,1} \mid \Psi_{nb,2} \rangle =$$
$$\langle \frac{1}{\sqrt{15}} (2\Phi_1 + 2\Phi_2 + 2\Phi_3 - \Phi_4 - \Phi_5 - \Phi_6) \mid (\xi\Phi_1 + \xi\Phi_2 + (2\xi+2\eta)\Phi_3 - (\xi+\eta)\Phi_4 + \eta\Phi_5 - (\xi+\eta)\Phi_6)$$
$$= \frac{1}{\sqrt{15}} (10\xi + 5\eta) = 0$$

$$\eta = -2\xi$$

$$
\begin{array}{c}
-2\xi \\
\xi \quad\quad \xi \\
\xi \quad\quad \xi \\
-2\xi
\end{array}
\quad
\xrightarrow[\xi = \frac{1}{2\sqrt{3}}]{\substack{\text{Normalization} \\ \xi^2(1+1+4+1+4+1)=1}}
\quad
\begin{array}{c}
-\frac{1}{\sqrt{3}} \\
\frac{1}{2\sqrt{3}} \quad\quad \frac{1}{2\sqrt{3}} \\
\frac{1}{2\sqrt{3}} \quad\quad \frac{1}{2\sqrt{3}} \\
-\frac{1}{\sqrt{3}}
\end{array}
$$

Problem 5.13: Calculate the charge orders of the following radicals and of their corresponding cations and anions:

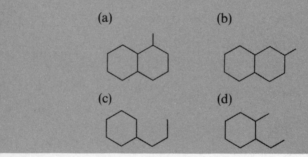

(a)   (b)

(c)   (d)

As demonstrated for the benzyl cation, radical, and anion in (5/43) through (5/45), the charge orders for the positively charged, neutral, and negatively charged π-electron systems (a) through (d) are calculated as follows:

(a) $c_{nb,\mu}^2$:

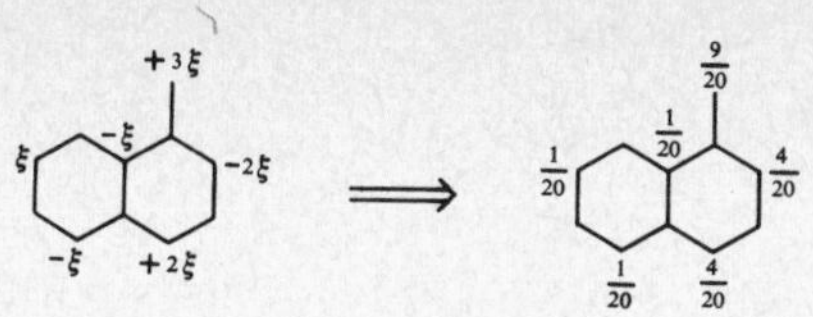

q_μ:

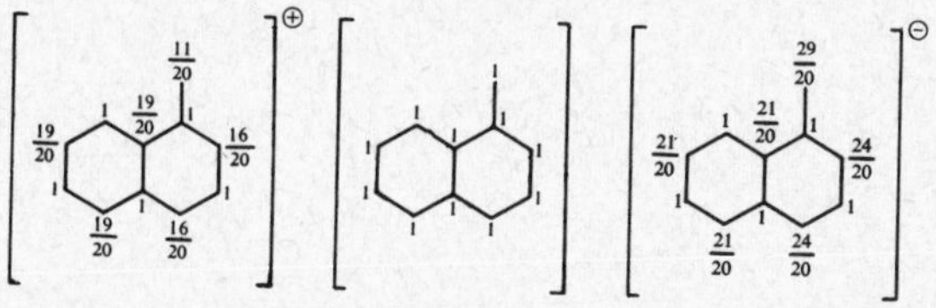

(b) $c_{nb,\mu}^2$:

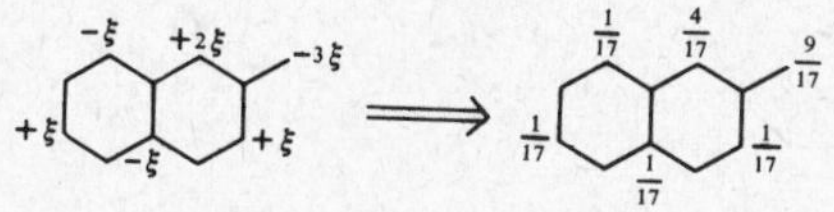

q_μ:

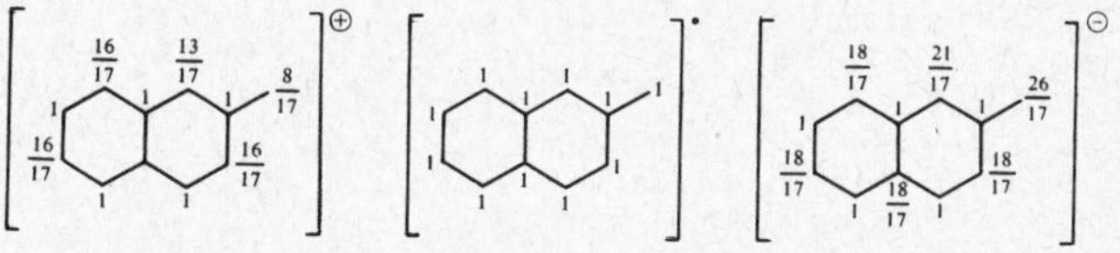

(c) $c_{nb,\mu}^2$:

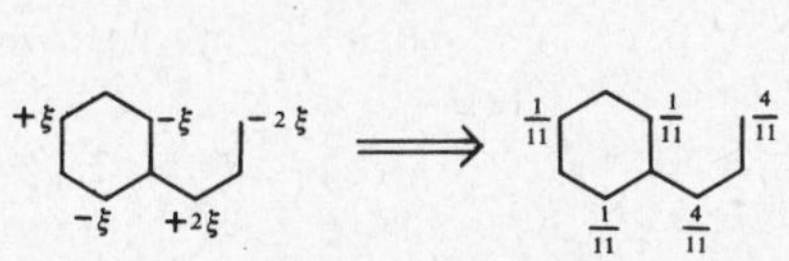

q_μ:

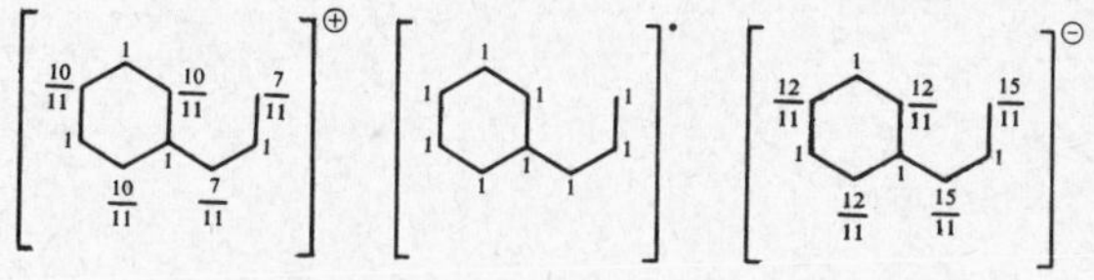

(d) $c_{nb,\mu}^2$:

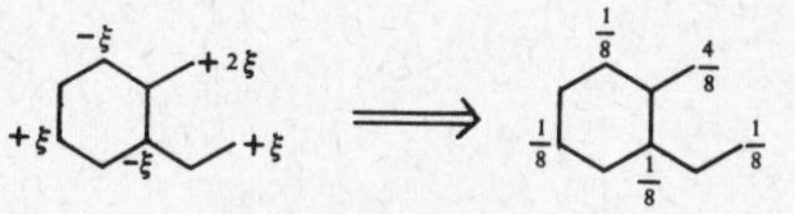

q_μ:

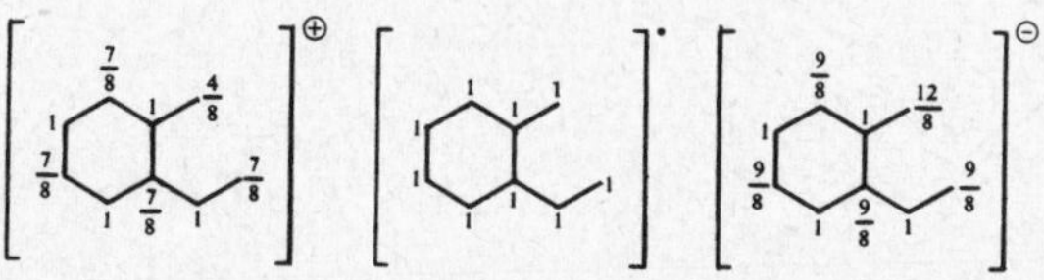

The π-electron systems (c) and (d) occur — as shall only be mentioned in passing — in the transition state of electrophilic and nucleophilic substitutions in naphthalene.

Problem 5.14: Determine the number of unexcited resonance structures (those with no 'long' bonds) for the following π-electron systems:

(a)   (b)   (c)   (d)

According to the counting rule [5.13], the number of resonance structures without "long" bonds in (a) through (d) is:

(a) 10 structures (cf. Problem 5.13)

The number of structures in which the electron is found at a given center is given by the coefficient of the relevant atomic orbital:

(b) 9 structures (cf. Problem 5.13)

(c) 40 structures

(d) 62 structures

In the two last cases — as mentioned in Vol. 1 — the number of resonance structures is proportional to the calculated coefficients, and is not identical with the multiplicands of the auxiliary value ξ as in examples (*a*) and (*b*).

Problem 5.15: Which of the following π-electron systems are alternant, which are nonalternant? Which have at least one nonbonding orbital? Which are probably stable as cations, and which as anions? Which may be predicted to have a doublet or triplet ground state?

(a)   (b) 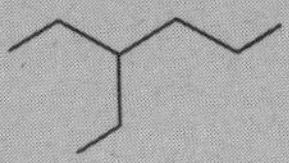   (c)

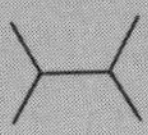

(d) 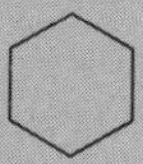   (e) 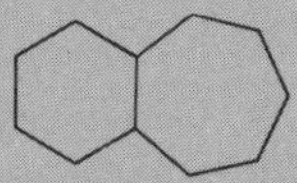   (f) 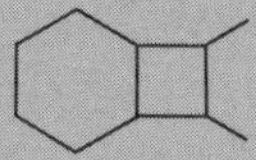   (g) 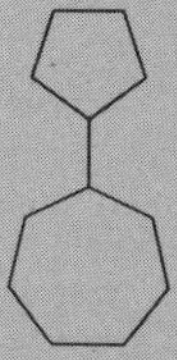   (h)

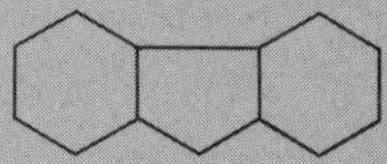

(i) 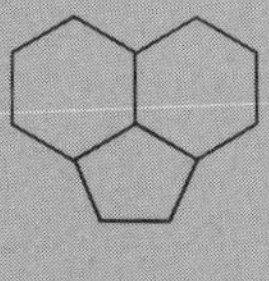   (j) 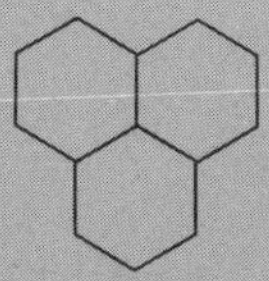   (k) 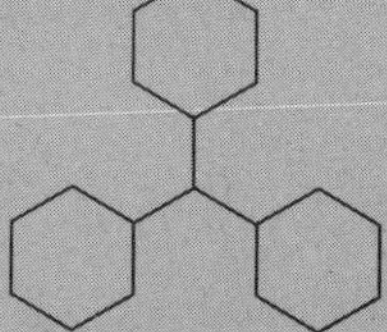   (l)

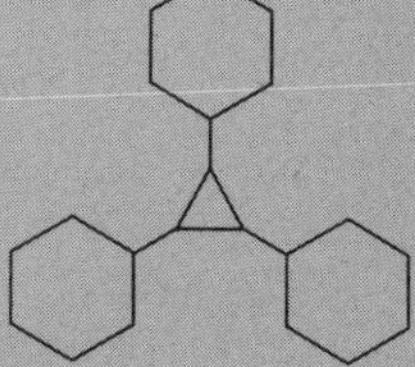

(m) 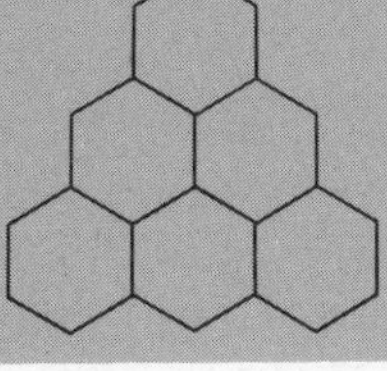   (n)

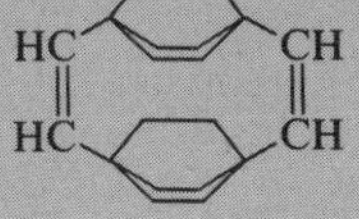

The desired properties of the π-electron systems (a) through (n) are listed in the table:

System	Alternant nonalternant	Nonbonding levels*	(Stable)** Molecular state	
(a)	alternant	1	radical (cation) (anion)	doublet
(b)	alternant	0	neutral	singlet
(c)	alternant	0 (2)	radical	triplet
(d)	alternant	0	neutral	singlet
(e)	nonalternant	(0)	cation	singlet
(f)	alternant	0	neutral	singlet
(g)	nonalternant	(0)	neutral	singlet
(h)	nonalternant	(1)	anion	singlet
(i)	nonalternant	(0)	neutral	singlet
(j)	alternant	1	radical (cation) (anion)	doublet
(k)	alternant	1	radical (cation) (anion)	doublet
(l)	nonalternant	(0)	cation	singlet
(m)	alternant	2	radical	triplet
(n)	alternant	0	neutral	singlet

* In parentheses: nonbonding levels that cannot be predicted from $|n^* - n^0|$

** As far as predictions are possible from the energy level schemes (a), (j), (k), (l) or from the *Hückel* rule (e), (h).

6. First Order Perturbation Treatment and Characteristic Quantities of π-Systems

6.1. First Order Perturbation Calculations

Problem 6.1: Draw the energy level schemes of azulene and 1-azaazulene (cf. HMO Table ⑤⑦)

assuming that replacement of a carbon atom at position 1 by a nitrogen atom causes a perturbation $\delta\alpha_1 = 0.5\,\beta$.

With the values of the HMO table, and according to the equation

$$\delta\epsilon_J = c_{j_1}^2\,\delta\alpha_1 \qquad (6/12)$$

we obtain the following changes in the orbital energies:

$\epsilon_J - \alpha$	$\delta\epsilon_J$	$\epsilon_J + \delta\epsilon_J - \alpha$
$-2.095\,\beta$	$(0.259)^2 \cdot 0.5\,\beta = 0.034\,\beta$	$-2.061\,\beta$
$-1.869\,\beta$	$(0.250)^2 = 0.031\,\beta$	$-1.838\,\beta$
$-1.579\,\beta$	$(0.436)^2 = 0.095\,\beta$	$-1.484\,\beta$
$-0.738\,\beta$	$(0.300)^2 = 0.045\,\beta$	$-0.693\,\beta$
$-0.400\,\beta$	$(0.063)^2 = 0.002\,\beta$	$-0.398\,\beta$
$0.477\,\beta$	$(0.543)^2 = 0.147\,\beta$	$0.624\,\beta$
$0.887\,\beta$	$(0.259)^2 = 0.034\,\beta$	$0.921\,\beta$
$1.356\,\beta$	$(0.221)^2 = 0.024\,\beta$	$1.380\,\beta$
$1.652\,\beta$	$(0.268)^2 = 0.036\,\beta$	$1.688\,\beta$
$2.310\,\beta$	$(0.323)^2 = 0.052\,\beta$	$2.362\,\beta$

The energy level scheme of the unperturbed and perturbed systems have the following appearance:

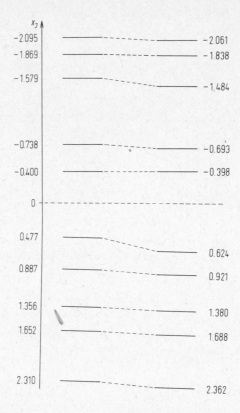

x_j		
-2.095	————————————	-2.061
-1.869	————————————	-1.838
-1.579	————————————	-1.484
-0.738	————————————	-0.693
-0.400	————————————	-0.398
0	————————————	
0.477	————————————	0.624
0.887	————————————	0.921
1.356	————————————	1.380
1.652	————————————	1.688
2.310	————————————	2.362

Problem 6.2: Within the HMO approximation, polarographic reduction of an 'aromatic' hydrocarbon can be described as insertion of an electron into the lowest antibonding molecular orbital, whose orbital energy ε_a can be correlated with the corresponding half-wave reduction potential $E_{1/2}$. Which of the three methyl-substituted anthracenes

is most easily reduced, assuming that the methyl group produces a perturbation $\delta\alpha_\rho = -0{\cdot}2\,\beta$?

Table ⑥⑥⑥ (Vol.3) gives the following values for the orbital energy ϵ_8 and the pertinent coefficient $c_{8\rho}$ of anthracene:

$$\epsilon_8 = -0.414\,\beta$$
$$c_{81} = -0.311 \qquad\qquad c_{82} = +0.220 \qquad\qquad c_{89} = +0.440$$

The resulting changes in the orbital energies

$$\delta\epsilon_J = c_{J\rho}^2 \cdot \delta\alpha_\rho \tag{6/12}$$

amount to

$$\delta\epsilon_8^{(1)} = 0.097\,(-0.2\,\beta) \qquad \delta\epsilon_8^{(2)} = 0.048\,(-0.2\,\beta) \qquad \delta\epsilon_8^{(9)} = 0.194\,(-0.2\,\beta)$$
$$= -0.019\,\beta \qquad\qquad\quad = -0.010\,\beta \qquad\qquad\quad = -0.039\,\beta$$

The level ϵ_8 generally rises under the influence of the perturbation $\delta\alpha_\rho$, so that methylanthracenes are more difficult to reduce than the unsubstituted hydrocarbon. Therefore, the half-wave potential will assume increasingly negative values along the series $2 < 1 < 9$, i.e. 2-methylanthracene is the easiest to reduce.

Problem 6.3: Draw the *Hückel* orbital energy scheme of styrene (cf. HMO Table ⑥—K_2) as a function of the angle Θ by which the vinyl group is continuously rotated out of the plane of the benzene π-electron system:

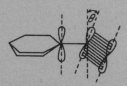

(According to convention, the perturbation formula holds only for small changes of angle $\Theta \leq 45°$. For $\Theta = 90°$, the π-system splits into a 'benzene' and an 'ethylene' π-system.) How does the position of the first intense absorption band ^1L_a in the electronic spectrum of styrene change if the vinyl group is rotated out of the plane of the ring due to steric hindrance?

According to

$$\delta\beta_{17} = -\beta(1 - \cos\Theta) \qquad\text{(cf. [6.2])}$$

the perturbation $\delta\beta_{17}$ assumes the following values upon twisting out of the plane:

Θ	26°	37°	45°	60°
$\cos\Theta$	0.9	0.8	0.7	0.5
$\delta\beta_{17}$	$-0.1\,\beta$	$-0.2\,\beta$	$-0.3\,\beta$	$-0.5\,\beta$

The perturbed orbital energies calculated according to

$$\delta\epsilon_J = 2c_{J1}\,c_{J7}\,\delta\beta_{17}; \quad \epsilon_J' = \epsilon_J + \delta\epsilon_J$$

are summarized in the appended table:

Θ	0°	26°	37°	45°	60°
ϵ_1'	2.136	2.104	2.073	2.041	1.978
ϵ_2'	1.414	1.379	1.343	1.308	1.237
ϵ_3'	1.000	1.000	1.000	1.000	1.000
ϵ_4'	0.662	0.688	0.715	0.741	0.794
ϵ_5'	−0.662	−0.688	−0.715	−0.741	−0.794
ϵ_6'	−1.000	−1.000	−1.000	−1.000	−1.000
ϵ_7'	−1.414	−1.379	−1.343	−1.308	−1.237
ϵ_8'	−2.136	−2.104	−2.073	−2.041	−1.978

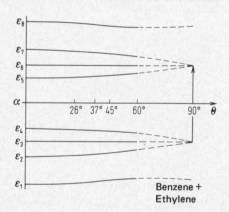

Benzene + Ethylene

It can be seen from the graphic representation that with increasing twisting of the vinyl group out of the plane of the ring, the excitation energy $\Delta E = \epsilon_5 - \epsilon_4$ increases and the (^1L_a) band consequently shifts to shorter wavelengths.

6.2. Relationships between Total π-Electron Energy, Charge Order, and Bond Order

Problem 6.4: Calculate the charge orders and the bond orders of butadiene and of methylenecyclopropene in the first electronically excited state, and compare the values obtained with those of the ground state.

The charge and bond orders for the first excited state are calculated with the values (6/15) according to

$$q_\rho = \sum_{J=1}^{n} b_J c_{J\rho}^2 \tag{4/52}$$

$$p_{\rho\sigma} = \sum_{J=1}^{n} b_J c_{J\rho} c_{J\sigma} \tag{6/24}$$

as follows:

(*a*) Butadiene:

$$\left.\begin{aligned}
q_1 &= 2c_{11}^2 + c_{21}^2 + c_{31}^2 \\
q_2 &= 2c_{12}^2 + c_{22}^2 + c_{32}^2 \\
q_3 &= 2c_{13}^2 + c_{23}^2 + c_{33}^2 \\
q_4 &= 2c_{14}^2 + c_{24}^2 + c_{34}^2
\end{aligned}\right\} = 2(\pm 0.372)^2 + 2(\pm 0.602)^2 = 1.000$$

$$\sum_{\rho=1}^{4} q_\rho = Z_\pi = \overline{4.000}$$

$$\left.\begin{aligned}
p_{12} &= 2c_{11}c_{12} + c_{21}c_{22} + c_{31}c_{32} \\
p_{34} &= 2c_{13}c_{14} + c_{23}c_{24} + c_{33}c_{34}
\end{aligned}\right\} = 2(0.372)(0.602) + (\pm 0.602)(\pm 0.372) + (0.602)(-0.37$$

$$= 0.447$$

$$p_{23} = 2c_{12}c_{13} + c_{22}c_{23} + c_{32}c_{33} = 2(0.602)_2 + (0.372)(-0.372) + (-0.372)^2 = 0.724$$

$$2 \sum_{(\rho-\sigma)} p_{\rho\sigma} = \sum_{J=1}^{4} b_J x_J = 3.236$$

From the molecular diagrams

Ground state	First excited state

we conclude that in the first excited state the charge orders $q_\mu = 1.000$ remain unchanged, since in alternant systems with n centers, the completely general relation $c_{\frac{n}{2}\mu}^{2} = c_{(\frac{n}{2}+1)\mu}^{2}$ is valid for the highest occupied (Ψ_n) and the lowest unoccupied ($\Psi_{\frac{n}{2}+1}$) levels. Only the bond orders change, the bond between the centers 2 and 3 being strengthened and those between the centers 1 and 2 and between 3 and 4 weakened, since the molecular orbital Ψ_3 displays a bonding interaction between the atomic orbitals Φ_2 and Φ_3 whereas a node lies between the centers 1 and 2 and between 3 and 4.

(b) Methylenecyclopropene:

$$
\begin{aligned}
q_1 &= 2c_{11}^2 + c_{21}^2 + c_{31}^2 = 2(0.282)^2 + (-0.815)^2 & &= 0.823 \\
q_2 &= 2c_{12}^2 + c_{22}^2 + c_{32}^2 = 2(0.612)^2 + (-0.254)^2 & &= 0.814 \\
\left.\begin{aligned} q_3 &= 2c_{13}^2 + c_{23}^2 + c_{33}^2 \\ q_4 &= 2c_{14}^2 + c_{24}^2 + c_{34}^2 \end{aligned}\right\} &= 2(0.523)^2 + (0.368)^2 + (\pm0.707)^2 & &= 1.182
\end{aligned}
$$

$$
\sum_{\rho=1}^{4} q_\rho = Z_\pi = \qquad 4.001
$$

$$
\begin{aligned}
p_{12} &= 2c_{11}c_{12} + c_{21}c_{22} + c_{31}c_{32} = 2(0.282)(0.612) + (-0.815)(-0.254) & &= 0.552 \\
\left.\begin{aligned} p_{23} &= 2c_{12}c_{13} + c_{22}c_{23} + c_{32}c_{33} \\ p_{24} &= 2c_{12}c_{14} + c_{22}c_{24} + c_{32}c_{34} \end{aligned}\right\} &= 2(0.602)(0.523) + (-0.254)(0.368) & &= 0.547 \\
p_{34} &= 2c_{13}c_{14} + c_{23}c_{24} + c_{33}c_{34} = 2(0.523)^2 + (0.368)^2 + (0.707)(-0.707) & &= 0.183
\end{aligned}
$$

$$
2\sum_{(\rho-\sigma)} p_{\rho\sigma} = \sum_{J=1}^{4} b_J x_J = \qquad 3.654
$$

The molecular diagrams

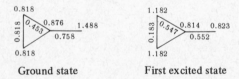

Ground state   First excited state

show that charge transfer occurs from center 1 to the centers 3 and 4 upon excitation. This behavior is typical for nonalternant systems, since in this specific case, no relation analogous to that for butadiene holds for the coefficients of the highest occupied and the lowest unoccupied molecular orbitals (here, $c_{2\mu}^2 \neq c_{3\mu}^2$). At the same time, the bond between the centers 3 and 4 is considerably weakened since the orbital Ψ_3 has a node at this position.

Problem 6.5: Within the HMO approximation, it can be shown that of any set of isomers of aromatic π-electron systems, it is always that isomer which has the greatest total π-electron energy that is thermodynamically most stable (assuming equal numbers of bonds of the same kind). Which isomer in each of the following pairs is predicted to have the greatest thermodynamic stability, assuming that substitution of a carbon atom by a nitrogen atom causes a perturbation $\delta\alpha_\rho = 0.5\,\beta$?

The values from the appropriate HMO Table (Vol. 3), substituted in the equation

$$\delta E_\pi = q_\rho\,\delta\alpha_\rho \tag{6/21}$$

lead to the following tabulated results.

System	q_ρ	δE_π	E_π		Stability
$(a)_1$	1.000	0.500 β	4 α +	4.972 β	
$(a)_2$	1.000	0.500 β	4 α +	4.972 β	
			$\Delta E_\pi =$	0.000 β	$(a)_1 = (a)_2$
$(b)_1$	0.814	0.408 β	8 α +	10.864 β	
$(b)_2$	1.173	0.587 β	8 α +	11.043 β	
			$\Delta E_\pi =$	-0.179 β	$(b)_2 > (b)_1$
$(c)_1$	1.097	0.549 β	10 α +	13.348 β	
$(c)_2$	0.976	0.488 β	10 α +	13.287 β	
			$\Delta E_\pi =$	+0.061 β	$(c)_1 > (c)_2$

System	q_ρ	δE_π	E_π	Stability
$(d)_1$	1.000	$0.500\,\beta$	$10\,\alpha\ +\ 14.183\,\beta$	
$(d)_2$	1.000	$0.500\,\beta$	$10\,\alpha\ +\ 14.183\,\beta$	
			$\Delta E_\pi =\ \ \ 0.000\,\beta$	$(d)_1 = (d)_2$
$(e)_1$	1.173	$0.587\,\beta$	$10\,\alpha\ +\ 13.951\,\beta$	
$(e)_2$	0.855	$0.428\,\beta$	$10\,\alpha\ +\ 13.792\,\beta$	
			$\Delta E_\pi =\ +0.159\,\beta$	$(e)_1 > (e)_2$

In the ground state of neutral alternant systems such as (a) or (d), all charge orders amount to

$$q_\mu = \sum_{J=1}^{n} b_J\, c_{J\mu}^2 = 1. \tag{5/27}$$

Consequently, the same perturbation energies $\delta E_\pi = \delta\alpha_\rho$ are obtained on replacement of any carbon center by a hetero atom. The expected differences are not derivable by a first order perturbation calculation. In contrast, first order perturbations already occur in nonalternant systems such as (b), (c), or (e) within the model used.

6.3. A Systematic Approach to First Order Perturbation Calculations: Generalized Bond Orders

Problem 6.6: Starting with the molecular orbitals of the cross-conjugated triene (a), calculate approximations to the orbital energies of fulvene (b)

(a)   (b)

and compare the results with the exact values from the HMO Table ⑤—.

Substitution of the tabulated coefficients of vinylbutadiene and of

$$\delta \epsilon_J = 2 c_{J2}\, c_{J3}\, \delta \beta_{23} \tag{6/14}$$

leads to the following changes in the orbital energies:

$$
\begin{aligned}
\delta\epsilon_1 &= 2(0.230)^2\,\beta &&= +0.106\,\beta & \epsilon_1' - \alpha &= +1.932\,\beta + 0.106\,\beta = &&2.038\,\beta \\
\delta\epsilon_2 &= -2(0.500)^2\,\beta &&= -0.500\,\beta & \epsilon_2' - \alpha &= +1.000\,\beta - 0.500\,\beta = &&0.500\,\beta \\
\delta\epsilon_3 &= 2(0.444)^2\,\beta &&= +0.394\,\beta & \epsilon_3' - \alpha &= +0.518\,\beta + 0.394\,\beta = &&0.912\,\beta \\
\delta\epsilon_4 &= 2(-0.444)^2\,\beta &&= +0.394\,\beta & \epsilon_4' - \alpha &= -0.518\,\beta + 0.394\,\beta = &&-0.124\,\beta \\
\delta\epsilon_5 &= -2(0.500)^2\,\beta &&= -0.500\,\beta & \epsilon_5' - \alpha &= -1.000\,\beta - 0.500\,\beta = &&-1.500\,\beta \\
\delta\epsilon_6 &= 2(0.230)^2\,\beta &&= +0.106\,\beta & \epsilon_6' - \alpha &= -1.932\,\beta + 0.106\,\beta = &&-1.826\,\beta
\end{aligned}
$$

The resulting orbital energies of the perturbed triene system are in good agreement with the exact *Hückel* values for fulvene, as shown by the energy level scheme:

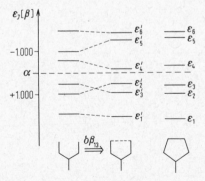

Problem 6.7: Calculate the shift of the orbital energies ε_J on conversion of s-trans- into s-cis-butadiene

by introducing an additional interaction corresponding to a resonance integral $\beta_{14} = \delta\beta$ between centres 1 and 4 in the latter conformation. Which of the two conformers absorbs at longer wavelengths?

The *Hückel* model, in which interactions β are stipulated to exist only between nearest neighbors, can differentiate between the above s-trans and s-cis conformations (in which the connections between the centers remain unchanged and the π-electron systems each lie in a plane) only if additional interactions are introduced between more distant centers. The changes in orbital energies thus calculated for s-cis-butadiene are

$\delta\epsilon_J = 2c_{J1}c_{J4}\,\delta\beta$	$\epsilon'_J - \alpha = \epsilon_J + \delta\epsilon_J - \alpha$
$\delta\epsilon_1 = +0.277\,\delta\beta$	$\epsilon'_1 - \alpha = 1.618\,\beta + 0.277\,\delta\beta$
$\delta\epsilon_2 = -0.725\,\delta\beta$	$\epsilon'_2 - \alpha = 0.618\,\beta - 0.725\,\delta\beta$
$\delta\epsilon_3 = +0.725\,\delta\beta$	$\epsilon'_3 - \alpha = -0.618\,\beta + 0.725\,\delta\beta$
$\delta\epsilon_4 = -0.277\,\delta\beta$	$\epsilon'_4 - \alpha = -1.618\,\beta - 0.277\,\delta\beta$

The perturbations of the levels ϵ_2 and ϵ_3 which happen to have opposite signs require that, within the framework of the present model, s-cis-butadiene absorbs at longer wavelengths, in agreement with experimental findings, e.g.:

$\tilde{\nu}_m = 44000\,\mathrm{cm}^{-1}$ $\qquad$ $\tilde{\nu}_m = 39000\,\mathrm{cm}^{-1}$

Problem 6.8: How large is the change in total π-electron energy on introduction of a bond between centres 2 and 3 in the following cross-conjugated triene?

The change in the total π-electron energy is obtained from

$$\delta E_\pi = 2 P_{23} \delta \beta_{23}. \qquad (6/55)$$

by introduction of the generalized bond order P_{23}. However, this is equal to zero according to (6/53) if two centers belonging to the same starred or unstarred set in an alternant system are linked together:

Thus within the framework of the above approximation, the total π-electron energies of vinylbutadiene and fulvene do not differ.

Problem 6.9: By assuming an additional resonance integral $\beta_{14} = \delta\beta$ to be operative in the s-cis conformation, calculate which of the two conformations

is the more stable from the point of view of HMO theory. In other words, on which side does the equilibrium lie?

The total π-electron energy of s-trans-butadiene is given in Vol. 3

$$E_{\pi,\,trans} = 4\,\alpha + 4.472\,\beta.$$

The perturbation $\beta_{14} = \delta\beta$ changes this value according to (6/55) as follows:

$$\delta E_\pi = 2 P_{14}\,\delta\beta = 2(-0.447)\delta\beta = -0.894\,\delta\beta.$$

The total π-electron energy of the s-cis compound thereby amounts to only

$$E_{\pi,\,cis} = 4\alpha + 4.472\,\beta - 0.894\,\delta\beta.$$

The s-cis conformer is thermodynamically less stable than the s-trans conformer with respect to its heat of formation, and the equilibrium lies on the side of the latter for negative $\delta\beta$ values. If the perturbation $\delta\beta$ reaches the full value β, then the π-electron system of cyclobutadiene is obtained, whose total π-electron energy only amounts to $4\,\alpha + 4\,\beta$.

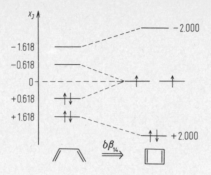

6.4. First Order Perturbation Calculations with Degenerate Eigenvalues

Problem 6.10: Assuming

$$\mathscr{R} \,\dot{\times}\, \Psi_J \doteq \Psi_J \quad \text{and} \quad \mathscr{R} \,\dot{\times}\, \Psi_K \doteq -\Psi_K$$

show that condition (6/67) holds if centres σ and τ, between which the perturbation $\delta\beta_{\sigma\tau}$ is introduced, are transformed into each other on application of the symmetry operation $\mathscr{R}$.

It is presumed that

$$\mathscr{R} \,\dot{\times}\, \Psi_J \doteq \Psi_J, \text{ i.e. } \mathscr{R} \,\dot{\times}\, \sum_\mu c_{J\mu} \Phi_\mu \doteq + \sum_\mu c_{J\mu} \Phi_\mu$$

$$\mathscr{R} \,\dot{\times}\, \Psi_K \doteq -\Psi_K, \text{ i.e. } \mathscr{R} \,\dot{\times}\, \sum_\mu c_{K\mu} \Phi_\mu \doteq - \sum_\mu c_{K\mu} \Phi_\mu$$

Since atomic orbitals Φ_σ and Φ_τ are interconverted by symmetry operation $\mathscr{R}$

$$\mathscr{R} \,\dot{\times}\, \Phi_\sigma \doteq \Phi_\tau,$$
$$\mathscr{R} \,\dot{\times}\, \Phi_\tau \doteq \Phi_\sigma,$$

the associated coefficients of the linear combinations change as follows:

$$c_{J\sigma} = c_{J\tau},$$
$$c_{K\sigma} = -c_{K\tau},$$

and a calculation of the matrix element H'_{JK} according to (6/65) yields

$$H'_{JK} = (c_{J\sigma}c_{KT} + c_{JT}c_{K\sigma})\,\delta\beta_{\sigma T}$$
$$= (c_{J\sigma}c_{KT} + c_{J\sigma}(-c_{KT}))\,\delta\beta_{\sigma T} = 0.$$

Problem 6.11: Using HMO Table ⑩, introduce a bond into a ten-membered ring between centres 1 and 6, or between centres 4 and 8 (or equivalently, 3 and 9) in such a way that the symmetry relative to a symmetry plane passing through atomic orbitals 1 and 6 is conserved.

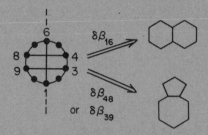

Compare the orbital energies so obtained for naphthalene and azulene with the exact values tabulated. What are the consequences of the perturbation with respect to the absorption of light by these systems?

The changes occurring in the orbital energies if the symmetry properties remain unaltered can be calculated according to

$$\delta\epsilon_J = 2c_{J\sigma}c_{JT}\,\delta\beta_{\sigma T} \tag{6/14}$$

in the following manner:
(a) Perturbation $\delta\beta_{16}$:

J	$\delta\epsilon_J$	$\epsilon_J^{10-Ring} - \alpha$	$\epsilon'_J - \alpha$	Naphthalene $\epsilon_J - \alpha$
1	$0.200\,\beta$	$2.000\,\beta$	$2.200\,\beta$	$2.303\,\beta$
2	$-0.400\,\beta$	$1.618\,\beta$	$1.218\,\beta$	$1.618\,\beta$
3	$0.000\,\beta$	$1.618\,\beta$	$1.618\,\beta$	$1.303\,\beta$
4	$0.400\,\beta$	$0.618\,\beta$	$1.018\,\beta$	$1.000\,\beta$
5	$0.000\,\beta$	$0.618\,\beta$	$0.618\,\beta$	$0.618\,\beta$
6	$-0.400\,\beta$	$-0.618\,\beta$	$-1.018\,\beta$	$-0.618\,\beta$
7	$0.000\,\beta$	$-0.618\,\beta$	$-0.618\,\beta$	$-1.000\,\beta$
8	$0.400\,\beta$	$-1.618\,\beta$	$-1.218\,\beta$	$-1.303\,\beta$
9	$0.000\,\beta$	$-1.618\,\beta$	$-1.618\,\beta$	$-1.618\,\beta$
10	$-0.200\,\beta$	$-2.000\,\beta$	$-2.200\,\beta$	$-2.303\,\beta$

The excitation energy $\Delta E = \epsilon_6 - \epsilon_5$ is not changed by the perturbation.

(b) Perturbation $\delta\beta_{39} = \delta\beta_{48}$:

J	$\delta\epsilon_J$	$\epsilon_J^{10\ Ring} - \alpha$	$\epsilon_J' - \alpha$	$\epsilon_J^{Azulene} - \alpha$
1	$0.200\ \beta$	$2.000\ \beta$	$2.200\ \beta$	$2.310\ \beta$
2	$0.038\ \beta$	$1.618\ \beta$	$1.656\ \beta$	$1.652\ \beta$
3	$-0.362\ \beta$	$1.618\ \beta$	$1.256\ \beta$	$1.356\ \beta$
4	$0.262\ \beta$	$0.618\ \beta$	$0.880\ \beta$	$0.887\ \beta$
5	$-0.138\ \beta$	$0.618\ \beta$	$0.480\ \beta$	$0.447\ \beta$
6	$0.262\ \beta$	$-0.618\ \beta$	$-0.356\ \beta$	$-0.400\ \beta$
7	$-0.138\ \beta$	$-0.618\ \beta$	$-0.756\ \beta$	$-0.738\ \beta$
8	$0.038\ \beta$	$-1.618\ \beta$	$-1.580\ \beta$	$-1.579\ \beta$
9	$-0.362\ \beta$	$-1.618\ \beta$	$-1.980\ \beta$	$-1.869\ \beta$
10	$0.200\ \beta$	$-2.000\ \beta$	$-1.800\ \beta$	$-2.095\ \beta$

Here the excitation energy $\Delta E = \epsilon_6 - \epsilon_5$ is lowered by the perturbation, i.e., in contrast to the naphthalene model obtained by perturbation of the ten-membered ring, the azulene model predicts a longer wavelength absorption in agreement with experience.

The results obtained are represented graphically in the following:

s = symmetrical orbital
a = antisymmetrical orbital $\Big\}$ with respect to symmetry plane σ

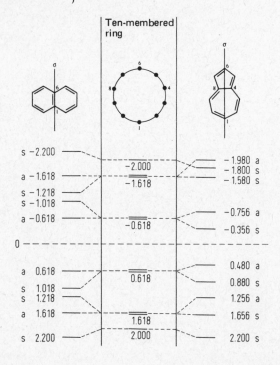

Problem 6.12: Starting from the HMO orbital energies of the 14 carbon ring (HMO Table ⑭), calculate approximations for the two highest bonding and for the two lowest antibonding *Hückel* molecular orbitals of phenanthrene.

The two bonds are introduced between centers 1 and 6, and also between 9 and 14 of the 14-perimeter.

The list of perturbations is therefore:

$$< \mu \mid h \mid \nu > = 0; \text{except} < 1 \mid h \mid 6 > = < 6 \mid h \mid 1 > = \beta$$
$$< 9 \mid h \mid 14 > = < 14 \mid h \mid 9 > = \beta$$

Since the symmetry properties (e.g. with reference to the reflection axis 1−8) are not conserved, the secular determinant has to be solved for the degenerate eigenvalues ϵ_6/ϵ_7 (*a*) and ϵ_8/ϵ_9 (*b*):

$$\left\| \begin{array}{cc} H'_{JJ} - \epsilon' & H'_{JK} \\ H'_{KJ} & H'_{KK} - \epsilon' \end{array} \right\| = 0 \qquad (6/60)$$

(*a*) The individual matrix elements (6/75) read

$$H'_{66} = x_6 + 2(c_{61}c_{66} + c_{69}c_{6\,14})$$
$$= 0.445 + 2(0.378 \cdot 0.341 - 0.084^2) \qquad\qquad = 0.689$$
$$H'_{77} = x_7 + 2(c_{71}c_{76} + c_{79}c_{7\,14})$$
$$= 0.445 + 2(0 \cdot 0.164 + 0.368^2) \qquad\qquad = 0.716$$
$$H'_{67} = H'_{76} = (c_{61}c_{76} + c_{66}c_{71} + c_{69}c_{7\,14} + c_{6\,14}c_{79})$$
$$= (0.378 \cdot 0.164 + 0.341 \cdot 0 + 0.084 \cdot 0.368 - 0.084 \cdot 0.368) = 0.062$$

Solution of the determinant yields the perturbed orbital energies:

$$\left\| \begin{array}{cc} 0.689 - x' & 0.062 \\ 0.062 & 0.716 - x' \end{array} \right\| = 0$$

$$(x')^2 - 1.405\,x' + 0.489 = 0$$
$$x' = 0.703 \pm 0.067$$
$$\epsilon'_6 = \alpha + 0.770\,\beta; \quad \epsilon'_7 = \alpha + 0.636\,\beta$$

(b) Since the alternancy of the system is conserved the energies of the antibonding molecular orbitals are

$$\epsilon_8 = \alpha - 0.636\,\beta; \quad \epsilon_9 = \alpha - 0.770\,\beta$$

As expected the perturbation expectedly eliminates the degeneracy of the orbital energies for the 14-perimeter, and the following pairs of molecular orbitals result for the alternant π-electron system:

$$\epsilon_6 = -\epsilon_9; \quad \epsilon_7 = -\epsilon_8$$

The following orbital energy scheme compares the results obtained with the exact HMO values of phenanthrene (Vol. 3).

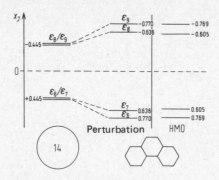

Agreement is seen to be satisfactory.

It can easily be shown that the problem — by analogy with Problem 6.1 — could also have been solved by a method avoiding the second order determinant. If the two additional bonds had been introduced between the centers 4/13 and 5/10, the orbital symmetry with respect to a plane of symmetry through the midpoints of the bonds 4/5 and 11/12 would have remained unaltered.

Problem 6.13:   As an extension of Problem 6.11, use the tabulated values for a 10-membered ring to calculate approximate orbital energies ε_4, ε_5, ε_6, and ε_7 for quinoline and for 1-azaazulene, introducing a perturbation of the *Coulomb* integral of $\delta\alpha_N = 0.5\beta$ for the nitrogen atoms.

By the simultaneous introduction of the perturbations $\delta\alpha$ and $\delta\beta$, the symmetry properties with respect to the reflection axis 1–6 (cf. Problem 6.11) disappear in the models and the secular determinant (6/64) therefore has to be solved in each case.

(a) Quinoline

The list of perturbations consists of

$$\langle \mu \mid h \mid \nu \rangle = 0; \text{except} \langle 2 \mid h \mid 2 \rangle = \delta_{\alpha_2} = 0.5\,\beta$$
$$\langle 1 \mid h \mid 6 \rangle = \langle 6 \mid h \mid 1 \rangle = \delta\beta_{16} = \beta$$

The individual matrix elements (6/75) read

$$
\begin{aligned}
H'_{44} &= x_4 + c_{42}^2 \cdot 0.5 + 2\,c_{41}\,c_{46} \\
&= 0.618 + 0.138^2 \cdot 0.5 + 2 \cdot 0.447^2 &&= 1.027 \\
H'_{55} &= x_5 + c_{52}^2 \cdot 0.5 + 2\,c_{51}\,c_{56} \\
&= 0.618 + 0.425^2 \cdot 0.5 + 2 \cdot 0 \cdot 0 &&= 0.708 \\
H'_{45} &= H'_{54} = c_{42} \cdot c_{52} \cdot 0.5 + (c_{41}\,c_{56} + c_{46}\,c_{51}) \\
&= 0.138 \cdot 0.425 \cdot 0.5 + 0.447 \cdot 0 \cdot 2 &&= 0.029
\end{aligned}
$$

The secular determinant gives the orbital energies

$$
\left\| \begin{array}{cc} 1.027 - x' & 0.029 \\ 0.029 & 0.708 - x' \end{array} \right\| = 0
$$

$$
\begin{aligned}
(x')^2 - 1.736\,x' + 0.728 &= 0 \\
x' &= 0.868 \pm 0.163 \\
x'_4 &= 1.031 \\
x'_5 &= 0.705
\end{aligned}
$$

In like manner, we obtain the energies x'_6 and x'_7.

$$
\left\| \begin{array}{cc} -1.008 - x' & 0.029 \\ 0.029 & -0.528 - x' \end{array} \right\| = 0
$$

$$
\begin{aligned}
(x')^2 + 1.536\,x' + 0.531 &= 0 \\
x' &= -0.768 \pm 0.242 \\
x'_6 &= -0.526 \\
x'_7 &= -1.010
\end{aligned}
$$

(b) 1-Azaazulene:

The list of perturbations comprises

$$\langle \mu \mid h \mid \nu \rangle = 0; \text{except} \langle 2 \mid h \mid 2 \rangle = \delta_{\alpha_2} = 0.5\,\beta$$
$$\langle 3 \mid h \mid 9 \rangle = \langle 9 \mid h \mid 3 \rangle = \delta\beta_{39} = \beta$$

The individual matrix elements (6/75) read

$$
\begin{aligned}
H'_{44} &= x_4 + c_{42}{}^2 \cdot 0.5 + 2c_{43}c_{49} \\
&= 0.618 + 0.138^2 \cdot 0.5 + 2 \cdot 0.362^2 \qquad = 0.890 \\
H'_{55} &= x_5 + c_{52}^2 \cdot 0.5 + 2c_{53}c_{59} \\
&= 0.618 + 0.425^2 \cdot 0.5 - 2 \cdot 0.263^2 \qquad = 0.570 \\
H'_{45} &= H'_{54} = c_{42} \cdot c_{52} \cdot 0.5 + (c_{43}c_{59} + c_{49}c_{53}) \\
&= 0.138 \cdot 0.425 \cdot 0.5 + 0 + 0 \qquad = 0.029
\end{aligned}
$$

The secular determinant gives the orbital energies:

$$
\begin{Vmatrix}
0.890 - x' & 0.029 \\
0.029 & 0.570 - x'
\end{Vmatrix} = 0
$$

$$
\begin{aligned}
(x')^2 - 1.460\,x' - 0.506 &= 0 \\
x' &= 0.730 \pm 0.163 \\
x'_4 &= 0.893 \\
x'_5 &= 0.567
\end{aligned}
$$

In like manner, we obtain the energies x'_6 and x'_7

$$
\begin{Vmatrix}
-0.346 - x' & 0.029 \\
0.029 & -0.666 - x'
\end{Vmatrix} = 0
$$

$$
\begin{aligned}
(x')^2 + 1.012\,x' + 0.230 &= 0 \\
x' &= -0.506 \pm 0.163 \\
x'_6 &= -0.343 \\
x'_7 &= -0.669
\end{aligned}
$$

Finally, let us compare the approximate values obtained with the exact HMO values.

		x_4	x_5	x_6	x_7
	Perturbation	1.031	0.705	−0.526	−1.010
	HMO	1.000	0.703	−0.527	−1.000
	Perturbation	0.893	0.567	−0.343	−0.669
	HMO	1.000	0.694	−0.396	−0.657

Furthermore, it should be noted that, as a result of the symmetry of the molecular orbitals employed, the crossterms $H_{JK} = H_{KJ}$ are determined only by the perturbations $\delta\alpha_2$ and are therefore small. For this reason the perturbed orbital energies can be satisfactorily reproduced by

$$H'_{JJ} = <\Psi_J \mid \mathcal{H}' \mid \Psi_J> = \epsilon'_J$$
$$H'_{KK} = <\Psi_K \mid \mathcal{H}' \mid \Psi_K> = \epsilon'_K$$

Problem 6.14: Within the framework of first order perturbation theory, calculate the resulting changes in total π-electron energy when a 14-membered ring is bridged by two additional bonds so as to form anthracene (a), phenanthrene (b), 1,2- (c), 4,5- (d), or 5,6-benzazulene (e):

(a)   (b)

(c)   (d)   (e)

In the present case involving multiple perturbations, the change in the π-electron energy δE_π for "closed-shell" systems is obtained according to

$$\delta E_\pi = \sum_{\mu=1}^{n} \sum_{\nu=1}^{n} P_{\mu\nu} < \mu \mid h \mid \nu >. \tag{6/56}$$

For the perturbation of the 14-perimeter according to (a) through (e), the following values result:

(a)/(b):

For the two benzenoid hydrocarbons, according to the list of perturbations

$$\langle \mu \mid h \mid \nu \rangle = 0, \text{ except } \langle 1 \mid h \mid 6 \rangle = \langle 6 \mid h \mid 1 \rangle = \beta$$
$$\langle 8 \mid h \mid 13 \rangle = \langle 13 \mid h \mid 8 \rangle = \beta$$
$$\langle 9 \mid h \mid 14 \rangle = \langle 14 \mid h \mid 9 \rangle = \beta$$

and because of the identity of the bond orders (Vol. 3)

$$P_{16} = P_{8\,13} = P_{9\,14} = 0.159$$

it turns out that, within the first order perturbation calculation, the same values result for the total π-electron energies

$$\delta E_\pi = 2\,(0.159 + 0.159) = 0.636\,\beta$$
$$E'_\pi = 14\alpha + (17.976 + 0.636)\beta = 14\alpha + 18.612\beta$$
$$E_\pi \text{ (Anthracene)} = 14\alpha + 19.314\beta$$
$$E_\pi \text{ (Phenanthrene)} = 14\alpha + 19.448\beta$$

$(c)/(d)/(e)$:

With the bond orders

$$P_{16} = 0.159$$
$$P_{8\,14} = P_{9\,13} = P_{10\,14} = 0$$

according to first order perturbation calculations the same total π-electron energy is likewise obtained for all three azulene derivatives.

$$\delta E_\pi = 2(P_{16} + 0) = 0.318$$
$$E'_\pi = 14\alpha + (17.976 + 0.318)\beta = 14\alpha + 18.294\beta$$
$$E_\pi^{(c)} = 14\alpha + 19.095\beta$$
$$E_\pi^{(d)} = 14\alpha + 19.109\beta$$
$$E_\pi^{(e)} = 14\alpha + 19.084\beta$$

Although first order perturbation calculations do indeed correctly reproduce the actual situation in a qualitative manner, the absolute values obtained are only about half as great as the change expected from exact HMO values. Moreover, the procedure makes no distinction between the individual benzenoid or non-benzenoid systems (cf. Problem 7.14).

6.5. Isoconjugate Systems and Perturbation Parameters for Hetero Atoms

Problem 6.15: Draw the isoconjugate models for the following compounds:

(a)   (b)   (c)   (d)

(e)   (f)   (g)   (h)

(i)   (j)   (k)   (l)

(m)   (n)   (o)   (p)

(q)   (r)

How many π-electrons do the individual centers contribute to the total π-electron system?

In the following isoconjugate models of molecules $(a) - (r)$, the individual hetero atoms X contribute z_X π-electrons each to the total π-electron number Z_π.

(a) Nitroethylene = 2-methylenebutadiene anion

$$Z_\pi = 6 \ (z_N = 2, \ z_O = 1)$$

In the nitro group $-N\lessgtr^O_O$ four electrons are formally distributed over three centers; the remaining free electron pairs of the oxygen atoms are orthogonal to the π-system and are therefore not included.

(*b*) Vinylacetylene = butadiene + ethylene

$$Z_\pi = 4 + 2$$

The second acetylene double bond lies in the plane of the π-system and therefore has to be considered as an additional perpendicular ethylene system.

(*c*) Acrolein = butadiene

$$Z_\pi = 4 \quad (z_O = 1)$$

The oxygen electron pairs are orthogonal to the π-electron system and make no contribution.

(*d*) Dimethylketene = ethylene + ethylene

$$Z_\pi = 2 + 2$$

If an interaction is postulated between the oxygen electron pair and one of the two crossed ethylene π-systems, we obtain as in isoconjugate model

Dimethylketene = allyl anion + ethylene

$$Z_\pi = 4 + 2 \quad (z_O = 2)$$

(*e*) Azomethane = ethylene

$$Z_\pi = 2 \quad (z_N = 1)$$

The free electron pairs of the sp^2-hybridized azo-nitrogens are orthogonal to the π-electron system, and are therefore neglected.

(*f*) Aniline = benzyl anion

$$Z_\pi = 8 \quad (z_N = 2)$$

Inclusion of the nitrogen electron pair is a good approximation if extensive sp^2 hybridization is assumed. However, this is not always the case, as shown for instance by the dipole moment of 1.57 D for *p*-phenylenediamine.

(*g*) Nitrobenzene = phenylallyl anion

$$Z_\pi = 10 \quad (z_N = 2, \; z_O = 1)$$

(cf.(*a*)).

(*h*) Phenol
(*i*) Phenolate anion } = benzyl anion

$$Z_\pi = 8 \quad (z_O = 2)$$

The isoconjugate models are identical, because the electron pairs of the phenol oxygens which lie in the plane of the ring are orthogonal to the π-electron system.

(*j*) *p*-Fluoroanisole = { benzyl anion (*A*)
p-quinodimethane dianion (*B*)

$$Z_\pi = 8 \quad (z_O = 2) \quad (A)$$

$$Z_\pi = 10 \quad (z_O = 2; \; z_F = 2) \quad (B)$$

The conjugative effect of the fluorine substituent is completely absent in model (*A*) with $F \sim CH_3$; in model (*B*), however, this effect is overemphasized because the substituent is considered equivalent to an anionic carbon atom.

(*k*) Hydroquinone = *p*-quinodimethane dianion

$$Z_\pi = 10 \quad (z_O = 2)$$

In this isoconjugate model, an interaction is assumed between the π-system and one electron pair of each of the oxygen atoms.

(*l*) *p*-Quinone = *p*-quinodimethane

$$Z_\pi = 8 \quad (z_O = 1)$$

(m) Benzaldehyde = styrene

$$Z_\pi = 8 \quad (z_O = 1)$$

(n) o-Fluorobenzonitrile = styrene

$$Z_\pi = 8 \quad (z_N = 1)$$

As in (j/A) the fluorine atom is considered equivalent to a methyl group. The nitrile group corresponds to an acetylene moiety (cf. (b)).

(o) p-Aminobenzoic acid = p-methylenephenylallyl dianion

$$Z_\pi = 12 \quad (z_N = 2, \ z_O = 1, \ z_{O^\bullet} = 2)$$

(p) Fulvene
(q) Azobenzene = stilbene

$$Z_\pi = 14 \quad (z_N = 1)$$

(cf. (e)).

(r) Borazole = benzene

$$Z_\pi = 6 \quad (z_B = 0, \ z_N = 2)$$

The boron/nitrogen bond here is isoelectronic with a carbon/carbon double bond.

Problem 6.16: In a chain of n centres, one or more p-atomic orbitals are to be replaced by d-atomic orbitals having equal *Coulomb* integrals ($\alpha_d = \alpha_p$) and equal resonance integrals ($\beta_{dp} = \beta_{pp}$). Show that the orbital energies $\varepsilon_J = \varepsilon_1$ to ε_n remain unchanged. How do the coefficients $c_{J\mu}$ of the associated molecular orbitals Ψ_J differ from those of a corresponding π-system composed of only p-atomic orbitals?

The starting point for the discussion is a linear chain of atomic p-orbitals.

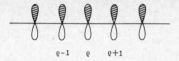

This is known to lead to the secular determinant

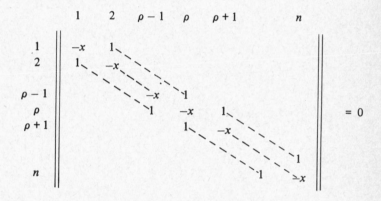

$$= 0$$

On replacement of the atomic p-orbital Φ_ρ by an atomic d-orbital

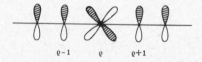

only the sign of the matrix elements $H_{\rho, \rho+1} = H_{\rho+1, \rho}$ changes in the secular determinant assuming $\alpha_p = \alpha_d$ and $\beta_{pp} = \beta_{pd}$ (i.e. -1 appears instead of $+1$ at the intersections of row ρ and column $\rho+1$ and row $\rho+1$ and column ρ). If all rows and columns with indices $\mu > \rho$ are multiplied by -1, the original secular determinant is obtained again. This is equivalent to the assumption that all atomic p-orbitals with indices $\mu \geqslant \rho+1$ are turned around in the basis set.

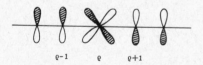

The orbital energies remain unchanged on replacement of an atomic p-orbital by an atomic d-orbital. This also applies to replacement of several atomic p-orbitals by atomic d-orbitals,

The coefficients $c_{J\mu}$ of the linear combinations also remain unchanged, since their calculation starts from the secular equations underlying the secular determinant so that they refer to a set of basis functions of corresponding sign.

Finally, it should be mentioned that the assumptions underlying the problem ($\alpha_p = \alpha_d$ and $\beta_{pp} = \beta_{pd}$) are not generally valid, and that the replacement of p-centers by d-centers is accompanied by far-reaching changes.

Problem 6.17: Calculate the orbital energies and orbitals of the cyclic π-electron system of the phosphonitrilic halides

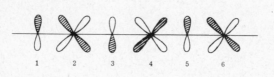

assuming that $\alpha_p = \alpha_N + \beta$.

Taking into consideration the conventions met in Problem 6.16, the calculations start from the basis functions

As can be seen, $\beta_{12} = \beta_{23} = \beta_{34} = \beta_{45} = \beta_{56} = \beta$. If the system is closed to from a ring

then it follows that $\beta_{16} = -\beta$. The resulting change of sign cannot be eliminated, in contrast to the example of Problem 6.16. Assuming $\alpha_p = \alpha_N + \beta$, we therefore obtain the *Hückel* determinant

$$\begin{Vmatrix} -x & 1 & & & & -1 \\ 1 & 1-x & 1 & & & \\ & 1 & -x & 1 & & \\ & & 1 & 1-x & 1 & \\ & & & 1 & -x & 1 \\ -1 & & & & 1 & 1-x \end{Vmatrix} = 0$$

The calculated orbital energies and linear combinations are summarized in the following table:

	1 2.303	2 2.303	3 1.000	4 0.000	5 -1.303	6 -1.303
1	0.491	0.000	0.000	0.577	-0.653	0.000
2	0.565	0.326	0.577	0.000	0.425	0.245
3	0.245	0.425	0.000	-0.577	-0.326	-0.565
4	0.000	0.653	-0.577	0.000	0.000	0.491
5	-0.245	0.425	0.000	0.577	0.326	-0.565
6	-0.565	0.326	0.577	0.000	-0.425	0.245

The energy level scheme has the following appearance:

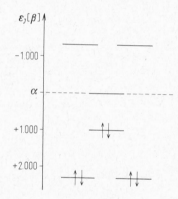

As can be seen, the sequence of the levels differs considerably from that of benzene.

6.6. Correlation Diagrams and First Order Perturbation Treatment

Problem 6.18: Construct a HMO correlation diagram for the *cis/trans* isomerization of 1,2-dideuterioethylene:

$$\underset{H}{\overset{D}{\diagdown}}C=C\underset{D}{\overset{H}{\diagup}} \rightleftarrows \underset{H}{\overset{D}{\diagdown}}C=C\underset{H}{\overset{D}{\diagup}}$$

The observed activation enthalpy $\Delta H^{\ne}$ is about 60 kcal mol^{-1}. What is the corresponding value of β? How would the reaction rate change if the isomerization were carried out not in the ground state but in the first electronically excited state?

The resonance integral of ethylene should change as a function of the angle of twist Θ according to

$$\beta(\Theta) = \beta \cos \Theta$$

which leads to the secular determinant

$$\begin{Vmatrix} -x & \cos \Theta \\ \cos \Theta & -x \end{Vmatrix} = 0.$$

Its solutions

$$\epsilon_1 = \alpha + \beta \cos \Theta$$
$$\epsilon_2 = \alpha - \beta \cos \Theta$$

afford the numerical values assembled in the following table:

Θ	$0°$	$30°$	$45°$	$60°$	$90°$
$\cos \Theta$	1	0.866	0.707	0.5	0
$\epsilon_1 - \alpha$	$1.000\,\beta$	$0.866\,\beta$	$0.707\,\beta$	$0.500\,\beta$	$0.000\,\beta$
$\epsilon_2 - \alpha$	$-1.000\,\beta$	$-0.866\,\beta$	$-0.707\,\beta$	$-0.500\,\beta$	$0.000\,\beta$

The corresponding correlation diagram has the simple form

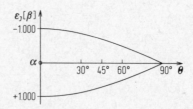

In the ground state ($b_1 = 2$, $b_2 = 0$) the total π-electron energy is

$$E_\pi = 2\alpha + 2\beta \cos \Theta$$

and the π-contribution to the activation energy is

$$\Delta E_\pi = E_\pi(90°) - E_\pi(0°) = -2\beta.$$

If ΔE_π is identified with the activation energy of 60 kcal/mol, then $\beta = -30$ kcal/mol.

In the first electronically excited state ($b_1 = 1$, $b_2 = 1$) the total π-electron energy is independent of the angle of twist Θ. Consequently, our simple model predicts that the isomerization in the first excited state should occur practically without activation energy, largely in agreement with experimental findings.

Problem 6.19: Draw the correlation diagram for a three-centre system X–C–X in which the *Coulomb* integral $\alpha_X = \alpha + h_X\beta$ is changed over the interval $0 \leq h_X \leq 2$ while the resonance integral β_{CX} remains constant.

The secular determinant of the three-center system

$$\begin{Vmatrix} h_X - x & 1 & \\ 1 & -x & 1 \\ & 1 & h_X - x \end{Vmatrix} = 0$$

can be factorized according to (4/98) because of the symmetry of the system

$$\begin{Vmatrix} h_X - x & \sqrt{2} & \\ \sqrt{2} & -x & \\ \hline & & h_X - x \end{Vmatrix} = 0.$$

The solutions are

$$x_1 = \frac{h_X}{2} + \sqrt{\left(\frac{h_X}{2}\right)^2 + 2}$$

$$x_2 = h_X$$

$$x_3 = \frac{h_X}{2} - \sqrt{\left(\frac{h_X}{2}\right)^2 + 2}$$

The following values are obtained:

h_X	0.0	0.5	1.0	1.5	2.0
x_3	−1.414	−1.186	−1.000	−0.851	−0.732
x_2	0.000	+0.500	+1.000	+1.500	+2.000
x_1	+1.414	+1.686	+2.000	+2.351	+2.732

The functions are presented graphically in the correlation diagram:

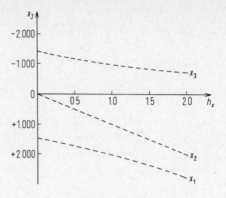

Problem 6.20: Prove formulae (6/99).

Starting from (6/98)

$$x_J(y) = v_{J0} + v_{J1} \cdot y + v_{J2} \cdot y^2 + v_{J3} \cdot y^3$$

the following relations should be valid:

$$\begin{aligned}
x_J(a) &= x_{Ja} \\
x_J(b) &= x_{Jb} \\
x'_J(a) &= x'_{Ja} \\
x'_J(b) &= x'_{Jb}
\end{aligned}$$

Furthermore, since

$$x'_J(y) = v_{J1} + 2v_{J2} \cdot y + 3v_{J3} \cdot y^2$$

the following four linear equations are found for the unknowns $v_{J0}, v_{J1}, v_{J2},$ and v_{J3}

$$\begin{aligned}
v_{J0} + av_{J1} + a^2 v_{J2} + a^3 v_{J3} &= x_{Ja} \\
v_{J0} + bv_{J1} + b^2 v_{J2} + b^3 v_{J3} &= x_{Jb} \\
v_{J1} + 2av_{J2} + 3a^2 v_{J3} &= x'_{Ja} \\
v_{J1} + 2bv_{J2} + 3b^2 v_{J3} &= x'_{Jb}
\end{aligned}$$

The change in coordinates $y' = y - a$ proposed in the text transforms the system of equations into

$$v_{J0} \hspace{5cm} = x_{Ja} \quad (1)$$
$$v_{J0} + (b-a)v_{J1} + (b-a)^2 v_{J2} + (b-a)^3 v_{J3} = x_{Jb} \quad (2)$$
$$v_{J1} \hspace{5cm} = x'_{Ja} \quad (3)$$
$$v_{J1} + 2(b-a)v_{J2} + 3(b-a)^2 v_{J3} = x'_{Jb} \quad (4)$$

Substitution of (1) and (3) into (2) and (4) leads to

$$(b-a)^2 v_{J2} + (b-a)^3 v_{J3} = x_{Jb} - x_{Ja} - (b-a)x'_{Ja},$$
$$2(b-a)v_{J2} + 3(b-a)^2 v_{J3} = x'_{Jb} - x'_{Ja}.$$

Solving for v_{J2}

$$3(b-a)^2 v_{J2} + 3(b-a)^3 v_{J3} = 3(x_{Jb} - x_{Ja}) - 3(b-a)x'_{Ja}$$
$$2(b-a)^2 v_{J2} + 3(b-a)^3 v_{J3} = (x'_{Jb} - x'_{Ja})(b-a)$$

$$(b-a)^2 v_{J2} \hspace{2cm} = 3(x_{Jb} - x_{Ja}) - 3(b-a)x'_{Ja} - (x'_{Jb} - x'_{Ja})(b-a)$$

$$v_{J2} = \frac{3(x_{Jb} - x_{Ja})}{(b-a)^2} - \frac{(x'_{Jb} + 2x'_{Ja})}{(b-a)}$$

and for v_{J3}

$$2(b-a)^2 v_{J2} + 2(b-a)^3 v_{J3} = 2(x_{Jb} - x_{Ja}) - 2(b-a)x'_{Ja}$$
$$2(b-a)^2 v_{J2} + 3(b-a)^3 v_{J3} = (x'_{Jb} - x'_{Ja})(b-a)$$

$$(b-a)^3 v_{J3} = (x'_{Jb} - x'_{Ja})(b-a) + 2(b-a)x'_{Ja} - 2(x_{Jb} - x_{Ja})$$

$$v_{J3} = \frac{x'_{Jb} + x'_{Ja}}{(b-a)^2} - \frac{2(x_{Jb} - x_{Ja})}{(b-a)^3}$$

affords the missing equations from (6/99).

Problem 6.21: Calculate the correlation lines for the model of Problem 6.19 according to formulae (6/99) and compare them with the exact values.

In Problem 6.19 the following expressions were obtained for x_1, x_2 and x_3 as functions of h_X

$$x_1(h_X) = \frac{h_X}{2} + \sqrt{\left(\frac{h_X}{2}\right)^2 + 2}$$

$$x_2(h_X) = h_X$$

$$x_3(h_X) = \frac{h_X}{2} - \sqrt{\left(\frac{h_X}{2}\right)^2 + 2}$$

The range of the parameter encompasses $0 \leqslant h_X \leqslant 2$. Since the case $x_2 (h_X)$ is trivial, only $x_1 (h_X)$ and $x_3 (h_X)$ are to be discussed below. The values of these quantities at the limits of the parameter range are

$$x_1 (0) = \sqrt{2}; \qquad x_1 (2) = 1 + \sqrt{3}$$

$$x_3 (0) = -\sqrt{2}; \qquad x_3 (2) = 1 - \sqrt{3}$$

Partial differention with respect to h_X

$$\frac{\partial x_1}{\partial h_X} = \frac{1}{2} + \frac{h_X}{4} \left(\left(\frac{h_X}{2} \right)^2 + 2 \right)^{-\frac{1}{2}}$$

$$\frac{\partial x_3}{\partial h_X} = \frac{1}{2} - \frac{h_X}{4} \left(\left(\frac{h_X}{2} \right)^2 + 2 \right)^{-\frac{1}{2}}$$

affords the following values at the limits of the parameter range:

$$\left(\frac{\partial x_1}{\partial h_X} \right)_{h_X=0} = \frac{1}{2}; \qquad \left(\frac{\partial x_1}{\partial h_X} \right)_{h_X=2} = \frac{1}{2} + \frac{1}{2\sqrt{3}}$$

$$\left(\frac{\partial x_3}{\partial h_X} \right)_{h_X=0} = \frac{1}{2}; \qquad \left(\frac{\partial x_3}{\partial h_X} \right)_{h_X=2} = \frac{1}{2} - \frac{1}{2\sqrt{3}}$$

The derivatives can, of course, also be obtained by way of the linear combinations (cf. (6/11) and (6/18)) belonging to the orbital energies for $h_X = 0$ and $h_X = 2$

$$h_X = 0: \ \Psi_1 = \frac{1}{2} \Phi_1 + \frac{1}{\sqrt{2}} \Phi_2 + \frac{1}{2} \Phi_3$$

$$\Psi_2 = \frac{1}{\sqrt{2}} \Phi_1 \qquad - \frac{1}{\sqrt{2}} \Phi_3$$

$$\Psi_3 = \frac{1}{2} \Phi_1 - \frac{1}{\sqrt{2}} \Phi_2 + \frac{1}{2} \Phi_3$$

$$h_X = 2: \quad \Psi_1 = \frac{1}{\sqrt{2(3-\sqrt{3})}} \, \Phi_1 + \frac{\sqrt{3}-1}{\sqrt{2(3-\sqrt{3})}} \, \Phi_2 + \frac{1}{\sqrt{2(3-\sqrt{3})}} \, \Phi_3$$

$$\Psi_2 = \frac{1}{\sqrt{2}} \, \Phi_1 \qquad\qquad - \frac{1}{\sqrt{2}} \Phi_3$$

$$\Psi_3 = \frac{1}{\sqrt{2(3+\sqrt{3})}} \, \Phi_1 - \frac{1+\sqrt{3}}{\sqrt{2(3+\sqrt{3})}} \, \Phi_2 + \frac{1}{\sqrt{2(3+\sqrt{3})}} \, \Phi_3$$

For the derivatives we therefore obtain:

$$h_X = 0: \quad \frac{\partial x_1}{\partial h_X} = c_{11}^2 + c_{13}^2 = \frac{1}{4} + \frac{1}{4} = \frac{1}{2}$$

$$\frac{\partial x_3}{\partial h_X} = c_{31}^2 + c_{33}^2 = \frac{1}{4} + \frac{1}{4} = \frac{1}{2}$$

$$h_X = 2: \quad \frac{\partial x_1}{\partial h_X} = c_{11}^2 + c_{13}^2 = 2 \cdot \frac{1}{2(3-\sqrt{3})} = \frac{1}{3-\sqrt{3}} \equiv \frac{1}{2} + \frac{1}{2\sqrt{3}} = 0.79$$

$$\frac{\partial x_3}{\partial h_X} = c_{31}^2 + c_{33}^2 = 2 \cdot \frac{1}{2(3+\sqrt{3})} = \frac{1}{3+\sqrt{3}} \equiv \frac{1}{2} - \frac{1}{2\sqrt{3}} = 0.21$$

These values are identical with those calculated first. Substitution in relation (6/99) gives the following constants v_{J0}, v_{J1}, v_{J2} and v_{J3} of the relevant polynomial (6/98).

$$x_1(h_X): \quad v_{10} = x_1(0) = \sqrt{2}$$

$$v_{11} = x'(0) = \frac{1}{2}$$

$$v_{12} = 3 \frac{x_1(2) - x_1(0)}{2^2} - \frac{x_1'(2) - 2x_1'(0)}{2}$$

$$= 3 \frac{(1+\sqrt{3}-\sqrt{2})}{4} - \frac{\dfrac{1}{3-\sqrt{3}} + 2 \cdot \dfrac{1}{2}}{2} = 0.0940$$

$$v_{13} = \frac{x_1'(2) + x_1'(0)}{2^2} - 2 \frac{x_1(2) - x_1(0)}{2^3}$$

$$= \frac{\dfrac{1}{3-\sqrt{3}} + \dfrac{1}{2}}{4} - 2 \frac{(1+\sqrt{3}-\sqrt{2})}{8} = -0.0073$$

$$x_3(h_X): \quad v_{30} = x_3(0) = -\sqrt{2}$$

$$v_{31} = x'_3(0) = \frac{1}{2}$$

$$v_{32} = 3\frac{x_3(2) - x_3(0)}{2^2} - \frac{x_3(2) + 2x'_3(0)}{2}$$

$$= 3\frac{(1 - \sqrt{3} + \sqrt{2})}{4} - \frac{\dfrac{1}{3+\sqrt{3}} + 2 \cdot \dfrac{1}{2}}{2} = -0.0940$$

$$v_{33} = \frac{x'_3(2) + x'_3(0)}{2^2} - 2\frac{x_3(2) - x_3(0)}{2^3}$$

$$= \frac{\dfrac{1}{3+\sqrt{3}} + \dfrac{1}{2}}{4} - 2\frac{(1 - \sqrt{3} + \sqrt{2})}{8} = 0.0073$$

With the constants, the polynomials (6/98) read

$$x_1(h_X) = 1.414 + 0.500\,h_X + 0.094\,h_X^2 - 0.0073\,h_X^3,$$
$$x_3(h_X) = -1.414 + 0.500\,h_X - 0.094\,h_X^2 + 0.0073\,h_X^3.$$

It can easily be demonstrated by substitution of the value h_X that the resulting values of $x_1(h_X)$ and $x_3(h_X)$ deviate only slightly from those calculated in Problem 6.19.

Second Order Perturbation Calculations and Polarizabilities

7.1. Second Order Perturbation Calculations for a Pair of Molecular Orbitals

Problem 7.1: As an extension of Problem 6.6, use the procedure just described to calculate the first and second order perturbations of orbital energies ε_3 and ε_4 on introduction of a bond between centres 2 and 3 of the cross-conjugated triene ($\delta\beta_{23} = \beta$):

Consider only the interactions between $\varepsilon_3 = \varepsilon_B$ and $\varepsilon_4 = \varepsilon_A$. Compare the results with the exact HMO values for the fulvene π-electron system (Table ⑤—).

On introduction of an additional bond between the centers 2 and 3 of vinylbutadiene, we obtain the following list of perturbations:

$$< \mu \mid h \mid \nu > = 0, \text{ except } < 2 \mid h \mid 3 > = < 3 \mid h \mid 2 > = \beta \text{ and } 1.$$

From Problem 6.6 it may be seen that first order perturbations transform the four inner molecular orbitals of the triene into corresponding approximate molecular orbitals of fulvene:

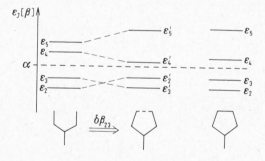

Obviously, both molecular orbitals Ψ_2 and Ψ_4 of the triene correspond to the inner molecular orbitals Ψ_3 und Ψ_4 of fulvene. Consequently, employing the nomenclature of the triene, the following perturbed orbital energies are required:

$$\epsilon_2' = \epsilon_2 + \delta^{(1)}\epsilon_2 + \delta^{(2)}\epsilon_2$$
$$\epsilon_4' = \epsilon_4 + \delta^{(1)}\epsilon_4 + \delta^{(2)}\epsilon_4$$

For reasons of symmetry, the second order perturbation $\delta^{(2)}\epsilon_2$ can only result from interaction with ϵ_5, and $\delta^{(2)}\epsilon_4$ only by interaction with ϵ_3. The slight interaction with ϵ_1 und ϵ_6 will be ignored. A second order perturbation calculation according to (7/14) gives

$$\delta^{(2)}\epsilon_2 = \frac{(H'_{25})^2}{\epsilon_2 - \epsilon_5} = \frac{(c_{22}c_{53} + c_{23}c_{52})^2\beta^2}{(\alpha + \beta) - (\alpha - \beta)}$$

$$= \frac{((0.500)(0.500) + (-0.500)(-0.500))^2\beta^2}{2\beta} = 0.125\beta$$

$$\delta^{(2)}\epsilon_4 = \frac{(H'_{43})^2}{\epsilon_4 - \epsilon_3} = \frac{(c_{42}c_{33} + c_{43}c_{32})^2\beta^2}{(\alpha - 0.518\beta) - (\alpha + 0.518\beta)}$$

$$= \frac{((0.444)(-0.444) + (0.444)(-0.444))^2\beta^2}{-1.036\beta} = -0.150\beta$$

Inclusion of the first order perturbation results from Problem 6.6 affords

$$\epsilon'_2 = \alpha + 1.000\beta - 0.500\beta + 0.125\beta = \alpha + 0.625\beta$$
$$\epsilon'_4 = \alpha - 0.518\beta + 0.394\beta - 0.150\beta = \alpha - 0.274\beta$$

A comparison of the results obtained from first and second order perturbation calculations with the exact HMO values of fulvene

	$\delta^{(1)}$	$\delta^{(2)}$	HMO
x_3	0.500	0.625	0.618
x_4	-0.124	-0.274	-0.254

demonstrates the good agreement with HMO values which one expects for second order perturbation.

Problem 7.2: Calculate the approximate coefficients of the linear combinations relating to Problem 7.1.

The orbitals Ψ_3 and Ψ_4 of the fulvene model derived from vinylbutadiene by intoducing an additional bond between the centers 2 and 3 are obtained as follows according to formulas (7/28):

$$\Psi_2' = \Psi_2 + \frac{H_{25}}{x_2 - x_5} \Psi_5 = \Psi_2 + 0.250\,\Psi_5$$

$$= (0.500 + 0.125)\Phi_1 + (0.500 - 0.125)\Phi_2 + (-0.500 + 0.125)\Phi_3 + (-0.500 - 0.125)\Phi_4$$
$$= 0.625\,\Phi_1 + 0.375\,\Phi_2 - 0.375\,\Phi_3 - 0.625\,\Phi_4$$

$$\Psi_4' = \Psi_4 + \frac{H_{43}}{x_4 - x_3} \Psi_3 = \Psi_4 + 0.381\,\Psi_3$$

$$= (+0.230 + 0.087)\Phi_1 + (-0.444 + 0.169)\Phi_2 + (-0.444 + 0.169)\Phi_3$$
$$+ (+0.230 + 0.087)\Phi_4 + (+0.325 - 0.123)\Phi_5 + (-0.628 - 0.239)\Phi_6$$
$$= +0.317\,\Phi_1 - 0.275\,\Phi_2 - 0.275\,\Phi_3 + 0.317\,\Phi_4 + 0.202\,\Phi_5 - 0.867\,\Phi_6$$

The resulting obitals are not strictly normalized, and must therefore each be multiplied by the factor

$$N = \frac{1}{\sqrt{1 + \left(\dfrac{H_{BA}}{x_B - x_A}\right)^2}} \qquad (7/30)$$

$$\Psi_{2,\,\text{norm.}}' = N_2\,\Psi_2' = 0.970\,\Psi_2'$$
$$= 0.606\,\Phi_1 + 0.364\,\Phi_2 - 0.364\,\Phi_3 - 0.606\,\Phi_4$$
$$\Psi_3^{(\text{Fulvene})} = 0.601\,\Phi_1 + 0.371\,\Phi_2 - 0.371\,\Phi_3 - 0.601\,\Phi_4$$

$$\Psi_{4,\,\text{norm.}}' = N_4\,\Psi_4' = 0.935\,\Psi_4'$$
$$= +0.296\,\Phi_1 - 0.257\,\Phi_2 - 0.257\,\Phi_3 + 0.296\,\Phi_4 + 0.189\,\Phi_5 - 0.810\,\Phi_6;$$
$$\Psi_4^{(\text{Fulvene})} = -0.350\,\Phi_1 + 0.280\,\Phi_2 + 0.280\,\Phi_3 - 0.350\,\Phi_4 - 0.190\,\Phi_5 + 0.749\,\Phi_6$$

The linear combination Ψ_4 of fulvene given in the HMO Table⑤– (Vol. 3)
has opposite sign. This is immaterial, however, and could have been corrected, for instance, by choice of the normalization coefficient $N_4 = -0.935$ which is just as compatible with (7/30) as that actually used.

Comparison with the exact HMO orbitals of fulvene Ψ_3 (Fulvene) and Ψ_4 (Fulvene) shows that the reproduction of the desired molecular orbitals is qualitatively correct. The quality of the approximation is excellent for the highest occupied molecular orbital Ψ_3 since the two antisymmetric eigenfunctions of the unperturbed system served as the basis of the perturbation calculation. In contrast, the linear combination of only two of the four existing symmetric molecular orbitals of the unperturbed system expectedly gives only a moderate approximation for the lowest unoccupied molecular orbital Ψ_4 of the fulvene model (cf. Problem 7.3).

7.2. General Formulation of Second Order Perturbation Calculations

> **Problem 7.3:** Starting with 2-vinylbutadiene (Problems 6.6 and 6.8) and using formulae (7/43) and (7/45), calculate the eigenvalues and eigenfunctions of fulvene.

For the fulvene model derived from 2-vinylbutadiene

the list of perturbations is

$$< \mu \mid h \mid \nu > = 0; \text{except} < 2 \mid h \mid 3 > = < 3 \mid h \mid 2 > = \beta \text{ and } 1.$$

The second order perturbations of the eigenvalues are calculated according to

$$\delta^{(2)} x_J = \sum_{K \neq J}^{n} \frac{< \Psi_J \mid h \mid \Psi_K >^2}{x_J - x_K} \tag{7/43}$$

as follows:

$$\delta^{(2)} x_1 = \frac{(c_{12}c_{33} + c_{13}c_{32})^2}{x_1 - x_3} + \frac{(c_{12}c_{43} + c_{13}c_{42})^2}{x_1 - x_4} + \frac{(c_{12}c_{63} + c_{13}c_{62})^2}{x_1 - x_6}$$

$$= \frac{(2 \cdot 0.230 \cdot 0.444)^2}{1.932 - 0.518} + \frac{(2 \cdot 0.230 \cdot (-0.444))^2}{1.932 - (-0.518)} + \frac{(2 \cdot -(0.230)^2)^2}{1.932 - (-1.932)} = +0.050$$

$$\delta^{(2)} x_2 = \frac{(c_{22}c_{53} + c_{23}c_{52})^2}{x_2 - x_5} = \frac{(2 \cdot -(0.500)^2)^2}{1.000 - (-1.000)} = +0.125$$

$$\delta^{(2)} x_3 = \frac{(c_{32}c_{13} + c_{33}c_{12})^2}{x_3 - x_1} + \frac{(c_{32}c_{43} + c_{33}c_{42})^2}{x_3 - x_4} + \frac{(c_{32}c_{63} + c_{33}c_{62})^2}{x_3 - x_6}$$

$$= \frac{(2 \cdot 0.230 \cdot 0.444)^2}{0.518 - 1.932} + \frac{(2 \cdot -(0.444)^2)^2}{0.518 - (-0.518)} + \frac{(2 \cdot (-0.230) \cdot 0.444)^2}{0.518 - (-1.932)} = +0.137$$

The second order perturbations $\delta^{(2)} x_4$, $\delta^{(2)} x_5$, and $\delta^{(2)} x_6$ differ only in sign since all cross terms appear as squares in the numerator while the denominator changes sign:

$$\delta^{(2)} x_4 = -\delta^{(2)} x_3 = -0.137$$
$$\delta^{(2)} x_5 = -\delta^{(2)} x_2 = -0.125$$
$$\delta^{(2)} x_6 = -\delta^{(2)} x_1 = -0.050$$

The alternancy of the starting system is already removed by the first order perturbation. In the appended energy scheme, the perturbed orbital energy coefficients $x_J^{(1)}$ from Problem 6.6 and the values of $x_J^{(2)}$ calculated here are compared with the exact HMO values (Vol. 3):

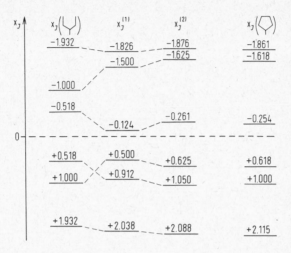

The second order perturbation calculation is now seen to give satisfactory agreement. The orbitals are obtained according to

$$\Psi'_J = \Psi_J + \sum_{K \neq J} \left(\frac{<\Psi_J|h|\Psi_K>}{x_J - x_K} \right) \Psi_K \tag{7/45}$$

with the same perturbation terms and with the normalization factor determined according to

$$N_J = \frac{1}{\sqrt{1 + \sum\limits_{K \neq J} \left(\dfrac{<\Psi_J|h|\Psi_K>}{x_J - x_K} \right)^2}} \tag{7/46}$$

One thus obtains:

$$
\begin{aligned}
\Psi'_1 &= N_1[\Psi_1 + 0.144\,\Psi_3 - 0.083\,\Psi_4 - 0.027\,\Psi_6] \\
&= 0.976[(0.444 + 0.033 - 0.019 - 0.012)\,\Phi_1 \\
&\quad + (0.230 + 0.064 + 0.037 + 0.006)\,\Phi_2 \\
&\quad + (0.230 + 0.064 + 0.037 + 0.006)\,\Phi_3 \\
&\quad + (0.444 + 0.033 - 0.019 - 0.012)\,\Phi_4 \\
&\quad + (0.628 - 0.047 - 0.027 + 0.017)\,\Phi_5 \\
&\quad + (0.325 - 0.090 + 0.052 - 0.009)\,\Phi_6] \\
&= 0.436\,\Phi_1 + 0.329\,\Phi_2 + 0.329\,\Phi_3 + 0.436\,\Phi_4 + 0.559\,\Phi_5 + 0.272\,\Phi_6 \\
\Psi_1^{HMO} &= 0.429\,\Phi_1 + 0.385\,\Phi_2 + 0.385\,\Phi_3 + 0.429\,\Phi_4 + 0.523\,\Phi_5 + 0.247\,\Phi_6
\end{aligned}
$$

$$\Psi_2' = N_2[\Psi_2 + 0.250\,\Psi_5]$$
$$= 0.969[(0.500 + 0.125)\,\Phi_1 + (0.500 - 0.125)\,\Phi_2 + (-0.500 + 0.125)\,\Phi_3$$
$$+ (-0.500 - 0.125)\,\Phi_4]$$
$$= 0.606\,\Phi_1 + 0.363\,\Phi_2 - 0.363\,\Phi_3 - 0.606\,\Phi_4$$
$$\Psi_3^{HMO} = 0.602\,\Phi_1 + 0.372\,\Phi_2 - 0.372\,\Phi_3 - 0.602\,\Phi_4$$

$$\Psi_3' = N_3[\Psi_3 - 0.144\,\Psi_1 - 0.380\,\Psi_4 - 0.083\,\Psi_6]$$
$$= 0.924[(0.230 - 0.064 - 0.087 - 0.037)\,\Phi_1$$
$$+ (0.444 - 0.033 + 0.169 + 0.019)\,\Phi_2$$
$$+ (0.444 - 0.033 + 0.169 + 0.019)\,\Phi_3$$
$$+ (0.230 - 0.064 - 0.087 - 0.037)\,\Phi_4$$
$$+ (-0.325 - 0.090 - 0.124 + 0.052)\,\Phi_5$$
$$+ (-0.628 - 0.047 + 0.239 - 0.027)\,\Phi_6]$$
$$= 0.039\,\Phi_1 + 0.553\,\Phi_2 + 0.553\,\Phi_3 + 0.039\,\Phi_4 - 0.450\,\Phi_5 - 0.428\,\Phi_6$$
$$\Psi_2^{HMO} = \qquad\quad + 0.500\,\Phi_2 + 0.500\,\Phi_3 \qquad\qquad - 0.500\,\Phi_5 - 0.500\,\Phi_6$$

$$\Psi_4' = N_4[\Psi_4 + 0.083\,\Psi_1 + 0.380\,\Psi_3 + 0.144\,\Psi_6]$$
$$= 0.924[(0.230 + 0.037 + 0.087 + 0.064)\,\Phi_1$$
$$+ (-0.444 + 0.019 + 0.169 - 0.033)\,\Phi_2$$
$$+ (-0.444 + 0.019 + 0.169 - 0.033)\,\Phi_3$$
$$+ \ \ (0.230 + 0.037 + 0.087 + 0.064)\,\Phi_4$$
$$+ \ \ (0.325 + 0.052 - 0.124 - 0.090)\,\Phi_5$$
$$+ (-0.628 + 0.027 - 0.239 + 0.047)\,\Phi_6]$$
$$= \ \ 0.388\,\Phi_1 - 0.268\,\Phi_2 - 0.268\,\Phi_3 + 0.388\,\Phi_4 + 0.150\,\Phi_5 - 0.732\,\Phi_6$$
$$\Psi_4^{HMO} = -0.350\,\Phi_1 + 0.280\,\Phi_2 + 0.280\,\Phi_3 - 0.350\,\Phi_4 - 0.190\,\Phi_5 + 0.750\,\Phi_6$$

$$\Psi_5' = N_5[\Psi_5 - 0.250\,\Psi_2]$$
$$= 0.969[(0.500 - 0.125)\,\Phi_1 + (-0.500 - 0.125)\,\Phi_2 + (0.500 + 0.125)\,\Phi_3$$
$$+ (-0.500 + 0.125)\,\Phi_4]$$
$$= \ \ 0.363\,\Phi_1 - 0.606\,\Phi_2 + 0.606\,\Phi_3 - 0.363\,\Phi_4$$
$$\Psi_5^{HMO} = -0.372\,\Phi_1 + 0.602\,\Phi_2 - 0.602\,\Phi_3 + 0.372\,\Phi_4$$

$$\Psi_6' = N_6[\Psi_6 + 0.027\,\Psi_1 + 0.083\,\Psi_3 - 0.144\,\Psi_4]$$
$$= 0.976[(0.444 + 0.012 + 0.019 - 0.033)\,\Phi_1$$
$$+ (-0.230 + 0.006 + 0.037 + 0.064)\,\Phi_2$$
$$+ (-0.230 + 0.006 + 0.037 + 0.064)\,\Phi_3$$
$$+ \ \ (0.444 + 0.012 + 0.019 - 0.033)\,\Phi_4$$
$$+ (-0.628 + 0.017 - 0.027 - 0.047)\,\Phi_5$$
$$+ \ \ (0.325 + 0.009 - 0.052 + 0.090)\,\Phi_6]$$
$$= \ \ 0.431\,\Phi_1 - 0.120\,\Phi_2 - 0.120\,\Phi_3 + 0.431\,\Phi_4 - 0.668\,\Phi_5 + 0.363\,\Phi_6$$
$$\Psi_6^{HMO} = -0.439\,\Phi_1 + 0.153\,\Phi_2 + 0.153\,\Phi_3 - 0.439\,\Phi_4 + 0.663\,\Phi_5 - 0.356\,\Phi_6$$

Concerning the approximate derivation of the molecular orbitals of fulvene from those of 2-vinylbutadiene we wish to draw attention to the following:

As already shown in Problem 6.6 Ψ_2' and Ψ_3' change places. Reversal of sign occurs for the orbitals Ψ_4', Ψ_5', and Ψ_6' because the absolute signs of the molecular orbitals of π-electron systems are arbitrarily assigned and the orbitals of another system obtained by perturbation calculations need agree only up to a factor ± 1. For the squares of the functions which alone have physical significance the absolute sign of the individual atomic orbitals is of no relevance.

Better agreement is generally achieved for energies than for orbitals since the former are subject to a correction of the second order while the latter are changed even in a first order correction. In exact HMO calculations, the energy minimum is found in terms of the coefficients so that the small changes in values of the coefficients hardly affect the energy. In contrast, the linear combinations of atomic orbitals change linearly with the coefficients:

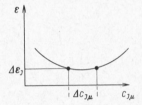 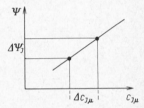

Problem 7.4: Using orbitals of a ten-membered ring (HMO Table ⑩) and taking symmetry into account, calculate approximately the orbital energies of the highest bonding and the lowest antibonding linear combinations of azulene.

The new bond introduced according to symmetry-correct manner (cf. Problem 6.11) between centers 3 and 9 leads to the list of perturbations

$$<\mu|h|\nu> = 0; \text{except} <3|h|9> = <9|h|3> = \beta \text{ and } 1.$$

According to (7/43) and (7/44) the coefficients of the inner orbital energies of azulene are approximated by

$$x_5'' = x_5 + \delta^{(1)}x_5 + \sum_{K \neq 5}^{n} \frac{<\Psi_5|h|\Psi_K>^2}{x_5 - x_K},$$

$$x_6'' = x_6 + \delta^{(1)}x_6 + \sum_{K \neq 6}^{n} \frac{<\Psi_6|h|\Psi_K>^2}{x_6 - x_K}.$$

Because of the symmetry of the starting orbitals the summation simplifies as follows:

$$\sum_{K \neq 5}^{n} \frac{<\Psi_5|h|\Psi_K>^2}{x_5 - x_K} = \frac{(c_{53}c_{39} + c_{59}c_{33})^2}{x_5 - x_3} + \frac{(c_{53}c_{79} + c_{59}c_{73})^2}{x_5 - x_7} + \frac{(c_{53}c_{99} + c_{59}c_{93})^2}{x_5 - x_9}$$

$$= \frac{(2 \cdot (-0.263) \cdot 0.425)^2}{0.618 - 1.618} + \frac{(2 \cdot (-0.263) \cdot 0.263)^2}{0.618 - (-0.618)} + \frac{(2 \cdot (-0.263) \cdot 0.425)^2}{0.618 - (-1.618)}$$

$$= -0.013$$

$$\sum_{K \neq 6}^{n} \frac{<\Psi_6|h|\Psi_K>^2}{x_6 - x_K} = \frac{(c_{63}c_{19} + c_{69}c_{13})^2}{x_6 - x_1} + \frac{(c_{63}c_{29} + c_{69}c_{23})^2}{x_6 - x_2} + \frac{(c_{63}c_{49} + c_{69}c_{43})^2}{x_6 - x_4}$$

$$+ \frac{(c_{63}c_{89} + c_{69}c_{83})^2}{x_6 - x_8} + \frac{(c_{63}c_{10/9} + c_{69}c_{10/3})^2}{x_6 - x_{10}}$$

$$= \frac{(2 \cdot 0.362 \cdot 0.316)^2}{-0.618 - 2.000} + \frac{(2 \cdot 0.362 \cdot 0.138)^2}{-0.618 - 1.618} + \frac{(2 \cdot 0.362 \cdot (-0.362))^2}{-0.618 - 0.618}$$

$$+ \frac{(2 \cdot 0.362 \cdot (-0.138))^2}{-0.618 - (-1.618)} + \frac{(2 \cdot 0.362 \cdot (-0.316))^2}{-0.618 - (-2.000)}$$

$$= -0.033$$

The resulting second order orbital energies calculated with the first oder perturbations from Problem 6.11 are

$$x_5'' = 0.480 - 0.013 = 0.467; \quad x_5^{HMO} = 0.477$$
$$x_6'' = -0.356 - 0.033 = -0.389; \quad x_6^{HMO} = -0.400$$

The orbitals

$$\Psi_J' = \Psi_J + \sum_{K \neq J}^{n} \left(\frac{<\Psi_J|h|\Psi_K>}{x_J - x_K} \right) \Psi_K \tag{7/45}$$

and the normalization factor

$$N_J = \frac{1}{\sqrt{1 + \sum_{K \neq J} \left(\frac{<\Psi_J|h|\Psi_K>}{x_J - x_K} \right)^2}} \tag{7/46}$$

are calculated again with the corresponding perturbation terms

$$
\begin{aligned}
\Psi_5' \quad &= N_5[\Psi_5 + 0.224\,\Psi_3 - 0.112\,\Psi_7 - 0.100\,\Psi_9] \\
&= 0.965\,[(0.000 \pm 0.000 \pm 0.000 \pm 0.000)\,\Phi_1 \\
&\quad + \ (0.425 + 0.059 + 0.048 + 0.026)\,\Phi_2 \\
&\quad + \ (0.263 + 0.095 - 0.029 - 0.043)\,\Phi_3 \\
&\quad + (-0.263 + 0.059 - 0.029 + 0.043)\,\Phi_4 \\
&\quad + (-0.425 + 0.095 + 0.048 - 0.026)\,\Phi_5 \\
&\quad + \ (0.000 \pm 0.000 \pm 0.000 \pm 0.000)\,\Phi_6 \\
&\quad + \ (0.425 - 0.059 - 0.048 + 0.026)\,\Phi_7 \\
&\quad + \ (0.263 - 0.095 + 0.029 - 0.043)\,\Phi_8 \\
&\quad + (-0.263 - 0.095 + 0.029 + 0.043)\,\Phi_9 \\
&\quad + (-0.425 - 0.059 - 0.048 - 0.026)\,\Phi_{10}] \\
&= 0.538\,\Phi_2 + 0.276\,\Phi_3 - 0.149\,\Phi_4 - 0.332\,\Phi_5 + 0.332\,\Phi_7 + 0.149\,\Phi_8 - 0.276\,\Phi_9 \\
&\qquad\qquad\qquad\qquad\qquad\qquad\qquad\qquad\qquad\qquad\qquad\qquad\qquad - 0.538\,\Phi_{10} \\
\Psi_5^{HMO} &= 0.543\,\Phi_2 + 0.259\,\Phi_3 - 0.160\,\Phi_4 - 0.335\,\Phi_5 + 0.335\,\Phi_7 + 0.160\,\Phi_8 - 0.259\,\Phi_9 \\
&\qquad\qquad\qquad\qquad\qquad\qquad\qquad\qquad\qquad\qquad\qquad\qquad\qquad - 0.542\,\Phi_{10}
\end{aligned}
$$

$$
\begin{aligned}
\Psi_6' \quad &= N_6[\Psi_6 + 0.087\,\Psi_1 + 0.045\,\Psi_2 - 0.212\,\Psi_4 - 0.100\,\Psi_8 - 0.166\,\Psi_{10}] \\
&= 0.957\,[(0.447 + 0.027 + 0.020 - 0.095 - 0.045 - 0.052)\,\Phi_1 \\
&\quad + (-0.138 + 0.027 + 0.016 - 0.029 + 0.036 + 0.052)\,\Phi_2 \\
&\quad + (-0.362 + 0.027 + 0.006 + 0.077 - 0.014 - 0.052)\,\Phi_3 \\
&\quad + \ (0.362 + 0.027 - 0.006 + 0.077 - 0.014 + 0.052)\,\Phi_4 \\
&\quad + \ (0.138 + 0.027 - 0.016 - 0.029 + 0.036 - 0.052)\,\Phi_5 \\
&\quad + (-0.447 + 0.027 - 0.020 - 0.095 - 0.045 + 0.052)\,\Phi_6 \\
&\quad + \ (0.138 + 0.027 - 0.016 - 0.029 + 0.036 - 0.052)\,\Phi_7 \\
&\quad + \ (0.362 + 0.027 - 0.006 + 0.077 - 0.014 + 0.052)\,\Phi_8 \\
&\quad + (-0.362 + 0.027 + 0.006 + 0.077 - 0.014 - 0.052)\,\Phi_9 \\
&\quad + (-0.138 + 0.027 + 0.016 - 0.029 + 0.036 + 0.052)\,\Phi_{10}] \\
&= \ \ 0.289\,\Phi_1 - 0.034\,\Phi_2 - 0.304\,\Phi_3 + 0.477\,\Phi_4 + 0.100\,\Phi_5 - 0.505\,\Phi_6 + 0.100\,\Phi_7 \\
&\qquad\qquad + 0.477\,\Phi_8 - 0.304\,\Phi_9 - 0.034\,\Phi_{10} \\
\Psi_6^{HMO} &= -0.316\,\Phi_1 + 0.063\,\Phi_2 + 0.290\,\Phi_3 - 0.470\,\Phi_4 - 0.102\,\Phi_5 + 0.510\,\Phi_6 - 0.102\,\Phi_7 \\
&\qquad\qquad - 0.470\,\Phi_8 + 0.290\,\Phi_9 + 0.063\,\Phi_{10}
\end{aligned}
$$

Sign inversion between the approximated and the exact orbitals Ψ_6 of azulene is due to the arbitrary assignment of the absolute sign and is without significance (cf. Problem 7.4).

7.3. Atom-Atom Polarizabilities

Problem 7.5:   Calculate the orbital energy ε_1 and the corresponding linear combination Ψ_1 of cyclopropenone

$$\triangleright C = O$$

using the values $\kappa_{\mu\rho}^{(1)}$ from Table (7/54) and the heteroatom parameter $h_0 = 1$ (6/80). Show that the same orbital energy ε_1 is obtained by using the partial atom–atom polarizability $\pi_{\mu\rho}^{(1)}$ from Table (7/62).

The approximate orbital energy $\epsilon_1' = \alpha + x_1'\beta$ of cyclopropenone can be calculated from that of the isoconjugate model (x_1) with the perturbation $\delta\alpha_1 = h_1\beta = \beta$ as follows:

$$x_J' = x_J + c_{J\rho}^2 h_\rho + \kappa_{\rho\rho}^{(J)} c_{J\rho} h_\rho^2$$
$$x_1' = x_1 + c_{11}^2 h_1 + \kappa_{11}^{(1)} c_{11} h_1^2$$
$$= 2.170 + (0.282)^2 + 0.121\,(0.282)$$
$$= 2.284$$

The approximate orbital Ψ_1 is obtained with the aid of the relation

$$c_{J\mu}' = c_{J\mu} + \kappa_{\mu\rho}^{(J)} \cdot h_\rho \tag{7/53}$$

in a simple manner:

$$\Psi_1' = (0.282 + 0.121)\,\Phi_1 + (0.612 + 0.005)\,\Phi_2 + (0.523 - 0.063)\,\Phi_3 + (0.523 - 0.063)\,\Phi_4$$
$$= 0.403\,\Phi_1 + 0.617\,\Phi_2 + 0.460\,\Phi_3 + 0.460\,\Phi_4$$

The exact HMO values

$$x_1^{HMO} = 2.303,$$
$$\Psi_1^{HMO} = 0.461\,\Phi_1 + 0.601\,\Phi_2 + 0.461\,\Phi_3 + 0.461\,\Phi_4$$

show the approximation to be satisfactory.

The approximate orbital energy $\epsilon_1 = \alpha + x_1\beta$ can also be calculated according to

$$x_J' = x_J + c_{J\rho}^2 h_\rho + \frac{1}{2}\pi_{\rho\rho}^{(J)} \cdot h_\rho^2$$

by using the partial atom-atom polarizability $\pi_{11}^{(1)} = 0.068$ from Table (7/62):

$$x_J' = 2.170 + (0.282)^2 + \frac{0.068}{2} = 2.284$$

Problem 7.6: Calculate the atom–atom polarizabilities π_{11}, π_{12}, and π_{13} of methylenecyclopropene using the coefficients and the eigenvalues from HMO Table ③—.

The atom-atom polarizabilities of methylenecyclopropene are obtained according to

$$\pi_{\mu\rho} = 2 \sum_{J=1}^{n} \sum_{K \neq J}^{n} b_J \frac{c_{J\rho}\, c_{K\rho}\, c_{J\mu}\, c_{K\mu}}{x_J - x_K} \tag{7/66}$$

in the following way:

$$\pi_{11} = 4 \left(\frac{c_{11}^2 c_{21}^2}{x_1 - x_2} + \frac{c_{11}^2 c_{31}^2}{x_1 - x_3} + \frac{c_{11}^2 c_{41}^2}{x_1 - x_4} + \frac{c_{21}^2 c_{11}^2}{x_2 - x_1} + \frac{c_{21}^2 c_{31}^2}{x_2 - x_3} + \frac{c_{21}^2 c_{41}^2}{x_2 - x_4} \right)$$

$$= 4 \left(\frac{(0.282)^2(-0.815)^2}{2.170 - 0.311} + 0 + \frac{(0.282)^2(0.506)^2}{2.170 - (-1.481)} + \frac{(-0.815)^2(0.282)^2}{0.311 - 2.170} + 0 + \right.$$

$$\left. + \frac{(-0.815)^2(0.506)^2}{0.311 - (-1.481)} \right)$$

$$= 0.402$$

$$\pi_{22} = 4 \left(\frac{c_{12}^2 c_{22}^2}{x_1 - x_2} + \frac{c_{12}^2 c_{32}^2}{x_1 - x_3} + \frac{c_{12}^2 c_{42}^2}{x_1 - x_4} + \frac{c_{22}^2 c_{12}^2}{x_2 - x_1} + \frac{c_{22}^2 c_{32}^2}{x_2 - x_3} + \frac{c_{22}^2 c_{42}^2}{x_2 - x_4} \right)$$

$$= 4 \left(\frac{(0.612)^2(-0.254)^2}{1.859} + 0 + \frac{(0.612)^2(-0.749)^2}{3.651} + \frac{(-0.254)^2(0.612)^2}{-1.859} + 0 + \right.$$

$$\left. + \frac{(-0.254)^2(-0.749)^2}{1.792} \right)$$

$$= 0.311$$

$$\pi_{33} = 4 \left(\frac{c_{13}^2 c_{23}^2}{x_1 - x_2} + \frac{c_{13}^2 c_{33}^2}{x_1 - x_3} + \frac{c_{13}^2 c_{43}^2}{x_1 - x_4} + \frac{c_{23}^2 c_{13}^2}{x_2 - x_1} + \frac{c_{23}^2 c_{33}^2}{x_2 - x_3} + \frac{c_{23}^2 c_{43}^2}{x_2 - x_4} \right)$$

$$= 4 \left(\frac{(0.523)^2(0.368)^2}{1.859} + \frac{(0.523)^2(0.707)^2}{3.170} + \frac{(0.523)^2(0.302)^2}{3.651} + \frac{(0.368)^2(0.523)^2}{-1.859} \right.$$

$$\left. + \frac{(0.368)^2(+0.707)^2}{1.311} + \frac{(0.368)^2(0.302)^2}{1.792} \right)$$

$$= 0.434$$

Problem 7.7: Derive the summation rule (7/69) for atom–atom polarizabilities from the general formula (7/66).

With the aid of the defining equation

$$\sum_{\mu=1}^{n} \pi_{\mu\rho} = 0 \tag{7/69}$$

proof of the summation rule for atom-atom polarizabilities

$$\pi_{\mu\rho} = 2 \sum_{J=1}^{n} \sum_{K \neq J}^{n} b_J \frac{c_{J\mu} c_{K\mu} c_{J\rho} c_{K\rho}}{x_J - x_K} \tag{7/66}$$

can be carried out as follows:

$$\sum_{\mu=1}^{n} \pi_{\mu\rho} = \sum_{\mu=1}^{n} 2 \sum_{J=1}^{n} \sum_{K \neq J}^{n} b_J \frac{c_{J\mu} c_{K\mu} c_{J\rho} c_{K\rho}}{x_J - x_K}$$

$$= 2 \sum_{J=1}^{n} \sum_{K \neq J}^{n} \left(b_J \frac{c_{J\rho} c_{K\rho}}{x_J - x_K} \sum_{\mu=1}^{n} c_{J\mu} c_{K\mu} \right)$$

From the general orthogonality condition for the *Hückel* orbitals

$$\langle \Psi_J | \Psi_K \rangle = \sum c_{J\mu} c_{K\mu} = 0 \quad (J \neq K) \tag{7/44}$$

and because of the summation over $K \neq J$, we obtain

$$\sum_{\mu=1}^{n} \pi_{\mu\rho} = 2 \sum_{J=1}^{n} \sum_{K \neq J}^{n} \left(b_J \frac{c_{J\rho} c_{K\rho}}{x_J - x_K} \cdot 0 \right) = 0. \tag{7/69}$$

Problem 7.8: Calculate the changes in charge orders q_μ and total π-electron energy E_π for 1-substituted methylenecyclopropene

assuming that the perturbation by the substituent R is purely inductive. Study both cases where $\delta\alpha_1 = 0\cdot5\beta$ and $\delta\alpha_1 = -0\cdot5\beta$.

The changes in the charge orders q_μ as well as in the total π-electron energies X_π are calculated according to

$$q'_\mu = q_\mu + \pi_{\mu\rho} \cdot h_\rho, \qquad (7/64)$$

$$X'_\pi = X_\pi + q_\rho h_\rho + \frac{1}{2}\pi_{\rho\rho} \cdot h_\rho^2 \qquad (7/71)$$

for the perturbations $h_\rho = \pm 0.5$ at center 1 of methylenecyclopropene as follows:

μ	q_μ	$\pi_{\mu 1}$	$q_\mu^{(+0.5)}$	$q_\mu^{(-0.5)}$
1	1.488	0.402	1.689	1.287
2	0.877	−0.247	0.754	1.000
3/4	0.818	−0.078	0.779	0.857

$$\Sigma = 4.001 \quad \Sigma = 4.001$$

$$X'_\pi(+0.5) = 4.962 + 1.488 \cdot 0.5 + \frac{1}{2} \cdot 0.402 \cdot 0.250 = 5.756$$

$$X'_\pi(-0.5) = 4.962 - 1.488 \cdot 0.5 + \frac{1}{2} \cdot 0.402 \cdot 0.250 = 4.268$$

According to (7/64) for perturbations of equal magnitude but opposite sign the q'_μ values are symmetrically disposed about the unperturbed charge order q_μ. For the total π-electron energies, however, the second order contribution according to (7/71) invariably results in a stabilization irrespective of the sign.

Problem 7.9: Starting from the relevant isoconjugate models and using the hetero atom parameters (6/80) and the atom–atom polarizabilities from the HMO tables, calculate the charge orders for the following compounds

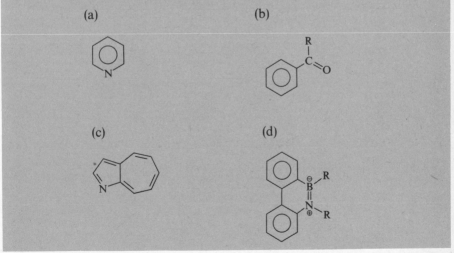

(a)

(b)

(c)

(d)

The charge order of the isoconjugate model which is modified by the influence of the perturbation $\delta\alpha_\rho$ is obtained from

$$q'_\mu = q_\mu + \pi_{\mu\,\rho} \cdot h_\rho. \tag{7/64}$$

Correspondingly, with several perturbations, as in example (d), the following relation holds

$$q'_\mu = q_\mu + \sum_\rho \pi_{\mu\,\rho} \cdot h_\rho.$$

The hetero parameters used are

$$
\begin{aligned}
h_{N.} &= 0.5 \ \text{(a), (c), (d)} \\
h_{O.} &= 1.0 \ \text{(b)} \\
h_B &= -1.0 \ \text{(d)}
\end{aligned}
$$

The results of the calculations are summarized in the following molecular (charge order) diagrams:

(a)

(b)

(c)

(d)

In the examples (a) – (d), the charge orders are influenced only by the atom-atom polarizabilities, since either the relation

$$k_{CC} = k_{CN} = k_{CO} = 1.0 \ \ \text{(a), (b), (c)} \tag{6/80}$$

holds, or otherwise alternant systems are being considered in which the atom-bond polarizabilities are identical to zero (d).

Problem 7.10: Which is the thermodynamically more stable isomer in each of the pairs (a) through (e) according to second order perturbations within the HMO framework, i.e. which one possesses the greater total π-electron energy?

(a)

(b)   (c)

(d)   (e)

Compare the results with those of Problem 6.5.

The change in total π-electron energy under the influence of the second order perturbation is calculated with

$$h_\rho = h_N = 0.5 \tag{6/80}$$

according to

$$X'_\pi = X_\pi + \delta^{(1)} X_\pi + \delta^{(2)} X_\pi$$

$$= X_\pi + q_\rho h_\rho + \frac{1}{2} \pi_{\rho\rho} \cdot h_\rho^2 \tag{7/71}$$

$$= X_\pi + \frac{1}{2} q_\rho + \frac{1}{8} \pi_{\rho\rho}.$$

Substitution of the tabulated atom-atom polarizabilities $\pi_{\rho\rho}$ gives the following results if the $\delta^{(1)}X_\pi$ values are taken from Problem 6.5.

System	$\pi_{\rho\rho}$	$\delta^{(2)}X_\pi$	$\delta^{(1)}X_\pi$	δX_π	Stability
$(a)_1$	0.626	0.078	0.500	0.578	
$(a)_2$	0.402	0.050	0.500	0.550	$(a)_1 > (a)_2$
$(b)_1$	0.513	0.064	0.407	0.471	
$(b)_2$	0.385	0.048	0.587	0.635	$(b)_1 < (b)_2$
$(c)_1$	0.608	0.076	0.549	0.625	
$(c)_2$	0.599	0.075	0.488	0.563	$(c)_1 > (c)_2$
$(d)_1$	0.443	0.055	0.500	0.555	
$(d)_2$	0.405	0.051	0.500	0.551	$(d)_1 > (d)_2$
$(e)_1$	0.425	0.053	0.587	0.640	
$(e)_2$	0.438	0.055	0.428	0.483	$(e)_1 > (e)_2$

In the case of azabutadienes (a) and azanaphthalenes (d), which as alternant system have equal charge orders and different atom/atom polarizabilities at the individual centers in the ground state, it is only the second order perturbation which determines, within the HMO approximation, the sequence of thermodynamic stabilities and total π-electron energies.

Problem 7.11: Which one of the five isomeric phenylazulenes $R - S$ possesses the highest total π-electron energy? Calculate the bond orders of the new bonds. (Use the HMO Tables ⑤⑦ and ⑥.)

For two partial system R and S joined at centers ρ and σ, the change in the total π-electron energy is approximately

$$\Delta E_\pi \cong (0.811 \sqrt{\pi_{\rho\rho}\pi_{\sigma\sigma}} + 0.062)\beta \qquad (7/77)$$

and the bond order of the new bond $\rho - \sigma$ is

$$p_{\rho\sigma} \cong 0.69 \sqrt{\pi_{\rho\rho}\pi_{\sigma\sigma}} + 0.10. \qquad (7/78)$$

Starting from the tabulated atom-atom polarizabilities of azulene $\pi_{\rho\rho}$ and of benzene $\pi_{\sigma\sigma}$, we obtain the following values:

	$\pi_{\rho\rho}$	$\pi_{\sigma\sigma}$	ΔE_{π}	$p_{\rho\sigma}$
1	0.425	0.398	0.396	0.384
2	0.419		0.393	0.382
4	0.438		0.401	0.388
5	0.429		0.397	0.385
6	0.424		0.395	0.383

4-Phenylazulene should accordingly be the most stable isomer. However, consideration of molecular models suggests that complete coplanarity is impossible in both the 1- and the 4-substituted compounds. Within the present approximation, 5-phenylazulene thus possesses the greatest total π-electron energy.

7.4. Bond-Atom-, Atom-Bond- and Bond-Bond Polarizabilities

Problem 7.12: Introduce bonds into a ten-membered ring between centres 1 and 6 or centres 1 and 5 using the bond–atom and the bond–bond polarizabilities (HMO Table ⑩, Volume 3).

Calculate the charge and the bond orders for the resulting models of naphthalene and of azulene and compare your answers with the tabulated values of the exact HMO models ⑥⑥ and ⑤⑦ (Volume 3).

The changes in the charge- and bond-orders of the 10-membered ring

$$\delta\beta_{16} = \delta\beta_{15} = \beta$$

are given, according to (7/92) and (7/93) as well as (7/89), by

$$q'_\mu = q_\mu + 2\pi_{\rho\sigma,\mu} \cdot \frac{\delta\beta_{\rho\sigma}}{\beta} = 1 + 2\pi_{1\sigma,\mu},$$

$$P'_{\mu\nu} = P_{\mu\nu} + \pi_{\mu\nu,\rho\sigma} \cdot \frac{\delta\beta_{\rho\sigma}}{\beta} = P_{\mu\nu} + \pi_{\mu\nu,1\sigma}.$$

The calculated values are compared with the corresponding exact HMO values in the following molecular diagrams:

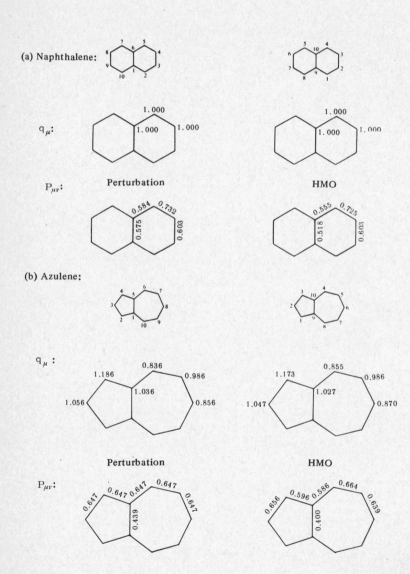

(a) Naphthalene:

q_μ:

$P_{\mu\nu}$:

Perturbation

HMO

(b) Azulene:

q_μ :

Perturbation

HMO

$P_{\mu\nu}$:

In the extreme case the deviation between the perturbational and HMO values amounts to about 0.05 units. The agreement for nonalternant azulene is hardly poorer than that for naphthalene.

Problem 7.13: How much do the charge and bond orders of styrene change if the vinyl group is twisted out of the plane of the ring by about 30°?

(Hint: For the perturbation $\delta\beta_{17}$, use $\delta\beta_{\rho\sigma} = -\beta(1 - \cos\Theta)$.)

The charge orders remain unchanged in the case of styrene, since the atom-bond polarizabilities in alternant π-electron systems are identically equal to zero. Writing

$$\delta\beta_{17} = -(1 - \cos 30°)\beta = -0.134\,\beta$$

we obtain from (7/93) the following formula for the change in bond order:

$$\delta P_{\mu\nu} = \pi_{\mu\nu,\rho\sigma} \cdot \frac{\delta\beta_{\rho\sigma}}{\beta} = -0.134 \cdot \pi_{\mu\nu,\,17.}$$

The calculated values are shown in the following molecular (bond order) diagram:

$$P_{\mu\nu}(\Theta = 0°) \qquad \delta P_{\mu\nu}(\Theta = 30°)$$

The bond orders of the 6-membered ring are seen to approach those of unsubstituted benzene ($P_{\mu\nu} = 0.667$) and of ethylene ($P_{17} \to 0$ and $P_{78} \to 1$). This extreme case is reached on twisting by 90°.

It should be noted that the above perturbation calculation gives a linear relationship only for small values of $\delta\beta$. Pronounced deviations occur for greater perturbations, as is apparent from the correlation diagram.

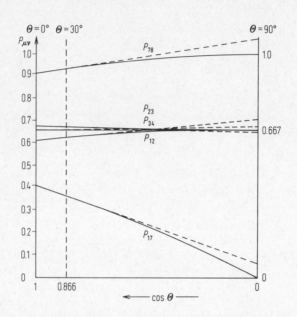

Problem 7.14: As an extension of Problem 6.14, calculate the second order changes in the total π-electron energy occurring on bridging of the 14-membered ring by two additional bonds leading to models for anthracene, phenanthrene, and 1,2-, 4,5-, and 5,6-benzazulenes. Use the bond–bond polarizabilities $\pi_{\rho\sigma,\rho\sigma}$ (HMO Table ⑭, Volume 3).

Owing to the identical bond orders in the starting system, the first order perturbation calculation (Problem 6.14) gave only a crude approximation, providing no more than a qualitative distinction between benzenoid and nonbenzenoid hydrocarbons. A second order perturbation calculation according to

$$X_{\pi}'' = X_{\pi} + \delta^{(1)} X_{\pi} + \delta^{(2)} X_{\pi} = X_{\pi}' + \pi_{\rho\sigma,\rho\sigma} \cdot k_{\rho\sigma}^2 \qquad (7/94)$$

and using the tabulated bond-bond self polarizabilities (Vol. 3) yields improved total π-electron energies:

(a)

$$X_\pi^{HMO} = 19.314$$

(b)

$$X_\pi^{HMO} = 19.448$$

$$X_\pi'' = X_\pi' + 2\pi_{16,16} \cdot k_{16}^2$$
$$= 18.612 + 2 \cdot 0.407 \cdot 1$$
$$= 19.426$$

(c)

$$X_\pi^{HMO} = 19.095$$

(d)

$$X_\pi^{HMO} = 19.109$$

$$X_\pi'' = X_\pi' + (\pi_{16,16} + \pi_{15,15})k_{\rho\sigma}^2$$
$$= 18.294 + (0.463 + 0.407) \cdot 1$$
$$= 19.164$$

(e)

$$X_\pi^{HMO} = 19.084$$

In contrast to first order perturbation, which gave less than half the true value for the difference between the total π-electron energies of the starting and final systems, the results show considerably better agreement with exact HMO values. However, distinctions within the benzenoid or nonbenzenoid hydrocarbons only become possible on inclusion of relevant bond-bond polarizabilities $\pi_{\mu\nu}, \rho\sigma$, in the second order perturbation calculation. These polarizabilities are listed for neighboring centers $\nu\mu$ and $\rho\sigma$ in the HMO tables (Vol. 3).

Problem 7.15: As an extension of Problem 7.13, calculate the extent to which the total π-electron energy of styrene changes if the vinyl group is twisted out of the plane of the ring by $30°$; use bond–bond polarizabilities $\pi_{17,17}$ (HMO Table ⑥—K_2, Volume 3). Compare the results of the first order (Problem 6.3) and the second order perturbation calculations.

In a second order perturbation calculation according to (7/96) and (7/97) the total π-electron energy of the styrene π-system twisted through $30°$ changes by

$$\delta^{(2)}E_\pi = \pi_{\rho\sigma,\rho\sigma} \cdot \frac{\delta\beta_{\rho\sigma}^2}{\beta}$$

$$= 0.339 \cdot (-0.134)^2\beta = 0.006\,\beta.$$

First order perturbation calculation gives

$$\delta^{(1)}E_\pi = 2P_{\rho\sigma} \cdot \delta\beta_{\rho\sigma} \qquad (6/55)$$

$$= 2 \cdot 0.406 \cdot (-0.134)\beta = -0.109\,\beta.$$

As already shown in the energy level scheme of Problem 6.3, first order perturbation of the bonding molecular orbitals leads to an overall destabilization whose magnitude is corrected by the second order perturbation.

Problem 7.16: Starting from the isoconjugate model of naphthalene, calculate charge and bond orders and total π-electron energy of phthalaldehyde

The list of perturbations in this case reads

$$\langle\mu|h|\nu\rangle = 0, \text{ except } \langle 2|h|2\rangle = \langle 3|h|3\rangle = \delta\alpha_\rho = h_o\beta = \beta$$

$$\langle 2|h|3\rangle = \langle 3|h|2\rangle = \delta\beta_{\rho\sigma} = k_{\rho\sigma}\beta = -\beta$$

The modified charge- and bond orders are calculated according to (7/67) and (7/91) through (7/94) as follows:

$$q'_\mu = q_\mu + \pi_{\mu\,\rho} \cdot h_\rho$$
$$P'_{\mu\nu} = P_{\mu\nu} + \pi_{\mu\nu,\rho} \cdot h_\rho$$

$$q'_\mu = q_\mu + \pi_{\mu,\rho\sigma} \cdot k_{\rho\sigma}$$
$$P'_{\mu\nu} = P_{\mu\nu} + \pi_{\mu\nu,\rho\sigma} \cdot k_{\rho\sigma}$$

For alternant π-electron systems, the atom-bond and bond-atom polarizabilities

$$\pi_{\mu,\rho\sigma} = 2\pi_{\rho\sigma,\mu} \qquad\qquad (7/89)$$

are identically equal to zero if ρ and σ belong to the same starred or unstarred set of atomic orbitals. For the individual cases we obtain:

$$
\begin{aligned}
q'_1 &= q'_4 &&= q_1 + \pi_{12} \cdot h_2 + \pi_{13} \cdot h_3 + 2\pi_{23,1} \cdot k_{23} \\
&&&= 1.000 + (-0.213) \cdot 1 + 0.018 \cdot 1 + 0 &&= 0.805 \\[4pt]
q'_2 &= q'_3 &&= 1.000 + 0.405 \cdot 1 + (-0.110) \cdot 1 &&= 1.295 \\[4pt]
q'_5 &= q'_8 &&= 1.000 + 0.006 \cdot 1 + (-0.032) \cdot 1 &&= 0.974 \\[4pt]
q'_6 &= q'_7 &&= 1.000 + (-0.033) \cdot 1 + (0.000) \cdot 1 &&= 0.967 \\[4pt]
q'_9 &= q'_{10} &&= 1.000 + 0.007 \cdot 1 + (-0.049) \cdot 1 &&= 0.958
\end{aligned}
$$

$$
\begin{aligned}
P'_{12} &= P'_{34} &&= P_{12} + 2\pi_{12,2} \cdot h_2 + 2\pi_{12,3} \cdot h_3 + \pi_{12,23} \cdot k_{23} \\
&&&= 0.725 + 0 + 0 + (-0.209)(-1) &&= 0.934 \\[4pt]
P'_{23} &&&= 0.603 + 0.295(-1) &&= 0.308 \\[4pt]
P'_{56} &= P'_{78} &&= 0.725 + 0.032(-1) &&= 0.693 \\[4pt]
P'_{67} &&&= 0.603 + (-0.032)(-1) &&= 0.635 \\[4pt]
P'_{19} &= P'_{4\,10} &&= 0.555 + 0.111(-1) &&= 0.444 \\[4pt]
P'_{5\,10} &= P'_{89} &&= 0.555 + (-0.045)(-1) &&= 0.600 \\[4pt]
P_{9\,10} &&&= 0.518 + (-0.041)(-1) &&= 0.559
\end{aligned}
$$

The following comparison with the exact HMO values shows that all the changes in charge- and bond orders are qualitatively correct. The observed deviations, which are considerable in some cases, arise because the atom-bond and bond-atom polarizabilities of alternant systems are identically equal to zero and the relevant correction terms therefore disappear.

q_μ

```
  1.000   1.000                    0.974    0.805                        0.929    0.649
1.000        1.000      1.000   0.964        0.958  O 1.245     0.949         0.979  O 1.494
                    ⟹                              O                                  O
```

HMO

$P_{\mu\nu}$

```
  0.725  0.555 0.555  0.725              0.693  0.600 0.444  0.934              0.662  0.617 0.437  0.988
0.603           0.518    0.603  ⟹  0.635         0.559    0.308       0.654        0.539    0.109
```

The total π-electron energy is calculated by generalization of (7/98) to three independent variables:

$$F(x+h, y+k, z+l) = F(xyz) + \frac{\partial F}{\partial x}h + \frac{\partial F}{\partial y}k + \frac{\partial F}{\partial z}l + \frac{1}{2}\frac{\partial^2 F}{\partial x^2}h^2 + \frac{1}{2}\frac{\partial^2 F}{\partial y^2}k^2 + \frac{1}{2}\frac{\partial^2 F}{\partial z^2}l^2 +$$

$$+ \frac{\partial^2 F}{\partial x \partial y}hk + \frac{\partial^2 F}{\partial x \partial z}hl + \frac{\partial^2 F}{\partial y \partial z}kl,$$

$$X'_\pi = X_\pi + q_2 h_2 + q_3 h_3 + 2p_{23}k_{23} + \frac{1}{2}\pi_{22}h_2^2 + \frac{1}{2}\pi_{33}h_3^2 + \pi_{23,23}k_{23}^2 + \pi_{2,3}h_2 h_3$$

$$+ 2\pi_{23,2}k_{23}h_2 + 2\pi_{23,3}k_{23}h_3$$

$$= 13.683 + 2 \cdot 1.000 \cdot 1 + 2 \cdot 0.603(-1) + 1^2 \cdot 0.405 +$$

$$+ (-1)^2 \cdot 0.295 + 1^2(-0.110) + 4 \cdot (0)1(-1)$$

$$= 15.067.$$

This result is in satisfactory agreement with the exact HMO coefficients of the total π-electron energy

$$X_\pi^{HMO} = 15.391$$

calculated according to (6/80).

7.5. Linear Combinations of Molecular Orbitals

Problem 7.17: Calculate the orbital energies of acrolein $H_2C=CH-CH=O$ by uniting the partial systems $C=C$ and $C=O$ [see (6.80) for parameters of $C=O$].

For the CO group, Ψ_1 and Ψ_2 represent molecular orbitals with the perturbation $h_{\dot{O}} = 1$

$$\left\| \begin{array}{cc} -x & 1 \\ 1 & 1-x \end{array} \right\| = 0$$

$$x^2 - x - 1 = 0$$

$$x = \frac{1}{2} \pm \sqrt{\frac{1}{4} + 1}$$

$$x_1 = -1.618$$
$$x_2 = -0.618$$

Ψ_2: $+0.618\,c_C + c_O = 0$ $c_C = 1$
$c_O = -0.618$

$$N = \frac{1}{\sqrt{1^2 + (-0.618)^2}} = 0.851$$

$$\Psi_2 = +0.851\,\Phi_3 - 0.526\,\Phi_4 = \Psi_{-CO}$$

Ψ_1: $-1.618\,c_C + c_O = 0$ $c_C = 1$
$c_O = +1.618$

$$N = \frac{1}{\sqrt{1^2 + (+1.618)^2}} = 0.526$$

$$\Psi_1 = +0.526\,\Phi_3 + 0.851\,\Phi_4 = \Psi_{+CO}$$

The LCMO calculation is based upon the following energy level scheme:

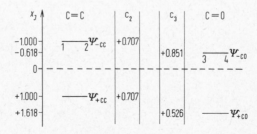

Considering only pairwise interaction between the two bonding molecular orbitals Ψ_{+CC} and Ψ_{+CO} as well as the antibonding molecular orbitals Ψ_{-CC} and Ψ_{-CO}, we obtain the approximate orbital energies as solutions of the following secular determinants:

$$x_3/x_4: \begin{Vmatrix} -1-x & 0.707 \cdot 0.851 \\ 0.707 \cdot 0.851 & -0.618-x \end{Vmatrix} = 0$$

$$x^2 + 1.618x + 0.256 = 0$$

$$x = -0.809 \pm \sqrt{0.398}$$
$$x_4 = -1.440$$
$$x_3 = -0.178$$

$$x_1/x_2: \begin{Vmatrix} +1-x & 0.707 \cdot 0.526 \\ 0.707 \cdot 0.526 & 1.618-x \end{Vmatrix} = 0$$

$$x^2 - 2.618x + 1.480 = 0$$

$$x = 1.309 \pm \sqrt{0.233}$$
$$x_2 = +0.826$$
$$x_1 = +1.792$$

On inclusion of all interactions in a fourth-order determinant

$$\begin{Vmatrix} -1-x & 0 & -0.602 & -0.372 \\ 0 & 1-x & 0.602 & 0.372 \\ -0.602 & 0.602 & -0.618-x & 0 \\ -0.372 & 0.372 & 0 & 1.618-x \end{Vmatrix} = 0$$

the solution leads of course to the exact HMO orbital energies:

$$x_1 = 1.878 \qquad x_2 = 1.000 \qquad x_3 = -0.347 \qquad x_4 = -1.531$$

Problem 7.18: On introduction of two additional bonds, the butadiene and ethylene systems can combine to yield a fulvene model:

Compare the approximate orbital energies calculated this way with the exact HMO values (HMO Table ⑤— Volume 3).

Calculation of the orbital energies starts from the following energy level scheme:

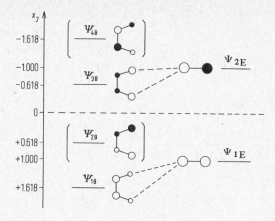

The molecular orbitals Ψ_2 and Ψ_4 of butadiene, in which the coefficients at the linkage sites have the same magnitude and opposite signs, clearly make no contribution to the LCMO calculation.

The list of perturbations reads:

$$\langle\mu|h|\nu\rangle = 0, \text{ except } \langle 1_B|h|1_E\rangle = \langle 1_E|h|1_B\rangle = \beta$$
$$\langle 4_B|h|1_E\rangle = \langle 1_E|h|4_B\rangle = \beta$$

The cross terms are therefore:

$$\langle\Psi_{B1}|h|\Psi_{E1}\rangle = (c_{B,11}c_{E,11} + c_{B,14}c_{E,11})\beta,$$
$$\langle\Psi_{B3}|h|\Psi_{E2}\rangle = (c_{B,31}c_{E,21} + c_{B,34}c_{E,21})\beta.$$

Considering only pairwise combination of the bonding and of the antibonding molecular orbitals without mutual interaction we can crudely approximate the orbital energies x_1, x_3, x_4, and x_6 of the fulvene model via the following secular determinants:

$$\begin{Vmatrix} -1-x & 2\cdot0.602\cdot0.707 \\ 2\cdot0.602\cdot0.707 & -0.618-x \end{Vmatrix} = 0$$

$$x^2 + 1.618x - 0.106 = 0$$
$$x = -0.809 \pm \sqrt{0.760}$$
$$x_6 = -1.681$$
$$x_4 = +0.063$$

$$\begin{Vmatrix} 1-x & 2 \cdot 0.372 \cdot 0.707 \\ 2 \cdot 0.372 \cdot 0.707 & 1.618-x \end{Vmatrix} = 0$$

$$x^2 - 2.618x + 1.341 = 0$$

$$x = +1.309 \pm \sqrt{0.372}$$
$$x_3 = +0.698$$
$$x_1 = +1.919$$

The orbital energies x_2 and x_5 are taken directly from butadiene:

$$x_5 = -1.618$$
$$x_2 = +0.618$$

Inclusion of all interaction terms between the molecular orbitals capable of combination gives the exact HMO values via the fourth order secular determinant:

$$\begin{Vmatrix} -1-x & 0 & 0.851 & 0.525 \\ 0 & 1-x & 0.851 & 0.525 \\ 0.851 & 0.851 & -0.618-x & 0 \\ 0.525 & 0.525 & 0 & 1.618-x \end{Vmatrix} = 0$$

$$x_6 = -1.861$$
$$x_4 = -0.254$$
$$x_3 = +1.000$$
$$x_1 = +2.115$$

The considerable error in the approximate values compared to the HMO orbital energies, especially the way in which x_4 has slipped down into the bonding region, arises from the neglect of interaction between the bonding molecular Ψ_{1B}, Ψ_{1E} and the antibonding molecular orbitals Ψ_{3B}, Ψ_{2E}. This interaction can be taken care of by a second order perturbation calculation (cf. Problem 7.21).

Problem 7.19: Starting from the symmetry-correct molecular orbitals of the cyclopentadienyl radical, calculate the two inner orbital energies of fulvalene

(Hint: Combine the orbitals symmetric to the long axis of fulvalene.)

Symmetry-correct linear combination is formed according to the appended scheme from the cyclopentadienyl molecular orbitals Ψ_3 and Ψ_4 of the HMO Tables (Vol. 3).

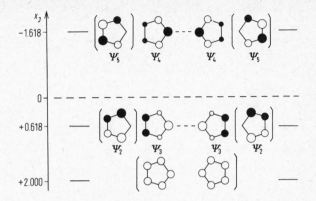

Using exclusively the pairwise combinations of Ψ_3/Ψ_3 and Ψ_4/Ψ_4, the following approximate orbital energies are obtained:

$$\left\| \begin{array}{cc} -1.618 - x & (-0.632)^2 \\ (-0.632)^2 & -1.618 - x \end{array} \right\| = 0$$

$$(-1.618 - x)^2 - (-0.632)^4 = 0$$

$$\begin{aligned} x &= -1.618 \pm 0.399 \\ x_{10} &= -2.017 & x_{10}^{HMO} &= -2.115 \\ x_7 &= -1.219 & x_7^{HMO} &= -1.303 \end{aligned}$$

$$\left\| \begin{array}{cc} 0.618 - x & (0.632)^2 \\ (0.632)^2 & 0.618 - x \end{array} \right\| = 0$$

$$(0.618 - x)^2 - (0.632)^4 = 0$$

$$\begin{aligned} x &= 0.618 \pm 0.399 \\ x_6 &= +0.219 & x_6^{HMO} &= +0.254 \\ x_3 &= +1.017 & x_3^{HMO} &= +1.000 \end{aligned}$$

Here, as is apparent from a comparison with the HMO values also given, the pairwise combination already leads to a satisfactory approximation. Solution of the secular determinant containing all interactions between the molecular orbitals Ψ_3 and Ψ_4

$$\left\| \begin{array}{cc|cc} -1.618 - x & 0 & 0.399 & -0.399 \\ 0 & 0.618 - x & -0.399 & 0.399 \\ \hline 0.399 & -0.399 & -1.618 - x & 0 \\ -0.399 & 0.399 & 0 & 0.618 - x \end{array} \right\| = 0$$

affords the following energy values:

$$x_{10} = -2.086$$
$$x_7 = -1.288$$
$$x_6 = +0.288$$
$$x_3 = +1.086$$

Problem 7.20: Calculate the LCMO functions belonging to the approximate orbital energies of acrolein (cf. Problem 7.17).

The approximate orbitals are obtained according to the statement

$$\Psi_{\substack{bonding \\ antibonding}} = c_{\pm CC}\Psi_{\pm CC} + c_{\pm CO}\Psi_{\pm CO}.$$

For this purpose the orbital energies are substituted as usual in the secular equations and thus the coefficients $c_{\pm CC}$ and $c_{\pm CO}$ of the linear combinations of the CC and CO molecular orbitals described in Problem 7.17 are obtained. The resulting approximate orbitals of the acrolein model are each compared with the respective HMO eigenfunctions:

Ψ_j: $\quad (-1-x)c_{-CC} + 0.602\,c_{-CO} = 0$

Ψ_4: $\quad 0.440\,c_{4,-CC} + 0.602\,c_{4,-CO} = 0 \qquad c_{4,-CC} = 1$
$$c_{4,-CO} = -0.731$$
$$N = \frac{1}{\sqrt{1.536}} = 0.807$$

$\Psi_4 \quad = 0.807\,\Psi_{-CC} - 0.590\,\Psi_{-CO}$
$\quad\quad = 0.807\,(-0.707\,\Phi_1 + 0.707\,\Phi_2) - 0.590\,(0.851\,\Phi_3 - 0.526\,\Phi_4)$
$\quad\quad = -0.570\,\Phi_1 + 0.570\,\Phi_2 - 0.502\,\Phi_3 + 0.310\,\Phi_4$
$\Psi_4^{HMO} = 0.429\,\Phi_1 - 0.656\,\Phi_2 + 0.577\,\Phi_3 - 0.228\,\Phi_4$

Ψ_3: $\quad -0.822\,c_{3,-CC} + 0.602\,c_{3,-CO} = 0 \qquad c_{3,-CC} = 1$
$$c_{3,-CO} = +1.368$$
$$N = \frac{1}{\sqrt{2.871}} = 0.590$$

$\Psi_3 \quad = 0.590\,\Psi_{-CC} + 0.807\,\Psi_{-CO}$
$\quad\quad = 0.590\,(-0.707\,\Phi_1 + 0.707\,\Phi_2) + 0.807\,(0.851\,\Phi_3 - 0.526\,\Phi_4)$
$\quad\quad = -0.417\,\Phi_1 + 0.417\,\Phi_2 + 0.687\,\Phi_3 - 0.424\,\Phi_4$
$\Psi_3^{HMO} = 0.657\,\Phi_1 - 0.228\,\Phi_2 - 0.577\,\Phi_3 + 0.429\,\Phi_4$

$\Psi_J:$ $(1-x)\,c_{2,+CC} + 0.372\,c_{2,+CO} = 0$

$\Psi_2:$ $0.174\,c_{2,+CC} + 0.372\,c_{2,+CO} = 0$ $\qquad c_{2,+CC} = 1$

$$c_{2,+CO} = -0.468$$

$$N = \frac{1}{\sqrt{1.220}} = 0.906$$

$\Psi_2 = 0.906\,\Psi_{+CC} - 0.424\,\Psi_{+CO}$

$\quad = 0.906\,(0.707\,\Phi_1 + 0.707\,\Phi_2) - 0.424\,(0.526\,\Phi_3 + 0.851\,\Phi_4)$

$\quad = 0.640\,\Phi_1 + 0.640\,\Phi_2 - 0.223\,\Phi_3 - 0.361\,\Phi_4$

$\Psi_2^{HMO} = 0.577\,\Phi_1 + 0.577\,\Phi_2 - 0.000\,\Phi_3 - 0.577\,\Phi_4$

$\Psi_1:$ $-0.792\,c_{1,+CC} + 0.372\,c_{1,+CO} = 0$ $\qquad c_{1,+CC} = 1$

$$c_{1,+CO} = +2.135$$

$$N = \frac{1}{\sqrt{5.558}} = 0.424$$

$\Psi_1 = 0.424\,\Psi_{+CC} + 0.905\,\Psi_{+CO}$

$\quad = 0.424\,(0.707\,\Phi_1 + 0.707\,\Phi_2) + 0.905\,(0.526\,\Phi_3 + 0.851\,\Phi_4)$

$\quad = 0.300\,\Phi_1 + 0.300\,\Phi_2 + 0.476\,\Phi_3 + 0.770\,\Phi_4$

$\Psi_1^{HMO} = 0.228\,\Phi_1 + 0.429\,\Phi_2 + 0.577\,\Phi_3 + 0.657\,\Phi_4$

Neglecting the interaction between bonding and antibonding molecular orbitals clearly leads to a qualitatively correct but very crude approximation. Further improvement is possible by a perturbation calculation; however, the complete fourth order determinant is relatively simple to solve. It should also be noted that sign inversion of the approximate orbitals Ψ_3 and Ψ_4 arises from the choice of the positive center as linkage site for the antibonding molecular orbitals. However, the absolute sign is immaterial (cf. Problems 7.3 and 7.4).

Problem 7.21: In continuation of Problem 7.18, calculate the LCMO functions of the fulvene model. Compare the functions obtained with those from the HMO Table ⑤— (Volume 3).

The first row of the secular determinant from Problem 7.18 furnishes as secular equation for the orbital energy $x_6 = -1.681$:

$$0.681\,c_{6,2E} + 0.851\,c_{6,3B}$$

The coefficients are those of the linear combination

$$\Psi_6 = c_{6,2E}\Psi_{2E} + c_{6,3B}\Psi_{3B}$$

and taking normalization into consideration we obtain

$$\Psi_6 = 0.781\,\Psi_{2E} - 0.625\,\Psi_{3B}.$$

For reasons of orthogonality

$$\Psi_4 = 0.625\,\Psi_{2E} + 0.781\,\Psi_{3B}.$$

Similarly, the secular determinants for the bonding molecular orbitals lead to

$$\Psi_3 = 0.868\,\Psi_{1E} - 0.496\,\Psi_{1B},$$
$$\Psi_1 = 0.496\,\Psi_{1E} + 0.868\,\Psi_{1B}.$$

The LCMO eigenfunctions of the fulvene model read:

$$\Psi_6 = 0.376\Phi_1 + 0.232\Phi_2 + 0.232\Phi_3 - 0.376\Phi_4 + 0.552\Phi_5 - 0.552\Phi_6$$
$$\Psi_5 = 0.372\Phi_1 - 0.602\Phi_2 + 0.602\Phi_3 - 0.372\Phi_4$$
$$\Psi_4 = 0.470\Phi_1 - 0.291\Phi_2 - 0.291\Phi_3 + 0.470\Phi_4 + 0.442\Phi_5 - 0.442\Phi_6$$
$$\Psi_2 = 0.602\Phi_1 + 0.372\Phi_2 - 0.372\Phi_3 - 0.602\Phi_4$$
$$\Psi_3 = 0.185\Phi_1 - 0.299\Phi_2 - 0.299\Phi_3 - 0.185\Phi_4 + 0.614\Phi_5 + 0.614\Phi_6$$
$$\Psi_1 = 0.323\Phi_1 + 0.523\Phi_2 + 0.523\Phi_3 + 0.323\Phi_4 + 0.351\Phi_5 + 0.351\Phi_6$$

The agreement with the HMO eigenfunctions of fulvene (Vol. 3) is not entirely satisfactory. In particular, no distinction is made between centers 5 and 6 within the framework of the chosen model. In the conclusion of Problem 7.18 it has been mentioned that the poor agreement between the approximate and the HMO orbital energies is due to the neglect of interactions between the bonding and the antibonding basis functions Ψ_{1E}, Ψ_{1B} and Ψ_{2E}, Ψ_{3B}. This interaction can also be accounted for using the linear combinations, as will be shown here for the orbital energy x_4. For the change δx_4, second order perturbation with the values from Problem 7.18 yields:

$$\delta x_4 = \frac{<\Psi_4|h|\Psi_3>^2}{x_4 - x_3} + \frac{<\Psi_4|h|\Psi_1>^2}{x_4 - x_1}$$

$$= \frac{(0.625\,(-0.496)<\Psi_{2E}|h|\Psi_{1B}> + 0.781 \cdot 0.868<\Psi_{1E}|h|\Psi_{3B}>)^2}{0.063 - 0.698}$$

$$+ \frac{(0.625 \cdot 0.868<\Psi_{2E}|h|\Psi_{1B}> + 0.781 \cdot 0.496<\Psi_{1E}|h|\Psi_{3B}>)^2}{0.063 - 1.919}$$

$$= \frac{(0.625(-0.496)\,0.525 + 0.781 \cdot 0.868 \cdot 0.851)^2}{0.063 - 0.698}$$

$$+ \frac{(0.625 \cdot 0.868 \cdot 0.525 + 0.781 \cdot 0.496 \cdot 0.851)^2}{0.063 - 1.919}$$

$$= -0.270 - 0.203 = -0.473$$

$$x'_4 = x_4 + \delta x_4 = 0.063 - 0.473 = -0.410$$
$$x_4^{HMO} = -0.254$$

As expected, the resulting correction is in the desired direction, but too large. This is because the cross terms in the fourth order secular determinant of Problem 7.18 are of the same order of magnitude as the energy differences between the starting orbitals.

Problem 7.22: From the 1-methylenenapththalene-, 2-methylenenaphthalene- and benzyl radicals, one can, for instance, construct models for the following annelated π-electron systems.

(k)   (l)   (m)

In each case, calculate the approximate orbital energies both for the highest bonding and the lowest antibonding levels.

The nonbonding orbitals of the alternant starting systems benzyl, 1-methylnaphthyl and 2-methylnaphthyl radical read

(A)

$$\Psi_A = \frac{1}{\sqrt{7}}(-\Phi_2 + \Phi_4 - \Phi_6 + 2\Phi_7) \qquad (5/32)$$

(B)

$$\Psi_B = \frac{1}{\sqrt{20}}(-2\Phi_2 + 2\Phi_4 - \Phi_5 + \Phi_7 - \Phi_9 + 3\Phi_{11})$$

(Problem 5.13)

(C)

$$\Psi_C = \frac{1}{\sqrt{17}}(-2\Phi_1 - \Phi_3 - \Phi_6 + \Phi_8 + \Phi_{10} + 3\Phi_{11})$$

(Problem 5.13)

Depending upon the way in which the individual components of the radicals are linked together, we obtain the two 'inner' orbital energies of the LCMO models (a) − (m) summarized in the following table. After improvement with the empirical multiplication factor $f = 0.8$ the LCMO values show remarkably good agreement with the exact HMO values (see page 175) given for comparison.

Model	Linkage systems	Linkage centers	Crossterms		x_J^{LCMO}	$0.8\, x_J^{LCMO}$	x_J^{HMO}
(a)	A/C	$7/3 + 2/11$	$\dfrac{2}{\sqrt{7}} \cdot \dfrac{1}{\sqrt{17}} + \dfrac{1}{\sqrt{7}} \cdot \dfrac{3}{\sqrt{17}}$		0.459	0.367	0.295
(b)	A/C	$7/3 + 2/11$	$\dfrac{2}{\sqrt{7}} \cdot \dfrac{2}{\sqrt{20}} + \dfrac{1}{\sqrt{7}} \cdot \dfrac{3}{\sqrt{20}}$		0.592	0.474	0.452
(c)	A/B	$7/11 + 2/2$	$\dfrac{2}{\sqrt{7}} \cdot \dfrac{3}{\sqrt{20}} + \dfrac{1}{\sqrt{7}} \cdot \dfrac{2}{\sqrt{20}}$		0.676	0.541	0.520
(d)	A/C	$7/11 + 2/1$	$\dfrac{2}{\sqrt{7}} \cdot \dfrac{3}{\sqrt{17}} + \dfrac{1}{\sqrt{7}} \cdot \dfrac{2}{\sqrt{17}}$		0.734	0.587	0.568
(e)	C/C	$11/3 + 3/11$	$\dfrac{3}{\sqrt{17}} \cdot \dfrac{1}{\sqrt{17}} + \dfrac{1}{\sqrt{17}} \cdot \dfrac{3}{\sqrt{17}}$		0.353	0.282	0.220
(f)	B/C	$1/11 + 2/11$	$\dfrac{2}{\sqrt{20}} \cdot \dfrac{3}{\sqrt{17}} + \dfrac{2}{\sqrt{20}} \cdot \dfrac{3}{\sqrt{17}}$		0.488	0.390	0.327
(g)	C/B	$11/11 + 3/2$	$\dfrac{3}{\sqrt{17}} \cdot \dfrac{3}{\sqrt{20}} + \dfrac{1}{\sqrt{17}} \cdot \dfrac{2}{\sqrt{20}}$		0.597	0.478	0.405
(h)	C/C	$11/11 + 3/1$	$\dfrac{3}{\sqrt{17}} \cdot \dfrac{3}{\sqrt{17}} + \dfrac{1}{\sqrt{17}} \cdot \dfrac{2}{\sqrt{17}}$		0.647	0.518	0.419
(i)	C/C	$11/11 + 3/3$	$\dfrac{3}{\sqrt{17}} \cdot \dfrac{3}{\sqrt{17}} + \dfrac{1}{\sqrt{17}} \cdot \dfrac{1}{\sqrt{17}}$		0.588	0.470	0.438
(j)	B/B	$11/2 + 2/11$	$\dfrac{3}{\sqrt{20}} \cdot \dfrac{2}{\sqrt{20}} + \dfrac{2}{\sqrt{20}} \cdot \dfrac{3}{\sqrt{20}}$		0.600	0.480	0.423
(k)	B/C	$11/1 + 2/11$	$\dfrac{3}{\sqrt{20}} \cdot \dfrac{2}{\sqrt{17}} + \dfrac{2}{\sqrt{20}} \cdot \dfrac{3}{\sqrt{17}}$		0.651	0.521	0.492
(l)	B/C	$11/11 + 2/1$	$\dfrac{3}{\sqrt{20}} \cdot \dfrac{3}{\sqrt{17}} + \dfrac{2}{\sqrt{20}} \cdot \dfrac{2}{\sqrt{17}}$		0.705	0.564	0.550
(m)	B/B	$11/11 + 2/2$	$\dfrac{3}{\sqrt{20}} \cdot \dfrac{3}{\sqrt{20}} + \dfrac{2}{\sqrt{20}} \cdot \dfrac{2}{\sqrt{20}}$		0.650	0.520	0.502

As will be shown for the example of 1,2-benzoanthracene, the given systems can often be built up in a variety of ways:

$$\left| x_J^{LCMO} \right| = 0.592$$

$$\left| x_J^{LCMO} \right| = 0.642$$

$$\left| x_J^{LCMO} \right| = 0.642$$

In such cases (b, f, j, k) the smallest perturbation should always be chosen since a second order interaction with the bonding and antibonding molecular orbitals of the overall system will reduce the corresponding splitting. This effect is therefore already minimized by the choice of the smallest splitting.

In this problem we were limited to the three partial systems given. Consideration of a greater number of potential building units often permits further reduction in the splitting, as will be discussed for some of the above examples in Problem 11.3.

Problem 7.23: Show that the graphical procedure described is entirely equivalent to that of solving the secular determinant

$$\left\| \begin{array}{cc} H_{AA} - \varepsilon & H_{AB} \\ H_{AB} & H_{BB} - \varepsilon \end{array} \right\|$$

and the corresponding secular equations.

Starting from the given secular determinant, we can undertake the following changes: Making the arbitrary assumption $H_{AA} > H_{BB}$, we define

$$H_{AA} - H_{BB} = 2 D_{AB}$$

and give all energies relative to the mean $(H_{AA}$ and $H_{BB})/2$ of the two energies. Thus

$$H_{AA} = \frac{H_{AA} + H_{BB}}{2} + D_{AB}$$

$$H_{BB} = \frac{H_{AA} + H_{BB}}{2} - D_{AB}$$

Now if the mean of the energies is taken as the zero point, the above secular determinant reads

$$\begin{Vmatrix} D_{AB} - \epsilon & H_{AB} \\ H_{AB} & -D_{AB} - \epsilon \end{Vmatrix} = 0$$

Expansion affords

$$\epsilon^2 - D_{AB}^2 - H_{AB}^2 = 0$$

$$\epsilon^2 = D_{AB}^2 + H_{AB}^2$$

This means that the energy ϵ is obtained as the hypotenuse of a right-angled triangle with the shorter sides H_{AB} and D_{AB} [7.14]. Relative to the mean $(H_{AA} + H_{BB})/2$ we obtain

$$|\epsilon_1| = |\epsilon_2| = |\sqrt{D_{AB}^2 + H_{AB}^2}|$$

where ϵ_1 is the negative (bonding) orbital energy and ϵ_2 is the positive (antibonding) value.

Substitution in one of the secular equations gives

$$(D_{AB} + |\epsilon_1|)c_{1A} + H_{AB} c_{1B} = 0$$

178

from which it follows that

$$\frac{|c_{1A}|}{|c_{1B}|} = \frac{|H_{AB}|}{|D_{AB} + |\epsilon_1||}$$

This proportionality corresponds to the construction underlying [7.15].

Problem 7.24: Determine graphically the orbital energies ε_1 and ε_2 as well as the associated linear combinations Ψ_1 and Ψ_2 of the imino group

$$\begin{array}{c} R \\ \diagdown \\ \diagup \\ R \end{array} C{=}NH \qquad (\alpha_N = \alpha + \beta;\ \beta_{CN} = \beta).$$

The construction according to [7.14] yields

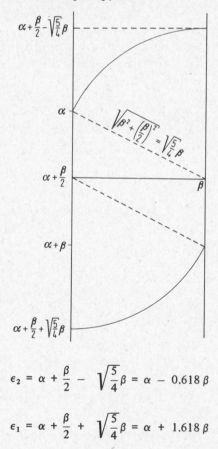

$$\epsilon_2 = \alpha + \frac{\beta}{2} - \sqrt{\frac{5}{4}}\beta = \alpha - 0.618\,\beta$$

$$\epsilon_1 = \alpha + \frac{\beta}{2} + \sqrt{\frac{5}{4}}\beta = \alpha + 1.618\,\beta$$

The construction according to [7.15] gives

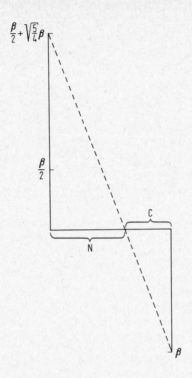

The ratio $N : C$ amounts to $0.62 : 0.38$. With the normalization coefficient

$$N = \frac{1}{\sqrt{0.62^2 + 0.38^2}} = 1.381$$

we obtain

$$c_{1C} = 0.523 \quad ; \quad c_{1N} = 0.853 .$$

From the orthogonality condition, it follows that

$$\Psi_2 = 0.853 \, \Phi_C - 0.523 \, \Phi_N .$$

7.6. Construction of Correlation Diagrams Using Second Order Perturbation Calculations

Problem 7.25: Protonation of cyclooctatetraene yields the homotropylium cation as the conjugate acid:

In this cation six π-electrons are delocalized over seven centres. Using a second order perturbation treatment construct a correlation diagram for the orbital energies ε_1 to ε_7 of the 1,7 bridged heptatrienylium cation (HMO Table $K_7^\oplus$, Volume 3) as a function of the perturbation $\beta_{17} = k\beta$ in the interval $0 < k < 1$

$$(\beta_{17} = 0; k = 0) \qquad (\beta_{17} = \beta; k = 1)$$

As a starting point, the molecular orbitals of the heptatrienyl cation (HMO Table $K_7^\oplus$, Vol. 3) are

$x_7 =$	-1.848	(A)	$c_{71}^2 =$	$c_{77}^2 =$	0.036
$x_6 =$	-1.414	(B)	$c_{61}^2 =$	$c_{67}^2 =$	0.125
$x_5 =$	-0.765	(A)	$c_{51}^2 =$	$c_{57}^2 =$	0.213
$x_4 =$	0.000	(B)	$c_{41}^2 =$	$c_{47}^2 =$	0.250
$x_3 =$	0.765	(A)	$c_{31}^2 =$	$c_{37}^2 =$	0.213
$x_2 =$	1.414	(B)	$c_{21}^2 =$	$c_{27}^2 =$	0.125
$x_1 =$	1.848	(A)	$c_{11}^2 =$	$c_{17}^2 =$	0.036

The perturbation operator h accounting for the additional bond between the atomic orbitals Φ_1 and Φ_7 is defined by the following list of perturbations:

$$<\mu|h|\nu> = 0; \text{except} <1|h|7> = <7|h|1> = k \cdot \beta,$$

where

$$0 \leqslant k \leqslant 1.$$

For $k = 0$, the orbital energies x_J previously introduced for the heptatrienyl cation $K_7^\oplus$ hold; for $K = 1$, those of the cycloheptatrienyl cation $\textcircled{7}^\oplus$, i.e. the tropylium cation (Vol. 3), apply:

$$x_7 = x_6 = -1.802$$
$$x_5 = x_4 = -0.445$$
$$x_3 = x_2 = 1.247$$
$$x_1 = 2.000$$

Perturbation calculations of first and second order give the following approximate orbital energies x_j' as functions of the parameter k:

(a) Representation A

$$x_7' = x_7 + 2\,c_{71}^2 k + 4\,c_{71}^2 k^2 \left(\frac{c_{11}^2}{x_7 - x_1} + \frac{c_{31}^2}{x_7 - x_3} + \frac{c_{51}^2}{x_7 - x_5} \right)$$

$$x_5' = x_5 + 2\,c_{51}^2 k + 4\,c_{51}^2 k^2 \left(\frac{c_{11}^2}{x_5 - x_1} + \frac{c_{31}^2}{x_5 - x_3} + \frac{c_{71}^2}{x_5 - x_7} \right)$$

$$x_3' = x_3 + 2\,c_{31}^2 k + 4\,c_{31}^2 k^2 \left(\frac{c_{11}^2}{x_3 - x_1} + \frac{c_{51}^2}{x_3 - x_5} + \frac{c_{71}^2}{x_3 - x_7} \right)$$

$$x_1' = x_1 + 2\,c_{11}^2 k + 4\,c_{11}^2 k^2 \left(\frac{c_{31}^2}{x_1 - x_3} + \frac{c_{51}^2}{x_1 - x_5} + \frac{c_{71}^2}{x_1 - x_7} \right)$$

(b) Representation B

$$x_6' = x_6 - 2\,c_{61}^2 k + 4\,c_{61}^2 k^2 \left(\frac{c_{21}^2}{x_6 - x_2} + \frac{c_{41}^2}{x_6 - x_4} \right)$$

$$x_4' = x_4 - 2\,c_{41}^2 k + 4\,c_{41}^2 k^2 \left(\frac{c_{21}^2}{x_4 - x_2} + \frac{c_{61}^2}{x_4 - x_6} \right)$$

$$x_2' = x_2 - 2\,c_{21}^2 k + 4\,c_{21}^2 k^2 \left(\frac{c_{41}^2}{x_2 - x_4} + \frac{c_{61}^2}{x_2 - x_6} \right)$$

Because of the alternancy of the starting system, i.e. because of the relations

$$c_{11}^2 = c_{71}^2 \quad , \quad c_{21}^2 = c_{61}^2 \quad , \quad c_{31}^2 = c_{51}^2 \quad ;$$

$$x_1 - x_3 = x_5 - x_7 \quad , \quad x_1 - x_5 = x_3 - x_7 \quad , \quad x_2 - x_4 = x_4 - x_6 \quad .$$

expressions (a) and (b) simplify to:

(a) Representation A

$$\begin{aligned}
x_7' &= -1.848 + 0.073\,k - 0.042\,k^2 \\
x_5' &= -0.765 + 0.427\,k - 0.102\,k^2 \\
x_3' &= 0.765 + 0.427\,k + 0.102\,k^2 \\
x_1' &= 1.848 + 0.073\,k + 0.042\,k^2
\end{aligned}$$

(b) Representation B

$$\begin{aligned}
x_6' &= -1.414 - 0.251\,k - 0.111\,k^2 \\
x_4' &= 0.000 - 0.500\,k \\
x_2' &= 1.414 - 0.251\,k + 0.111\,k^2
\end{aligned}$$

182

We thus obtain the following correlation diagram:

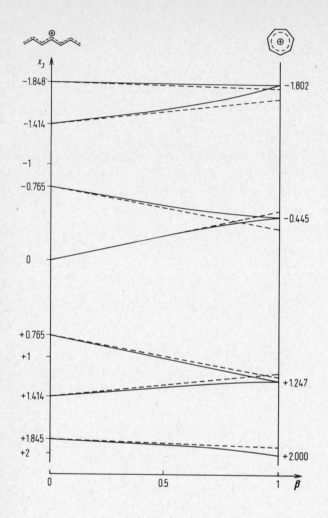

8. Qualitative HMO Theory

8.1. Basic Rules

Problem 8.1: Prove the formula (8/19) for the case in which none of the coefficients of the molecular orbital considered is zero.

Assuming that all $a_{J\mu} \neq 0$ and all $a_{J\nu} \neq 0$, the relation

$$\epsilon_J^0 = \alpha + 2N_J^{0^2}(Z_{BJ} - Z_{AJ})\beta \qquad (8/19)$$

can be proved as follows:

$$
\begin{aligned}
\epsilon_J^0 = H_{JJ}^0 &= \langle \Psi_J^0 | \mathcal{H} | \Psi_J^0 \rangle \\
&= N_J^{0^2} \langle \sum_\mu^n a_{J\mu} \Phi_\mu | \mathcal{H} | \sum_\nu^n a_{J\nu} \Phi_\nu \rangle \\
&= N_J^{0^2} \sum_\mu^n \sum_\nu^n a_{J\mu} a_{J\nu} \langle \Phi_\mu | \mathcal{H} | \Phi_\nu \rangle \\
&= N_J^{0^2} \sum_\mu^n a_{J\mu}^2 \langle \Phi_\mu | \mathcal{H} | \Phi_\mu \rangle + \sum_{\mu}^n \sum_{\nu \neq \mu} a_{J\mu} a_{J\nu} \langle \Phi_\mu | \mathcal{H} | \Phi_\nu \rangle
\end{aligned}
$$

Since the magnitudes of the coefficients $|a_{J\mu}| = 1$ by definition, it follows that

$$\sum_{\mu=1}^n a_{J\mu}^2 = n \quad ; \quad N_J^0 = \frac{1}{\sqrt{n}} \ .$$

The integrals $\langle \Phi_\mu | \mathcal{H} | \Phi_\nu \rangle$ have the value β only for the centers $(\nu \to \mu)$ bonded to each other and are equal to zero in all other cases.

$$\epsilon_J^0 = \frac{1}{n} \cdot n \cdot \alpha + N_J^{0^2} \left(\sum_\mu^n \sum_{\substack{\nu \neq \mu \\ (\nu \to \mu)}} a_{J\mu} a_{J\nu} \right) \beta \ .$$

The products $a_{J\mu} \cdot a_{J\nu}$ lead to a bonding contribution $Z_{BJ} = +1$ for coefficients having the same sign and to an antibonding contribution $Z_{AJ} = -1$ for coefficients with opposite signs. We thus obtain

$$\epsilon_J^0 = \alpha + 2N_J^{0^2}(Z_{BJ} - Z_{AJ})\beta \ .$$

Problem 8.2: Using formula (8/19), show that for alternant π-electron systems the relation $x_{n-J+1}^0 = -x_J^0$ is fulfilled.

By definition bonds occur only between starred and unstarred centers in alternant systems. By going from a bonding molecular orbital to the corresponding antibonding molecular orbital Ψ^0_{n-J+1}, the coefficients of either the starred or the unstarred set change sign (cf. (5/25) and (5/26)). All bonding interactions of the original orbital Ψ^0_J are transformed into antibonding ones and vice versa.

$$\Psi^0_J: \quad \begin{matrix} Z_{BJ} \\ \\ Z_{AJ} \end{matrix} \quad \Rightarrow \quad \Psi^0_{n-J+1}: \quad \begin{matrix} Z_{AJ} \\ \\ Z_{BJ} \end{matrix}$$

From the relation

$$\epsilon^0_J = \alpha + x^0_J \beta = \alpha + 2 N^{0^2}_J (Z_{BJ} - Z_{AJ}) \beta \qquad (8/19)$$

it therefore follows that

$$x^0_{n-J+1} = 2 N^{0^2}_J (Z_{AJ} - Z_{BJ})$$

$$= -2 N^{0^2}_J (Z_{BJ} - Z_{AJ}) = -x^0_J \quad .$$

Problem 8.3: Using Rules (A) through (I), determine qualitative orbitals and orbital energies of the π-electron systems:

(a) (b) (c)

Compare the results with the exact HMO values (Table K_6, ⑥⑥, and ⑤⑤, Volume 3).

(a) Hexatriene:

Acording to Rule (A) six qualitative molecular orbitals are expected for the alternant 6-center π-system of which Ψ^0_1 can be derived directly from Rule (B); Ψ^0_6 can then be derived from Ψ^0_1 according to Rule (F).

$$\psi^0_1 \qquad\qquad \psi^0_6$$

According to Rule (D), the approximate orbitals Ψ_J^0 always have $J - 1$ nodes, so that the remaining qualitative molecular orbitals are obtained taking into account the change of sign in the starred set according to Rule (F).

ψ_2^0 $\qquad$ ψ_5^0

ψ_3^0 $\qquad$ ψ_4^0

The qualitative orbital energies estimated according to (8/19) agree with the corresponding HMO values from Table K_6 (Vol. 3):

J	1/6	2/5	3/4
x_J^0	±1.7	±1.0	±0.3
x_J^{HMO}	±1.802	±1.247	±0.445

(b) Naphthalene:

$SE(2)$

$SE(1)$

Of the ten qualitative molecular orbitals expected according to Rule (A), Ψ_1 and Ψ_{10} are again given by Rules (B) and (F).

ψ_1^0 $\qquad$ ψ_{10}^0

The remaining eight qualitative molecular orbitals can be derived by considering the symmetry of the system according to Rule (H). The next higher orbital must have a nodal plane according to Rule (C), i.e. must be antisymmetric relative to the symmetry plane SE(1) or SE(2). The following sets of atomic orbitals are antisymmetric with respect to SE(1), since Φ_9 and Φ_{10} cannot appear because of their symmetry:

$$\{\Phi_1 - \Phi_8\} \quad ; \quad \{\Phi_2 - \Phi_7\} \quad ; \quad \{\Phi_3 - \Phi_6\} \quad ; \quad \{\Phi_4 - \Phi_5\} \quad .$$

By combining and changing signs according to Rule (F), we obtain

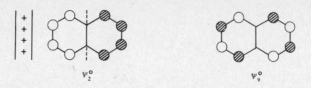

$$\psi_2^0 \qquad\qquad \psi_9^0$$

With respect to SE(2) the following sets of atomic orbitals exist:

$$\{\Phi_1 - \Phi_4\} \quad ; \quad \{\Phi_2 - \Phi_3\} \quad ; \quad \{\Phi_8 - \Phi_5\} \quad ; \quad \{\Phi_7 - \Phi_6\} \quad ; \quad \{\Phi_9 - \Phi_{10}\}$$

From these we obtain the qualitative molecular orbitals

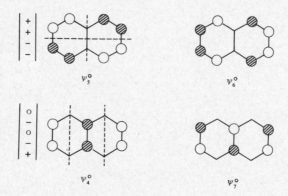

$$\psi_3^0 \qquad\qquad \psi_8^0$$

The estimates of the qualitative orbital energies entered in the concluding table leads to the given assignment of Ψ_2^0/Ψ_9^0 and Ψ_3^0/Ψ_8^0. The four approximate orbitals still required — of which the bonding ones should have at least two nodal planes according to Rule (G) — are obtained by further combination of sets of atomic orbitals and sign changes according to Rule (F):

$$\psi_5^0 \qquad\qquad \psi_6^0$$

$$\psi_4^0 \qquad\qquad \psi_7^0$$

The sequence of the qualitative molecular orbitals can be determined from the qualitative orbital energies calculated according to (8/19). Comparison with the exact HMO values (Vol. 3) indicates that the energy levels x_3^0/x_4^0 and x_7^0/x_8^0 are accidentally degenerate:

J	1/10	2/9	3/8	4/7	5/6
x_J^0	±2.2	±1.5	±1.0	±1.0	±0.5
x_J^{HMO}	±2.303	±1.618	±1.303	±1.000	±0.618

(c) Pentalene:

$$SE(2)—5 \; \substack{6 \; 7 \; 1 \\ 8 \\ 4 \; 3} \; 2—$$

SE(1)

The nonalternance of the pentalene π-electron system limits the number of applicable rules. Of the eight qualitative molecular orbitals expected from Rule (A), only Ψ_1^0 is determined according to Rule (B):

ψ_1^0

In order to progress further we have to exploit the symmetry of the system: with respect to the two mirror planes SE(1) and SE(2), four possible types of functions result:

	I	II	III	IV
SE(1)	+	+	−	−
SE(2)	+	−	+	−

Type I, to which Ψ_1^0 also belongs, is represented by the following sets of atomic orbitals of corresponding symmetry

$$\{\Phi_1 + \Phi_3 + \Phi_4 + \Phi_6\} \quad ; \quad \{\Phi_2 + \Phi_5\} \quad ; \quad \{\Phi_7 + \Phi_8\} \quad .$$

Combination with unchanged sign of the first set gives the following molecular orbital diagrams, which are symmetric with respect to SE(1) and SE(2):

$\psi_1^0 \qquad \psi_4^0 \qquad \psi_4^0 \qquad \psi_7^0$

Two of the resulting qualitative molecular orbitals have equal energy according to (8/19) and differ only in the position of the two nodal planes located at right angles to the long molecular axis, i.e. there are two possibilities for the same molecular orbital of which preference is to be given to the first one according to Rule (I) on account of the more symmetrical arrangement of the nodal planes.

Because of the symmetric behavior of the atomic orbitals at centers 2 and 5, the type II function antisymmetric to SE(2) contains only the following sets of atomic orbitals

$$\{\Phi_1 - \Phi_3 - \Phi_4 + \Phi_6\} \quad ; \quad \{\Phi_7 - \Phi_8\} \quad .$$

Combination with the same or opposite signs of the second set leads to

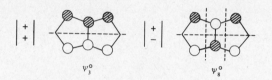

$$\psi_3^0 \qquad\qquad \psi_8^0$$

The functions of type III must be antisymmetric with respect to SE(1), and consequently the coefficients of atomic orbitals Φ_7 and Φ_8 are zero.

$$\{\Phi_1 + \Phi_3 - \Phi_4 - \Phi_6\} \quad ; \quad \{\Phi_5 - \Phi_2\}$$

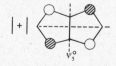

$$\psi_2^0 \qquad\qquad \psi_6^0$$

Finally, in type IV, because of simultaneous antisymmetry with respect to the two mirror planes, both the atomic orbitals Φ_2 and Φ_5 and the atomic orbitals Φ_7 and Φ_8 are missing. The remaining set

$$\{\Phi_1 - \Phi_3 + \Phi_4 - \Phi_6\}$$

affords the last qualitative molecular orbital:

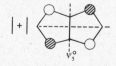

$$\psi_5^0$$

The sequence of the qualitative molecular orbitals follows from the qualitative orbital energy estimated according to (8/19):

J	x_J^0	x_J^{HMO}
8	-1.7	-2.000
7	-1.8	-1.814
6	-1.3	-1.414
5	0.0	0.000
4	$+0.3$	$+0.471$
3	$+1.0$	$+1.000$
2	$+1.3$	$+1.414$
1	$+2.3$	$+2.343$

Comparison with the exact HMO values and the symmetry classification (Problem 4.11 (b)), shows that the results agree except for the interchanged approximate orbitals Ψ_7^0 and Ψ_8^0.

8.2. Systematic Use of Symmetry

Problem 8.4: Determine the symmetry group of each of the following molecules:

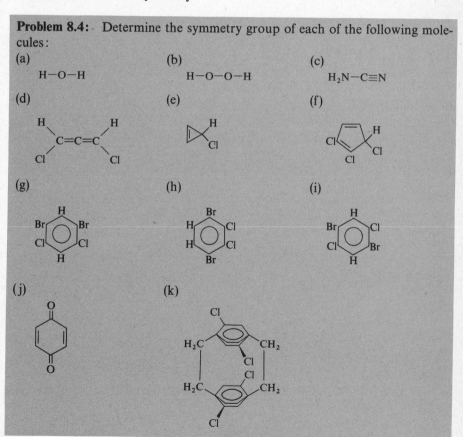

(a)

   H—O—H

(b)

   H—O—O—H

(c)

   $H_2N—C\equiv N$

(d)

(e)

(f)

(g)

(h)

(i)

(j)

(k)

The molecules $(a)-(k)$ contain the given symmetry elements and according to $(8/37)$ belong to the following symmetry groups:

(a) The water molecule is bent:

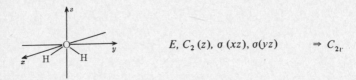

$E, C_2(z), \sigma(xz), \sigma(yz)$ $\Rightarrow C_{2v}$

(b) The hydrogen peroxide molecule in the crystalline state possesses the energetically favored conformation with a dihedral angle $\theta \sim 90°$ (cf. Problem 2.22):

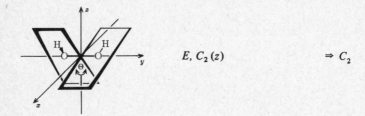

$E, C_2(z)$ $\Rightarrow C_2$

(c) Cyanamide has a largely sp^3 hybridized amino nitrogen:

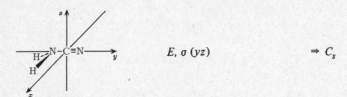

$E, \sigma(yz)$ $\Rightarrow C_s$

(d) 1,3-Dichloroallene contains two crossed double bonds:

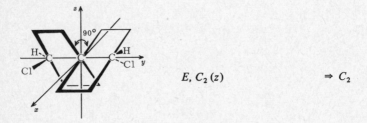

$E, C_2(z)$ $\Rightarrow C_2$

(e) 1-Chloro-2-cyclopropene:

$E, \sigma(yz)$ $\Rightarrow C_s$

(f) 1,2,3-Trichlorocyclopentadiene:

$$E \qquad\qquad \Rightarrow C_1$$

(g) 1,3-Dibromo-4,6-dichlorobenzene:

$$E, C_2\,(z), \sigma\,(xz), \sigma\,(yz) \quad \Rightarrow C_{2v}$$

(h) 1,4-Dibromo-2,3-dichlorobenzene:

$$E, C_2\,(z), \sigma\,(xz), \sigma\,(yz) \quad \Rightarrow C_{2v}$$

(i) 1,4-Dibromo-3,6-dichlorobenzene:

$$E, C_2\,(z), \sigma\,(xy), i \qquad \Rightarrow C_{2h}$$

(j) p-Quinone:

$$\left.\begin{array}{l} E, C_2\,(z), C_2\,(y), C_2\,(x) \\ i, \sigma\,(xy), \sigma\,(xz), \sigma\,(yz) \end{array}\right\} \Rightarrow D_{2h}$$

(k) Tetrachloro-[2,2]-paracyclophane:

$$E, C_2\,(z), C_2\,(y), C_2\,(x) \quad \Rightarrow D_2$$

Problem 8.5: To which irreducible representations do the following molecular orbitals of diphenylene belong?

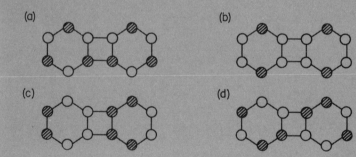

Diphenylene, having the symmetry elements

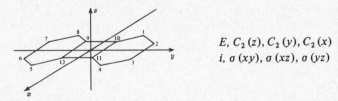

$$E, C_2\,(z), C_2\,(y), C_2\,(x)$$
$$i, \sigma\,(xy), \sigma\,(xz), \sigma\,(yz)$$

belongs to the group D_{2h}. As follows from the individual symmetry operations, only E and $\sigma(xy)$ give non-zero contributions to the reducible representation Γ, which contains the irreducible representations

$$\Gamma = 3 \times A_u + 3 \times B_{1u} + 3 \times B_{2g} + 3 \times B_{3g} \quad.$$

These differ in their symmetry behavior with respect to the mirror planes $\sigma(xz)$ and $\sigma(yz)$ as follows:

	A_u	B_{1u}	B_{2g}	B_{3g}
$\sigma(xz)$	−1	+1	+1	−1
$\sigma(yz)$	−1	+1	−1	+1
	$(d) : \Psi_{10}^0$	$(b) : \Psi_8^0$	$(a) : \Psi_{11}^0$	$(c) : \Psi_6^0$

The qualitative molecular orbitals (a)-(d) thus belong to the above irreducible representations.

Problem 8.6 Derive the qualitative molecular orbitals belonging to the individual irreducible representations for the π-electron systems used as examples in Section 8.1:

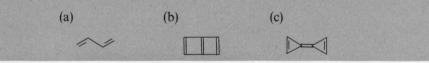

Corresponding to the procedure described in Section 8.2, the qualitative molecular orbitals belonging to the irreducible representations are determined in the following manner:

(a) Butadiene:

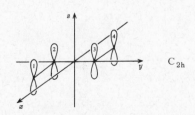

C_{2h}	E	$C_2(z)$	$\sigma(xy)$	i	
A_g	1	1	1	1	0
A_u	1	1	−1	−1	8
B_g	1	−1	−1	1	8
B_u	1	−1	1	−1	0
Γ	4	0	−4	0	

$$\Gamma = 2 \overset{\times}{} A_u \overset{\cdot}{+} 2 \overset{\times}{} B_g$$

The molecular orbitals belong to the irreducible representations shown:

A_u (symmetric with respect to $C_2(z)$):

$$\{\Phi_1 + \Phi_4\} \quad ; \quad \{\Phi_2 + \Phi_3\}$$

B_g (antisymmetric with respect to $C_2(z)$):

$$\{\Phi_1 - \Phi_4\} \quad ; \quad \{\Phi_2 - \Phi_3\}$$

The orbital energies are given in (8/20).

(b) 1,4-Dehydrobenzene:

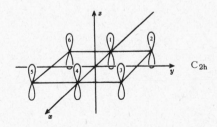

194

With the aid of the character table given in (8/51) we obtain:

D_{2h}	E	$C_2(z)$	$C_2(y)$	$C_2(x)$	i	$\sigma(xy)$	$\sigma(xz)$	$\sigma(yz)$
Γ	6	0	0	-2	0	-6	$+2$	0

$$\Gamma = 2 \, \dot{\times} \, B_{2g} \, \dot{+} \, 1 \, \dot{\times} \, B_{3g} \, \dot{+} \, 1 \, \dot{\times} \, A_u \, \dot{+} \, 2 \, \dot{\times} \, B_{1u}$$

To the irreducible representations belong the following molecular orbitals:

B_{2g} (antisymmetric with respect to $\sigma(yz)$/symmetric with respect to $\sigma(xz)$):

$$\{\Phi_1 - \Phi_4\} \quad ; \quad \{\Phi_2 - \Phi_3 - \Phi_5 + \Phi_6\}$$

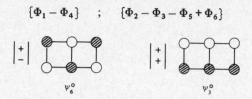

A_u (antisymmetric with respect to $\sigma(yz)$/antisymmetric with respect to $\sigma(xz)$):

$$\{\Phi_2 - \Phi_3 + \Phi_5 - \Phi_6\}$$

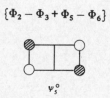

B_{3g} (symmetric with respect to $\sigma(yz)$/antisymmetric with respect to $\sigma(xz)$):

$$\{\Phi_2 + \Phi_3 - \Phi_5 - \Phi_6\}$$

ψ_2°

B_{1u} (symmetric with respect to $\sigma(yz)$/symmetric with respect to $\sigma(xz)$):

$$\{\Phi_1 + \Phi_4\} \quad ; \quad \{\Phi_2 + \Phi_3 + \Phi_5 + \Phi_6\}$$

$\psi_1^\circ \qquad \psi_4^\circ$

The orbital energies are given in (8/26).

(c) Trifulvalene:

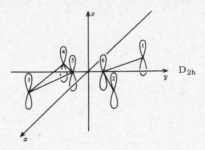

With the aid of character table (8/51) we obtain:

D_{2h}	E	$C_2(z)$	$C_2(y)$	$C_2(x)$	i	$\sigma(xy)$	$\sigma(xz)$	$\sigma(yz)$
Γ	+6	0	−2	0	0	−6	0	+2

$$\Gamma = 1 \overset{.}{\times} B_{2g} \dotplus 2 \overset{.}{\times} B_{3g} \dotplus 1 \overset{.}{\times} A_u \dotplus 2 \overset{.}{\times} B_{1u}$$

To the irreducible representations belong the following molecular orbitals:

B_{2g} (symmetric with respect to $\sigma(xz)$/antisymmetric with respect to $\sigma(yz)$):

B_{1u} (symmetric with respect to $\sigma(xz)$/symmetric with respect to $\sigma(yz)$):

A_u (antisymmetric with respect to $\sigma(xz)$/antisymmetric with respect to $\sigma(yz)$):

196

B_{3g} (antisymmetric with respect to $\sigma\,(xz)$/symmetric with respect to $\sigma\,(yz)$):

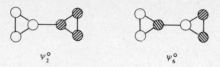

$$\psi_2^{\,0} \qquad\qquad\qquad \psi_6^{\,0}$$

The orbital energies are given in (8/28).

Problem 8.7: As an extension of Problem 8.3, determine the qualitative molecular orbitals of the following π-electron systems using symmetry criteria

(a)   (b)   (c)

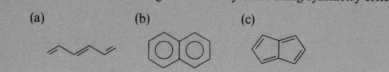

Corresponding to the treatment described in Section 8.2, the qualitative molecular orbitals belonging to the irreducible representations are established in the following manner:

(a) Hexatriene:

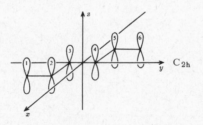

With the aid of the character table given in Problem 8.6, we obtain

C_{2h}	E	$C_2(z)$	$\sigma(xy)$	i
Γ	+6	0	−6	0

$$\Gamma = 3\overset{\times}{}A_u \dotplus 3\overset{\times}{}B_g$$

To the irreducible representations belong the following molecular orbitals:

A_u (symmetric with respect to $C_2(z)$):

$$\{\Phi_1 + \Phi_6\} \; ; \{\Phi_2 + \Phi_5\} \; ; \{\Phi_3 + \Phi_4\}$$

B_g (antisymmetric with respect to $C_2(z)$):

$$\{\Phi_1 - \Phi_6\} \; ; \{\Phi_2 - \Phi_5\} \; ; \{\Phi_3 - \Phi_4\}$$

The approximate orbital energies are given in Problem 8.3.

(b) Naphthalene:

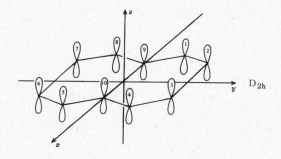

D_{2h}	E	$C_2(z)$	$C_2(y)$	$C_2(x)$	i	$\sigma(xy)$	$\sigma(xz)$	$\sigma(yz)$
Γ	+10	0	0	−2	0	−10	+2	0

$$\Gamma = 3\dot{\times}B_{2g} + 2\dot{\times}B_{3g} + 2\dot{\times}A_u + 3\dot{\times}B_{1u}$$

To the irreducible representations belong the following molecular orbitals:

B_{2g} (antisymmetric with respect to $\sigma(yz)$/symmetric with respect to $\sigma(xz)$):

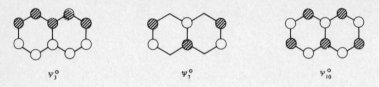

A_u (antisymmetric with respect to $\sigma(yz)$/antisymmetric with respect to $\sigma(xz)$):

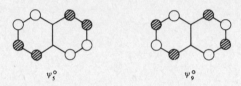

B_{3g} (symmetric with respect to $\sigma(yz)$/antisymmetric with respect to $\sigma(xz)$):

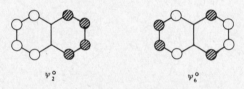

B_{1u} (symmetric with respect to $\sigma(yz)$/symmetric with respect to $\sigma(xz)$):

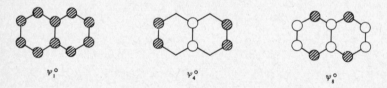

The approximate orbital energies are given in Problem 8.3. The results obtained here provide an insight into the symmetry classification of the *Hückel* molecular orbitals of naphthalene in [4.10].

(c) Pentalene:

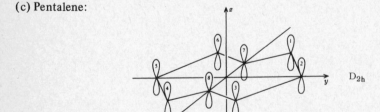

D_{2h}	E	$C_2(z)$	$C_2(y)$	$C_2(x)$	i	$\sigma(xy)$	$\sigma(xz)$	$\sigma(yz)$
Γ	+8	0	−2	−2	0	−8	+2	+2

$$\Gamma = 2\dot{\times}B_{2g} \dot{+} 2\dot{\times}B_{3g} \dot{+} 1\dot{\times}A_u \dot{+} 3\dot{\times}B_{1u}$$

To the irreducible representations belong the following molecular orbitals:

B_{2g} (antisymmetric with respect to $\sigma(yz)$/symmetric with respect to $\sigma(xz)$):

A_u (antisymmetric with respect to $\sigma(yz)$/antisymmetric with respect to $\sigma(xz)$):

B_{3g} (symmetric with respect to $\sigma(yz)$/antisymmetric with respect to $\sigma(xz)$):

B_{1u} (symmetric with respect to $\sigma(yz)$/symmetric with respect to $\sigma(xz)$):

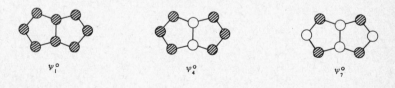

The approximate orbital energies are given in Problem 8.3. The results obtained here provide an insight into the symmetry classification of the *Hückel* molecular orbitals of pentalene (Problem 4.11(b)).

Problem 8.8: An electron moves in a 'three-dimensional box' of edge lengths $L_x = 2L$, $L_y = 3L$, $L_z = L$. To which irreducible representations do the eigenfunctions of the eight eigenvalues E_{n_x, n_y, n_z} with the quantum numbers n_x, n_y, n_z = 1, 1, 1; 1, 1, 2; ...; 2, 2, 2 belong?

A three-dimensional box with different side lengths belongs to the symmetry group D_{2h} on the basis of its inherent symmetry elements:

$$\left. \begin{array}{cccc} E & C_2(z) & C_2(y) & C_2(x) \\ i & \sigma(xy) & \sigma(xz) & \sigma(yz) \end{array} \right\} \quad \Rightarrow \quad D_{2h}$$

Since the number of eigenfunctions $\Psi_{n_x n_y n_z}$ is unlimited, each irreducible representation necessarily contains an infinite number of functions. Assignment to a given irreducible representation can be accomplished by considering whether the quantum numbers n_x, n_y and n_z are even or odd.

n_x	n_y	n_z	Irreducible representation
u	u	u	A_g
g	g	u	B_{1g}
g	u	g	B_{2g}
u	g	g	B_{3g}
g	g	g	A_u
u	u	g	B_{1u}
u	g	u	B_{2u}
g	u	u	B_{3u}

The given eigenfunctions $\Psi_{n_x n_y n_z}$ consequently belong to the following irreducible representations:

n_x	n_y	n_z	$\Psi n_x n_y n_z$	E	$C_2(z)$	$C_2(y)$	$C_2(x)$	i	$\sigma(xy)$	$\sigma(xz)$	$\sigma(yz)$	
1	1	1		1	1	1	1	1	1	1	1	A_g
2	2	1		1	1	−1	−1	1	1	−1	−1	B_{1g}
2	1	2		1	−1	1	−1	1	−1	1	−1	B_{2g}
1	2	2		1	−1	−1	1	1	−1	−1	1	B_{3g}
2	2	2		1	1	1	1	−1	−1	−1	−1	A_u
1	1	2		1	1	−1	−1	−1	−1	1	1	B_{1u}
1	2	1		1	−1	1	−1	−1	1	−1	1	B_{2u}
2	1	1		1	−1	−1	1	−1	1	1	−1	B_{3u}

8.3. Improvement of Qualitative Molecular Orbitals by Second Order Perturbation Calculations

Problem 8.9:   Prove that the determinant (8/69) is identical to that part of the factorized *Hückel* determinant of dimethylenecyclobutene which belongs to the representation A_2. (Hint: Since this is a so-called 'basis-transformation', it is expedient to start from a comparison of the HMO orbitals with the qualitative molecular orbitals to determine the necessary calculation operations for the determinant.)

The *Hückel* determinant of dimethylenecyclobutene can be factorized according to (4/98) as follows:

$$
\begin{array}{c}
(1+6) \\
(2+5) \\
(3+4) \\
(1-6) \\
(2-5) \\
(3-4)
\end{array}
\left\|
\begin{array}{cccccc}
-x & 1 & & & & \\
1 & -x & 1 & & 1 & \\
 & 1 & -x & 1 & & \\
 & & 1 & -x & 1 & \\
 & 1 & & 1 & -x & 1 \\
 & & & & 1 & -x
\end{array}
\right\|
\Rightarrow
$$

$$
\begin{array}{c}
B_1 \\
\left\|
\begin{array}{ccc|ccc}
-x & 1 & & & & \\
1 & 1-x & 1 & & & \\
 & 1 & 1-x & & & \\
\hline
 & & & -x & 1 & \\
 & & & 1 & -1-x & 1 \\
 & & & & 1 & -1-x
\end{array}
\right\| \\
A_2
\end{array}
$$

The part of the step-determinant belonging to the irreducible representation A_2 is related to the HMO basis set:

$$\varphi_1 = \frac{1}{\sqrt{2}} (\Phi_1 - \Phi_6)$$

$$\varphi_2 = \frac{1}{\sqrt{2}} (\Phi_2 - \Phi_5)$$

$$\varphi_3 = \frac{1}{\sqrt{2}} (\Phi_3 - \Phi_4)$$

The QMO approach (8/69) starts from the following qualitative basis functions (cf. (8/46)):

$$\Psi_2^0 = \frac{1}{\sqrt{6}} (\Phi_1 + \Phi_2 + \Phi_3 - \Phi_4 - \Phi_5 - \Phi_6)$$

$$\Psi_4^0 = \frac{1}{2} (\Phi_1 - \Phi_3 + \Phi_4 - \Phi_6)$$

$$\Psi_6^0 = \frac{1}{\sqrt{6}} (\Phi_1 - \Phi_2 + \Phi_3 - \Phi_4 + \Phi_5 - \Phi_6)$$

A comparison of the HMO and QMO basis functions affords:

$$\Psi_2^0 = \frac{1}{\sqrt{3}} (\varphi_1 + \varphi_2 + \varphi_3)$$

$$\Psi_4^0 = \frac{1}{\sqrt{2}} (\varphi_1 - \varphi_3)$$

$$\Psi_6^0 = \frac{1}{\sqrt{3}} (\varphi_1 - \varphi_2 + \varphi_3)$$

Thus the operations required to transform that part of the *Hückel* determinant belonging to A_2 into the corresponding QMO determinant (8/69) are:

$$(\varphi_1 + \varphi_2 + \varphi_3)(\varphi_1 - \varphi_3)(\varphi_1 - \varphi_2 + \varphi_3)$$

$$
\begin{array}{l}
\varphi_1 \\
\varphi_2 \\
\varphi_3
\end{array}
\begin{Vmatrix}
-x & 1 & \\
1 & -1-x & 1 \\
 & 1 & -1-x
\end{Vmatrix}
\quad
\begin{array}{c}
\text{(Columns)} \\
\Rightarrow
\end{array}
\quad
\begin{Vmatrix}
1-x & -x & -x-1 \\
1-x & 0 & 3+x \\
-x & 1+x & -2-x
\end{Vmatrix}
$$

$$\Downarrow \quad \text{(Rows)}$$

$$
\begin{Vmatrix}
\dfrac{2}{3}-x & \dfrac{1}{\sqrt{6}} & -\dfrac{x}{3} \\[2mm]
\dfrac{1}{\sqrt{6}} & -\dfrac{1}{2}-x & \dfrac{1}{\sqrt{6}} \\[2mm]
-\dfrac{x}{3} & \dfrac{1}{\sqrt{6}} & -2-x
\end{Vmatrix}
\quad \Leftarrow \quad
\begin{Vmatrix}
2-3x & 1 & -x \\
1 & -1-2x & 1 \\
-x & 1 & -6-3x
\end{Vmatrix}
\begin{array}{l}
\cdot\dfrac{1}{\sqrt{3}} \\[2mm]
\cdot\dfrac{1}{\sqrt{2}} \\[2mm]
\cdot\dfrac{1}{\sqrt{3}}
\end{array}
$$

$$\cdot\frac{1}{\sqrt{3}} \qquad \cdot\frac{1}{\sqrt{2}} \qquad \cdot\frac{1}{\sqrt{3}}$$

For the reverse transformation of the determinant (8/69) into the *Hückel* determinant belonging to representation A_2, corresponding comparison of the HMO and QMO basis functions gives:

$$\sqrt{3}\,\Psi_2^0 = \varphi_1 + \varphi_2 + \varphi_3$$

$$\sqrt{2}\,\Psi_4^0 = \varphi_1 - \varphi_3$$

$$\sqrt{3}\,\Psi_6^0 = \varphi_1 - \varphi_2 + \varphi_3$$

$$\frac{\sqrt{3}}{2}(\Psi_2^0 + \Psi_6^0) = \varphi_1 + \varphi_3$$

$$\frac{\sqrt{3}}{2}(\Psi_2^0 + \Psi_6^0) + \sqrt{2}\,\Psi_4^0 = 2\varphi_1$$

$$\varphi_1 = \frac{\sqrt{3}}{4}\,\Psi_2^0 + \frac{1}{\sqrt{2}}\,\Psi_4^0 + \frac{\sqrt{3}}{4}\,\Psi_6^0$$

$$\varphi_2 = \frac{\sqrt{3}}{2}(\Psi_2^0 - \Psi_6^0)$$

$$\varphi_3 = \frac{\sqrt{3}}{2}(\Psi_2^0 + \Psi_6^0) - \varphi_1$$

$$= \frac{\sqrt{3}}{4}\,\Psi_2^0 - \frac{1}{\sqrt{2}}\,\Psi_4^0 + \frac{\sqrt{3}}{4}\,\Psi_6^0$$

The above basis transformations are valid because the qualitative molecular orbitals Ψ_J^0 ($J=1,2\ldots n$) are linearly independent, and as a result the atomic orbitals Φ_μ can be described by

$$\Phi_\mu = \sum_J k_J \Psi_J^0$$

This change of basis corresponds to the choice of a new coordinate system:

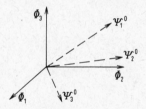

In matrix notation, the first transformation reads:

$$\begin{pmatrix} \Psi_2^0 \\ \\ \Psi_4^0 \\ \\ \Psi_6^0 \end{pmatrix} = \begin{pmatrix} \dfrac{1}{\sqrt{3}} & \dfrac{1}{\sqrt{3}} & \dfrac{1}{\sqrt{3}} \\ \\ \dfrac{1}{\sqrt{2}} & 0 & -\dfrac{1}{\sqrt{2}} \\ \\ \dfrac{1}{\sqrt{3}} & -\dfrac{1}{\sqrt{3}} & \dfrac{1}{\sqrt{3}} \end{pmatrix} \begin{pmatrix} \varphi_1 \\ \\ \varphi_2 \\ \\ \varphi_3 \end{pmatrix} = M(\varphi) = (\Psi_J^0)$$

According to the rules of matrix algebra the reverse transformation reads:

$$(\varphi) = M^{-1}(\Psi_j^0)$$

where M^{-1} has already been calculated above:

$$\begin{pmatrix} \varphi_1 \\ \varphi_2 \\ \varphi_3 \end{pmatrix} = \begin{pmatrix} \dfrac{\sqrt{3}}{4} & \dfrac{1}{\sqrt{2}} & \dfrac{\sqrt{3}}{4} \\ \dfrac{\sqrt{3}}{2} & 0 & -\dfrac{\sqrt{3}}{2} \\ \dfrac{\sqrt{3}}{4} & -\dfrac{1}{\sqrt{2}} & \dfrac{\sqrt{3}}{4} \end{pmatrix} \begin{pmatrix} \Psi_2^0 \\ \Psi_4^0 \\ \Psi_6^0 \end{pmatrix}$$

It can easily be verified that:

$$\begin{pmatrix} \dfrac{1}{\sqrt{3}} & \dfrac{1}{\sqrt{3}} & \dfrac{1}{\sqrt{3}} \\ \dfrac{1}{\sqrt{2}} & 0 & -\dfrac{1}{\sqrt{2}} \\ \dfrac{1}{\sqrt{3}} & -\dfrac{1}{\sqrt{3}} & \dfrac{1}{\sqrt{3}} \end{pmatrix} \begin{pmatrix} \dfrac{\sqrt{3}}{4} & \dfrac{1}{\sqrt{2}} & \dfrac{\sqrt{3}}{4} \\ \dfrac{\sqrt{3}}{2} & 0 & -\dfrac{\sqrt{3}}{2} \\ \dfrac{\sqrt{3}}{4} & -\dfrac{1}{\sqrt{2}} & \dfrac{\sqrt{3}}{4} \end{pmatrix} = \begin{pmatrix} 1 & 0 & 0 \\ 0 & 1 & 0 \\ 0 & 0 & 1 \end{pmatrix}$$

Problem 8.10: Use of another combination of the atomic orbitals yields less satisfactory qualitative molecular orbitals (8/48) for dimethylenecyclobutene, which leads to the degeneracies $x_2^0 = x_3^0$ and $x_4^0 = x_5^0$. Show that improved eigenvalues can be obtained by perturbation calculations.

Dimethylenecyclobutene is an alternant π-electron system so that a complete calculation of orbital energies merely requires combination of the molecular orbitals belonging to one irreducible representation.

B_1:

(8/46)

(8/48)

$$\psi_1^0 \qquad\qquad \psi_3^0 \qquad\qquad \psi_5^0$$

$$x_1^0 = 2 \qquad x_3^0 = \frac{2}{3} \qquad x_5^0 = -\frac{2}{3}$$

The improved energy values $x_J^{0'}$ are calculated according to (8/71)

$$x_J^{0'} = x_J^0 + \sum_{K \neq J} \frac{(H_{JK} - S_{JK} x_J^0)^2}{x_J^0 - x_K^0}.$$

In simplified form the matrix elements H_{JK} and S_{JK} read

$$H_{11} = 2 \qquad H_{33} = \frac{2}{3} \qquad S_{13} = -\frac{1}{3}$$

$$H_{13} = -\frac{4}{3} \qquad H_{35} = -\frac{2}{3} \qquad S_{15} = +\frac{1}{3}$$

$$H_{15} = 0 \qquad H_{55} = -\frac{2}{3} \qquad S_{35} = +\frac{1}{3}$$

$$(H_{JK} = H_{KJ} ; S_{JK} = S_{KJ})$$

Substitution yields

$$x_5^{0'} = x_5^0 + \frac{(H_{15} - S_{15} x_5)^2}{x_5 - x_1} + \frac{(H_{53} - S_{53} x_5)^2}{x_5 - x_3}$$

$$= -\frac{2}{3} + \frac{\left(0 - \frac{1}{3} \cdot \left(-\frac{2}{3}\right)\right)^2}{-\frac{2}{3} - 2} + \frac{\left(-\frac{2}{3} - \frac{1}{3}\left(-\frac{2}{3}\right)\right)^2}{-\frac{2}{3} - \frac{2}{3}} = -\frac{2}{3} - \frac{1}{54} - \frac{8}{54} = -0.8$$

$$x_3^{0'} = x_3^0 + \frac{(H_{13} - S_{13} x_3)^2}{x_3 - x_1} + \frac{(H_{53} - S_{53} x_3)^2}{x_3 - x_5}$$

$$= \frac{2}{3} + \frac{\left(-\frac{4}{3} - \left(-\frac{1}{3} \cdot \frac{2}{3}\right)\right)^2}{\frac{2}{3} - 2} + \frac{\left(-\frac{2}{3} - \frac{1}{3} \cdot \frac{2}{3}\right)^2}{\frac{2}{3} - \left(-\frac{2}{3}\right)} = \frac{2}{3} - \frac{25}{27} + \frac{16}{27} = +0.333$$

$$x_1^{0'} = x_1^0 + \frac{(H_{13} - S_{13} x_1)^2}{x_1 - x_3} + \frac{(H_{15} - S_{15} x_1)^2}{x_1 - x_5}$$

$$= 2 + \frac{\left(-\frac{4}{3} - \left(-\frac{1}{3} \cdot 2\right)\right)^2}{2 - \frac{2}{3}} + \frac{\left(0 - \frac{1}{3} \cdot 2\right)^2}{2 - \left(-\frac{2}{3}\right)} = 2 + \frac{1}{3} + \frac{1}{6} = +2.500$$

Comparison with exact HMO values

J	x_J^0	$x_J^{0'}$	x_J^{HMO}
1/6	±2.000	±2.500	±2.247
2/5	±0.667	±0.833	±0.802
3/4	±0.500	±0.333	±0.555

shows that $x_1^{0'}$ lies too low, while $x_3^{0'}$ is too high. This is because the interaction between the two starting orbitals is too large relative to their separation, i.e. the magnitude of the cross term corresponds roughly to the difference in energies, and consequently a point has been reached where a second order perturbation can only be used with reservation.

Problem 8.11: Improve the qualitative molecular orbitals of the nonalternant molecule triafulvalene (8/28) by means of a second order perturbation calculation.

The molecular orbitals of trifulvalene (8/28) show the following symmetry behavior with respect to the symmetry planes $SE(1)$ and $SE(2)$:

Ψ_J^0	$SE(1)$	$SE(2)$	x_J^0
Ψ_6^0	a	s	−1.000
Ψ_5^0	a	a	−1.000
Ψ_4^0	s	a	−1.000
Ψ_3^0	s	s	−0.333
Ψ_2^0	a	s	+1.667
Ψ_1^0	s	s	+2.333

Consequently interaction can only occur between the functions Ψ_1^0/Ψ_3^0 and Ψ_2^0/Ψ_6^0 possessing the same symmetry. The orbital energies x_4^0 and x_5^0 accordingly correspond to the exact HMO values. The changes in the remaining orbital energies are obtained according to (8/71)

$$x_J^{0'} = x_J^0 + \sum_{K \neq J} \frac{(H_{JK} - S_{JK} x_J^0)^2}{x_J^0 - x_K^0}$$

as follows:

$$S_{26} = \frac{2}{6} = \frac{1}{3} \qquad x_6^{0'} = x_6^0 + \frac{(H_{26} - S_{26} x_6^0)^2}{x_6^0 - x_2^0}$$

$$H_{26} = \frac{6}{6} = 1$$

$$= -1 + \frac{\left(1 - \left(\frac{1}{3} \cdot -1\right)\right)^2}{-1 - \frac{5}{3}} = -1 - \frac{2}{3} = -1.667$$

$$x_2^{0'} = +\frac{5}{3} + \frac{\left(1 - \frac{1}{3} \cdot \frac{5}{3}\right)^2}{\frac{5}{3} - (-1)} = \frac{5}{3} + \frac{2}{27} = +1.741$$

$$S_{13} = \frac{2}{6} = \frac{1}{3} \qquad x_3^{0'} = x_3^0 + \frac{(H_{13} - S_{13} x_3^0)^2}{x_3 - x_1}$$

$$H_{13} = \frac{2}{6} = \frac{1}{3}$$

$$= -\frac{1}{3} + \frac{\left(\frac{1}{3} - \left(\frac{1}{3} \cdot -\frac{1}{3}\right)\right)^2}{-\frac{1}{3} - \frac{7}{3}} = -\frac{1}{3} - \frac{2}{27} = -0.407$$

$$x_1^{0'} = \frac{7}{3} + \frac{\left(\frac{1}{3} - \frac{1}{3} \cdot \frac{7}{3}\right)^2}{\frac{7}{3} - \left(-\frac{1}{3}\right)} = \frac{7}{3} + \frac{2}{27} = +2.407$$

The improvement upon the qualitative values x_J^0 is considerable for x_6.

J	x_J^0	$x_J^{0'}$	x_J^{HMO}
6	−1.000	−1.667	−1.732
3	−0.333	−0.407	−0.414
2	+1.700	+1.741	+1.732
1	+2.333	+2.407	+2.414

The difference in magnitude of the perturbations for x_2^0 and x_6^0 is attributable to the non-orthogonality of the function pair Ψ_2^0/Ψ_6^0.

Problem 8.12: Calculate the improved eigenvalues $x_J^{0'}$ and eigenfunctions $\Psi_J^{0'}$ of fulvene starting from qualitative molecular orbitals. Compare the results with the HMO eigenvalues from Table ⑤— (Vol. 3).

The nonalternant π-electron system of fulvene belongs to the symmetry group c_{2v} [4.8] and, according to the reducible representation

$$\Gamma = 2\overset{\times}{}A_2 + 4\overset{\times}{}B_1$$

possesses two antisymmetric (A_2) and four symmetric (B_1) molecular orbitals, with reference to the discriminating symmetry plane $\sigma(xz)$. These molecular orbitals can be constructed from basis sets of atomic orbitals

$$\{\Phi_1 \pm \Phi_4\} \;;\; \{\Phi_2 \pm \Phi_3\} \;;\; \{\Phi_5\} \;;\; \{\Phi_6\}$$

according to Rules (A), (B), (C), and (I) from Section 8.1.

	Ψ_1^0	Ψ_2^0	Ψ_3^0	Ψ_4^0	Ψ_5^0	Ψ_6^0
$\sigma(xz)$	s	s	as	s	as	s
N_J^0	$\dfrac{1}{\sqrt{6}}$	$\dfrac{1}{\sqrt{4}}$	$\dfrac{1}{\sqrt{4}}$	$\dfrac{1}{\sqrt{6}}$	$\dfrac{1}{\sqrt{4}}$	$\dfrac{1}{\sqrt{6}}$
x_J^0	2	1	$\dfrac{1}{2}$	0	$-\dfrac{3}{2}$	$-\dfrac{4}{3}$

The normalization factors N_J^0 are calculated according to (8/16) and the orbital energies x_J^0 according to (8/19).

The functions Ψ_1^0, Ψ_2^0, Ψ_4^0, and Ψ_6^0, which are symmetric with respect to $\sigma(xz)$, do not combine with the antisymmetric functions Ψ_3^0 and Ψ_5^0. The improved orbital energies $x_J^{0'}$ are consequently obtained according to (8/71)

$$x_J^{0'} = x_J^0 + \sum_{K \neq J} \frac{(H_{JK} - S_{JK}\, x_J^0)^2}{x_J^0 - x_K^0}$$

from the pertinent function sets as follows:

$$x_6^{0'} = x_6^0 + \frac{(H_{61} - S_{61}x_6^0)^2}{x_6^0 - x_1^0} + \frac{(H_{62} - S_{62}x_6^0)^2}{x_6^0 - x_2^0} + \frac{(H_{64} - S_{64}x_6^0)^2}{x_6^0 - x_4^0}$$

$$= -\frac{4}{3} + \frac{\left(\frac{1}{3} - 0\right)^2}{-\frac{4}{3} - 2} + \frac{\left(\frac{1}{\sqrt{6}} - \frac{1}{\sqrt{6}} \cdot \left(-\frac{4}{3}\right)\right)^2}{-\frac{4}{3} - 1} + \frac{\left(0 - \frac{1}{3}\left(-\frac{4}{3}\right)\right)^2}{-\frac{4}{3} - 0}$$

$$= -\frac{4}{3} - \frac{1}{30} - \frac{7}{18} - \frac{4}{27} = -1.903$$

$$x_6^{HMO} = -1.861$$

$$x_5^{0'} = x_5^0 + \frac{(H_{53} - S_{53}x_5^0)^2}{x_5^0 - x_3^0}$$

$$= -\frac{3}{2} + \frac{\left(-\frac{1}{2} - 0\right)^2}{-\frac{3}{2} - \frac{1}{2}} = -\frac{3}{2} - \frac{1}{8} = -1.625$$

$$x_5^{HMO} = -1.618$$

$$x_4^{0'} = x_4^0 + \frac{(H_{41} - S_{41}x_4^0)^2}{x_4^0 - x_1^0} + \frac{(H_{42} - S_{42}x_4^0)^2}{x_4^0 - x_2^0} + \frac{(H_{46} - S_{46}x_4^0)^2}{x_4^0 - x_6^0}$$

$$= 0 + \frac{\left(-\frac{1}{3} - 0\right)^2}{0 - 2} + \frac{\left(\frac{1}{\sqrt{6}} - 0\right)^2}{0 - 1} + \frac{(0 - 0)^2}{0 - \left(-\frac{4}{3}\right)} = -\frac{1}{18} - \frac{1}{6} = -0.222$$

$$x_4^{HMO} = -0.254$$

$$x_3^{0'} = x_3^0 + \frac{(H_{35} - S_{35}x_3^0)^2}{x_3^0 - x_5^0}$$

$$= \frac{1}{2} + \frac{\left(-\frac{1}{2} - 0\right)^2}{\frac{1}{2} - \left(-\frac{3}{2}\right)} = \frac{1}{2} + \frac{1}{8} = +0.625$$

$$x_3^{HMO} = +0.618$$

$$x_2^{0'} = x_2^0 + \frac{(H_{21} - S_{21}x_2^0)^2}{x_2^0 - x_1^0} + \frac{(H_{24} - S_{24}x_2^0)^2}{x_2^0 - x_4^0} + \frac{(H_{26} - S_{26}x_2^0)^2}{x_2^0 - x_6^0}$$

$$= 1 + \frac{(0-0)^2}{1-2} + \frac{\left(\frac{1}{\sqrt{6}} - \frac{1}{\sqrt{6}} \cdot 1\right)^2}{1-0} + \frac{\left(\frac{1}{\sqrt{6}} - \frac{1}{\sqrt{6}} \cdot 1\right)^2}{1 - \left(-\frac{4}{3}\right)} = 1 + 0 = +1.000$$

$$x_2^{HMO} = +1.000$$

$$x_1^{0'} = x_1^0 + \frac{(H_{12} - S_{12}x_1^0)^2}{x_1^0 - x_2^0} + \frac{(H_{14} - S_{14}x_1^0)^2}{x_1^0 - x_4^0} + \frac{(H_{16} - S_{16}x_1^0)^2}{x_1^0 - x_6^0}$$

$$= 2 + \frac{(0-0)^2}{2-1} + \frac{\left(-\frac{1}{3} - 0\right)^2}{2-0} + \frac{\left(\frac{1}{3} - 0\right)^2}{2 - \left(-\frac{4}{3}\right)} = 2 + \frac{1}{18} + \frac{1}{30} = +2.089$$

$$x_1^{HMO} = +2.115$$

Remarkably good agreement with the exact HMO values is achieved in spite of the qualitative starting orbitals.

According to (8/74), the improved molecular orbitals $\Psi_J^{0'}$

$$\Psi_J^{0'} = \left(\Psi_J^0 + \sum_{K \neq J} \frac{(H_{JK} - S_{JK}x_J^0)}{x_J^0 - x_K^0} \Psi_K\right) N_J$$

$$N_J = \frac{1}{\sqrt{\sum_\mu c_{J\mu}^2}}$$

are obtained in the schematic summation (8/76) as follows:

$$\Psi_6^{0'} = N_6 \left(\Psi_6^0 - \frac{1}{10}\Psi_1^0 - \frac{1}{\sqrt{6}}\Psi_2^0 - \frac{1}{3}\Psi_4^0\right)$$

$$\Psi_5^{0\prime} = N_5 \left(\Psi_5^0 - \frac{1}{4}\,\Psi_3^0 \right)$$

$$= N_5 \left[(1)\ \text{(pentagon: } \tfrac{1}{2},\ -\tfrac{1}{2},\ -\tfrac{1}{2},\ \tfrac{1}{2}) \ -\left(\tfrac{1}{4}\right)\ \text{(pentagon: } \tfrac{1}{2},\ -\tfrac{1}{2},\ \tfrac{1}{2},\ -\tfrac{1}{2}) \right]$$

$$= 0.970 \left[\text{(pentagon: } \tfrac{5}{8},\ -\tfrac{5}{8},\ -\tfrac{3}{8},\ \tfrac{3}{8}) \right] = \text{(pentagon: } 0.606,\ -0.606,\ -0.364,\ 0.364)$$

$$\Psi_4^{0\prime} = N_4 \left(\Psi_4^0 + \frac{1}{6}\,\Psi_1^0 - \frac{1}{\sqrt{6}}\,\Psi_2^0 - 0\cdot\Psi_6^0 \right)$$

$$= N_4 \left[(1)\ \text{(pentagon: } \tfrac{1}{\sqrt6},\ \tfrac{1}{\sqrt6},\ -\tfrac{1}{\sqrt6},\ -\tfrac{1}{\sqrt6},\ -\tfrac{1}{\sqrt6},\ +\tfrac{1}{\sqrt6}) + \left(\tfrac{1}{6}\right)\ \text{(pentagon: } \tfrac{1}{\sqrt6},\ \tfrac{1}{\sqrt6},\ \tfrac{1}{\sqrt6},\ \tfrac{1}{\sqrt6},\ \tfrac{1}{\sqrt6},\ \tfrac{1}{\sqrt6}) - \left(\tfrac{1}{\sqrt6}\right)\ \text{(pentagon: } \tfrac{1}{2},\ \tfrac{1}{2},\ -\tfrac{1}{2},\ -\tfrac{1}{2}) \right]$$

$$= 0.180 \left[\text{(pentagon: } \tfrac{4}{\sqrt6},\ \tfrac{4}{\sqrt6},\ -\tfrac{5}{\sqrt6},\ -\tfrac{5}{\sqrt6},\ -\tfrac{2}{\sqrt6},\ \tfrac{10}{\sqrt6}) \right] = \text{(pentagon: } 0.293,\ -0.367,\ -0.147,\ 0.733)$$

$$\Psi_3^{0\prime} = N_3 \left(\Psi_3^0 - \frac{1}{4} \Psi_5^0 \right)$$

$$= N_3 \left[(1) \, \frac{1}{2} \middle\langle\text{pentagon: } -\tfrac{1}{2}, -\tfrac{1}{2}, \tfrac{1}{2}, \tfrac{1}{2}\middle\rangle - \left(\frac{1}{4}\right) \middle\langle\text{pentagon: } \tfrac{1}{2}, -\tfrac{1}{2}, -\tfrac{1}{2}, \tfrac{1}{2}\middle\rangle \right]$$

$$= 0.970 \left[\middle\langle\text{pentagon: } \tfrac{3}{8}, -\tfrac{1}{8}, \tfrac{5}{8}, -\tfrac{5}{8}\middle\rangle \right] = \middle\langle\text{pentagon: } 0.364, -0.364, 0.606, -0.606\middle\rangle$$

$$\Psi_2^{0\prime} = N_2 \left(\Psi_2^0 + 0 \cdot \Psi_1^0 + 0 \cdot \Psi_4^0 + 0 \cdot \Psi_6^0 \right) = \middle\langle\text{pentagon: } 0.500, 0.500, -0.500, -0.500\middle\rangle$$

$$\Psi_1^{0\prime} = N_1 \left(\Psi_1^0 - 0 \cdot \Psi_2^0 - \frac{1}{6} \Psi_4^0 + \frac{1}{10} \Psi_6^0 \right)$$

$$= N_1 \left[(1) \, \frac{1}{\sqrt6} \middle\langle\text{pentagon: } \tfrac{1}{\sqrt6}, \tfrac{1}{\sqrt6}, \tfrac{1}{\sqrt6}, \tfrac{1}{\sqrt6}, \tfrac{1}{\sqrt6}\middle\rangle - \left(\frac{1}{6}\right) \middle\langle\text{pentagon: } -\tfrac{1}{\sqrt6}, \tfrac{1}{\sqrt6}, -\tfrac{1}{\sqrt6}, -\tfrac{1}{\sqrt6}, -\tfrac{1}{\sqrt6}\middle\rangle + \left(\frac{1}{10}\right) \middle\langle\text{pentagon: } \tfrac{1}{\sqrt6}, \tfrac{1}{\sqrt6}, -\tfrac{1}{\sqrt6}, -\tfrac{1}{\sqrt6}, \tfrac{1}{\sqrt6}\middle\rangle \right]$$

$$= 0.032 \left[\middle\langle\text{pentagon: } \tfrac{28}{\sqrt6}, \tfrac{28}{\sqrt6}, \tfrac{32}{\sqrt6}, \tfrac{38}{\sqrt6}, \tfrac{22}{\sqrt6}\middle\rangle \right] = \middle\langle\text{pentagon: } 0.376, 0.430, 0.510, 0.295\middle\rangle$$

The coefficients of the linear combinations obtained by second order pertubation calculation from the qualitative molecular orbitals are in good agreement with the exact HMO values, as is convincingly demonstrated by reference to the HMO Table ⑤ — (Vol. 3).

9. Application of HMO Theory

9.2. Elements of Linear Regression Calculations

Problem 9.1: Calculate the regression line for nitration of phenanthrene [9.2], given the four corresponding pairs of values

i	1	2	3	4
RN_i	1·86	2·18	2·04	1·80
$\log v_i$	−0·139	−0·725	−0·219	0·000

(Hint: The RN_i value corresponds to the dependent variable y_i, and $\log v_i$ values relate to the independent variables x_i).

The quantities (9/4) through (9/12) are obtained from the given pairs of values as follows:

$$T_x = \sum_i x_i \qquad\qquad = -1.0830 \tag{9/4}$$

$$T_y = \sum_i y_i \qquad\qquad = +7.8800 \tag{9/5}$$

$$\bar{x} = \frac{T_x}{N} \qquad\qquad = -0.2707 \tag{9/6}$$

$$\bar{y} = \frac{T_y}{N} \qquad\qquad = +1.9700 \tag{9/7}$$

$$S_{xx} = \sum_i x_i^2 - \frac{T_x^2}{N} = +0.2997 \tag{9/8}$$

$$S_{yy} = \sum_i y_i^2 - \frac{T_y^2}{N} = +0.0900 \tag{9/9}$$

$$S_{xy} = \sum_i x_i y_i - \frac{T_x T_y}{N} = -0.1523 \tag{9/10}$$

$$b = \frac{S_{xy}}{S_{xx}} \qquad\qquad = -0.508 \tag{9/11}$$

$$a = \bar{y} - b\bar{x} \qquad = +1.832 \tag{9/12}$$

The desired regression line is

$$Y = a + bx = 1.832 - 0.508\,x$$
$$RN_i = 1.832 - 0.508\,lg\,v_i \qquad (9/13)$$

The following points lie on the regression line:

$$\bar{x} = -0.271 \quad / \quad \bar{y} = +1.970$$
$$x = -1 \quad / \quad y = +2.341$$
$$x = 0 \quad / \quad y = +1.832$$

Problem 9.2: Starting from Problem 9.1 (nitration of phenanthrene), calculate the standard deviations $SE(a)$ and $SE(b)$ and thence the upper and lower confidence limits of the regression parameters for $P = 0.9$ and $P = 0.7$.

The standard deviations and limits of confidence sought can be obtained using the values from Problem 9.1 by a variance analysis according to (9/22):

Source	SQ	Φ	DQ
Due to regr.	0.0774	1	0.0774
About regr.	0.0126	2	0.0063
Total	0.0900	3	

$$SE(y) = \sqrt{0.0063} = 0.079 \qquad (9/24)$$

$$SE(a) = SE(y)\sqrt{\frac{1}{N} + \frac{\bar{x}^2}{S_{xx}}} = 0.079\sqrt{\frac{1}{4} + \frac{0.0733}{0.2997}} = 0.056 \qquad (9/25)$$

$$SE(b) = \frac{SE(y)}{\sqrt{S_{xx}}} = \frac{0.079}{0.5474} = 0.145 \qquad (9/26)$$

For the degree of freedom $\Phi = N - 2 = 2$ the t-values for a two-sided test, $t_{0.9} = 2.92$ and $t_{0.7} = 1.39$, are obtained for the probabilities $P = 0.9$ and $P = 0.7$. The confidence limits are consequently

$$P = 0.9: \quad a_u = 1.8324 + 2.92 \cdot 0.056 = 1.995$$
$$a_l = 1.8324 - 2.92 \cdot 0.056 = 1.669$$
$$b_u = 0.5082 + 2.92 \cdot 0.144 = 0.929 \left.\rule{0pt}{1.3em}\right\}$$
$$b_l = 0.5082 - 2.92 \cdot 0.144 = 0.088 \left.\rule{0pt}{1.3em}\right\} \quad !$$

$$P = 0.7. \quad a_u = 1.8324 + 1.39 \cdot 0.056 = 1.910$$
$$a_l = 1.8324 - 1.39 \cdot 0.056 = 1.755$$
$$b_u = 0.5082 + 1.39 \cdot 0.144 = 0.708$$
$$b_l = 0.5082 - 1.39 \cdot 0.144 = 0.309$$

Considering the very widely spaced limits of confidence for the slope b, the regression [9.2] based on only four points is only barely assured in spite of it pleasing appearance.

Problem 9.3: The eigenvalues (7/131) obtained according to LCMO approximation procedures can be improved by an empirical factor $f = 0.8$. Calculate the optimal factor f for the LCMO and HMO eigenvalues compared in Problem 7.22 and discuss its confidence limits.

From the 13 pairs of values of Problem 7.22

x^{HMO}	x^{LCMO}
0.295	0.459
0.452	0.592
0.520	0.676
0.568	0.734
0.220	0.353
0.327	0.488
0.405	0.597
0.419	0.647
0.438	0.588
0.423	0.600
0.492	0.651
0.550	0.705
0.502	0.650

the quantites $(9/4) - (9/12)$ are obtained as follows:

$$T_x = \Sigma\, x_i \qquad\qquad\qquad = 5.611 \qquad\qquad (9/4)$$

$$T_y = \Sigma\, y_i \qquad\qquad\qquad = 7.740 \qquad\qquad (9/5)$$

$$\bar{x} = \frac{T_x}{N} \qquad\qquad\qquad = 0.4316 \qquad\qquad (9/6)$$

$$\bar{y} = \frac{T_y}{N} \qquad\qquad\qquad = 0.5954 \qquad\qquad (9/7)$$

$$S_{xx} = \Sigma\, x_i^2 \; - \frac{T_x^2}{N} \quad = 2.5466 - 2.4218 = 0.1248 \qquad\qquad (9/8)$$

$$S_{yy} = \Sigma\, y_i^2 \; - \frac{T_y^2}{N} \quad = 4.8471 - 4.7173 = 0.1354 \qquad\qquad (9/9)$$

$$S_{xy} = \Sigma\, x_i y_i - \frac{T_x T_y}{N} = 3.5032 - 3.3800 = 0.1265 \qquad\qquad (9/10)$$

$$b = \frac{S_{xy}}{S_{xx}} \qquad\qquad\qquad = 1.0136 \qquad\qquad (9/11)$$

$$a = \bar{y} - b\bar{x} \qquad\qquad\qquad = 0.1578 \qquad\qquad (9/12)$$

The regression line

$$x^{\text{LCMO}} = 0.158 + 1.014\, x^{\text{HMO}}$$

does not pass through the origin. On the other hand, in the interval $0.2 < x^{\text{HMO}} < 0.6$ the approximate and the exact orbital energies differ by a constant amount:

$$x^{\text{LCMO}} \approx 0.16 + x^{\text{HMO}}$$

If we insist that for $x^{\text{HMO}} = 0$, it is necessary to have $x^{\text{LCMO}} = 0$, then the line is compelled to pass through the origin. In this case, however, the standard deviation is no longer independent of x^{HMO} and x^{LCMO} and the evaluation of the line must be performed as follows:

Calculation of quantities $Z = x^{LCMO} / x^{HMO}$ gives the following table of values (column Z):

Z	$0.713\, x^{LCMO}$
1.556	0.327
1.310	0.422
1.300	0.482
1.292	0.523
1.605	0.252
1.492	0.348
1.474	0.426
1.544	0.461
1.342	0.419
1.418	0.428
1.323	0.464
1.282	0.503
1.295	0.463

It can be shown that for a regression line compelled to pass through the origin, the standard error of the ratio Z is independent of the value of Z, so that the 13 values of Z can be evaluated as a random sample according to known statistical procedures in the following way:

$$T_z = \Sigma Z_i = 18.234; \quad \bar{Z} = \frac{T_z}{N} = \frac{18.234}{13} = 1.403.$$

Thus the conversion factor for transforming LCMO values into HMO values amounts to

$$x^{HMO} = \frac{x^{LCMO}}{1.403} = 0.713\, x^{LCMO}.$$

The second column of the above table contains the approximate values $0.713\, x^{LCMO}$. The standard deviation is calculated as

$$\sqrt{\frac{\Sigma (Z - \bar{Z})^2}{13 - 1}} = 0.117,$$

so that about 2/3 of the Z values lie within the limits $1.403 - 0.117 = 1.286$ and $1.403 + 0.117 = 1.520$. On conversion of the x^{LCMO} values into x^{HMO} about 2/3 will thus lie in an interval which is determined by

$$x^{HMO}_{upper} = \frac{1}{1.286}\, x^{LCMO} = 0.778\, x^{LCMO},$$

$$x^{HMO}_{lower} = \frac{1}{1.520}\, x^{LCMO} = 0.658\, x^{LCMO}$$

If higher probabilities are desired for the confidence limits, the values have to be multiplied by the corresponding *Student's t*-value for 12 degrees of freedom (Table (9/56), Vol. I, p. 291).

Problem 9.4: For the regression of phenanthrene nitration [9.2], calculate the confidence limits for the value $\log v_4 = -0.809$ at a level $P = 0.8$, and using the theoretical value for the reactivity number $RN = 1.97$. Show that the experimental value v_4 lies outside the calculated confidence limits.

Starting with the standard deviation $SE(y)$ from Problem 9.2 and with the values encountered in Problem 9.1, calculation of the confidence limits for the point $\log v_4/RN_4$ is carried out according to

$$SE(Y) = SE(y) \sqrt{1 + \frac{1}{N} + \frac{(x - \bar{x})^2}{S_{xx}}} \qquad (9/32)$$

$$= 0.079 \sqrt{1 + 0.25 + \frac{(-0.809 + 0.2707)^2}{0.2997}} = 0.118.$$

For the degree of freedom $\Phi = N - 2 = 2$ and the probability $P = 0.8$, we find the value $t_{P,\Phi} = 1.89$ in Table (9/56), Vol. 1, p 291 and obtain as limits of confidence

$$Y \quad = 1.8324 - 0.5082 \cdot (-0.809) = 2.2435$$

$$Y_o \quad = Y + t_{P,\Phi} SE(Y) \qquad (9/33)$$

$$RN_{4,u} = 2.2435 + 1.89 \cdot 0.117 = 2.466$$

$$Y_l \quad = Y - t_{P,\Phi} SE(Y) \qquad (9/33)$$

$$RN_{4,l} = 2.2435 - 1.89 \cdot 0.117 = 2.021$$

As a consequence $RN_4 = 1.97$ lies significantly outside the confidence limits, on a probability level $P = 0.8$.

9.3. Use of Correlation Diagrams

Problem 9.5: Rotation of an RHC grouping converts 1,3-dialkylallene (a) into the diastereomer (b):

(a)   (b)

Use the relevant *Hückel* determinant to calculate the orbital energies ε_1 through ε_4 of the allene π-electron system as a function of the angle of twist ω.

Allene possesses two crossed π-electron systems:

The corresponding *Hückel* determinant, starting from the linear combination

$$\Psi = \sum_{\mu=1}^{4} c_\mu \Phi_\mu$$

reads

$$\begin{Vmatrix} -x & 1 & 0 & 0 \\ 1 & -x & 0 & 0 \\ 0 & 0 & -x & 1 \\ 0 & 0 & 1 & -x \end{Vmatrix} = 0$$

Upon twisting of the terminal RHC group by an angle ω relative to its initial position. the resonance integral β_{34} is reduced to $\beta_{34} = \beta \cos \omega$, while the corresponding value between Φ_2 and Φ_4 is $\beta_{24} = \beta \sin \omega$. Thus the determinant for the perturbed system is

$$\begin{Vmatrix} -x & 1 & 0 & 0 \\ 1 & -x & 0 & \sin \omega \\ 0 & 0 & -x & \cos \omega \\ 0 & \sin \omega & \cos \omega & -x \end{Vmatrix} = 0$$

Expansion of the determinant gives
$$x^4 - 2x^2 + \cos^2 \omega = 0,$$
$$x^2 = 1 \pm \sqrt{1 - \cos^2 \omega}$$
which yields the solutions
$$x = \pm \sqrt{1 \pm \sin \omega}.$$

The results are plotted for the range $0° < \omega < 180°$ in the following correlation diagram:

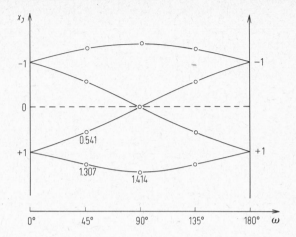

Identical solutions are obtained if the right hand RHC grouping is twisted by an angle $\omega / 2$ in a positive direction and the left-hand one is twisted by $- \omega / 2$ in a negative direction. The corresponding determinant

$$
\begin{vmatrix}
-x & \cos \dfrac{\omega}{2} & \sin \dfrac{\omega}{2} & 0 \\
\cos \dfrac{\omega}{2} & -x & 0 & \sin \dfrac{\omega}{2} \\
\sin \dfrac{\omega}{2} & 0 & -x & \cos \dfrac{\omega}{2} \\
0 & \sin \dfrac{\omega}{2} & \cos \dfrac{\omega}{2} & -x
\end{vmatrix} = 0
$$

affords the same polynomial

$$
x^4 - 2x^2 + \cos^2 \omega = 0
$$

and hence the same orbital energy coefficients.

Problem 9.6 : Construct the qualitative and the semiquantitative correlation diagram of the configurations of the ground state and of all excited states in the manner shown above for the angles $\omega = 0°$ through $\omega = 180°$ for the transition from s-cis- to s-trans-butadiene.

The problem is solved in complete analogy to the derivation of the correlation diagram for the cis-trans isomerization of hexatriene. The molecular orbital diagram for the conversion s-cis$\rightarrow s$-trans is first constructed as in [9.9]:

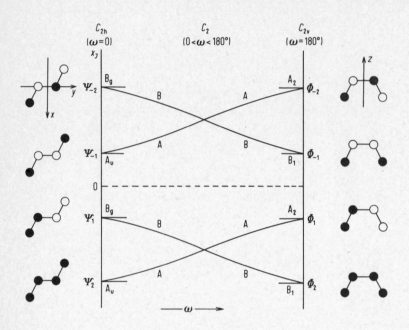

The assignments of the molecular orbitals to the representations of the relevant symmetry groups are also indicated. While s-trans-butadiene belongs to the symmetry group C_{2h} and s-cis-butadiene to C_{2v} for all conformations $0 < \omega < \pi$ the symmetry group C_2 applies, so that the corresponding molecular orbitals can be assigned either to representation A or B. Referred to this reduced symmetry, the following configurations listed with their energies belong to the representations indicated:

Γ $(\Psi_2)^2(\Psi_1)^2 \longrightarrow (\Phi_2)^2(\Phi_1)^2$, $E_\pi = 2\epsilon_2 + 2\epsilon_1 = 4\alpha + 4.472\,\beta$

$A \overset{\times}{\times} A \overset{\times}{\times} B \overset{\times}{\times} B \doteq A$ $\quad B \overset{\times}{\times} B \overset{\times}{\times} A \overset{\times}{\times} A \doteq A$

χ_1^{-1} $(\Psi_2)^2(\Psi_1)^1(\Psi_{-1})^1 \searrow (\Phi_2)^2(\Phi_1)^1(\Phi_{-1})^1$, $E_\pi = 2\epsilon_2 + \epsilon_1 + \epsilon_{-1} = 4\alpha + 3.236\,\beta$

$A \overset{\times}{\times} A \overset{\times}{\times} B \overset{\times}{\times} A \doteq B$ $\quad B \overset{\times}{\times} B \overset{\times}{\times} A \overset{\times}{\times} B \doteq B$

χ_2^{-2} $(\Psi_2)^1(\Psi_1)^2(\Psi_{-2})^1 \nearrow (\Phi_2)^1(\Phi_1)^2(\Phi_{-2})^1$, $E_\pi = \epsilon_2 + 2\epsilon_1 + \epsilon_{-2} = 4\alpha + 1.236\,\beta$

$A \overset{\times}{\times} B \overset{\times}{\times} B \overset{\times}{\times} B \doteq B$ $\quad B \overset{\times}{\times} A \overset{\times}{\times} A \overset{\times}{\times} A \doteq B$

$$\chi_1^{-2} \quad (\Psi_2)^2(\Psi_1)^1(\Psi_{-2})^1$$
$$A \overset{\times}{\cdot} A \overset{\times}{\cdot} B \overset{\times}{\cdot} B \doteq A$$

$$(\Phi_2)^2(\Phi_1)^1(\Phi_{-2})^1, \; E_\pi = 2\epsilon_2 + \epsilon_1 + \epsilon_{-2} = 4\alpha + 2.236\,\beta$$
$$B \overset{\times}{\cdot} B \overset{\times}{\cdot} A \overset{\times}{\cdot} A \doteq A$$

$$\chi_2^{-1} \quad (\Psi_2)^1(\Psi_1)^2(\Psi_{-1})^1$$
$$A \overset{\times}{\cdot} B \overset{\times}{\cdot} B \overset{\times}{\cdot} A \doteq A$$

$$(\Phi_2)^1(\Phi_1)^2(\Phi_{-1})^1, \; E_\pi = \epsilon_2 + 2\epsilon_1 + \epsilon_{-1} = 4\alpha + 2.236\,\beta$$
$$B \overset{\times}{\cdot} A \overset{\times}{\cdot} A \overset{\times}{\cdot} B \doteq A$$

It is also shown which configurations are subject to mutual interconversion.

The resulting correlation diagram of the configurations thus has the appearance:

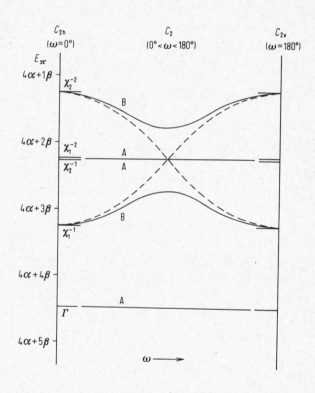

10. Molecules in Their Electronic Ground States

10.1. Interatomic Distances in π-Electron Systems

Problem 10.1: Calibrate the relationship (10/11) on the basis of interatomic distances $R_{\mu\nu}^{\text{exp}}$ and HMO bond orders $p_{\mu\nu}$ of

	$R_{\mu\nu}^{\text{exp}}$	$p_{\mu\nu}$
Ethylene	1·34 Å	1·000
Benzene	1·39 Å	0·667
Graphite	1·42 Å	0·535

using formulae (9/4) through (9/13). Calculate the slope β' of the function $\beta = \beta(R)$. (Hint: The force constant k for σ-bonds between sp^2-hybridized carbon atoms is about 5×10^5 dyn/cm $= 7 \times 10^2$ kcal Å^2/mol).

The desired regression line is obtained from the given pairs of values as follows:

$$R_{\mu\nu} = R_0 - \frac{2\beta'}{k}\, p_{\mu\nu} \tag{10/11}$$

$$y = a + b \cdot x$$

x	y
1.000	1.34
0.667	1.39
0.535	1.42

$$T_x = \sum_{i=1}^{N} x_i = 2.202 \quad ; \quad \bar{x} = \frac{T_x}{N} = 0.734$$

$$T_y = \sum_{i=1}^{N} y_i = 4.15 \quad ; \quad \bar{y} = \frac{T_y}{N} = 1.3833$$

$$S_{xx} = \sum_{i=1}^{N} x_i^2 - \frac{T_x^2}{N} = 1.7311 - \frac{2.202^2}{3} = 0.1148$$

$$S_{xy} = \sum_{i=1}^{N} x_i y_i - \frac{T_x T_y}{N} = 3.0268 - \frac{2.202 \cdot 4.15}{3} = -0.0193$$

$$b = \frac{S_{xy}}{S_{xx}} = -0.1678$$

$$a = \bar{y} - b\bar{x} = 1.3833 - (-0.1678) \cdot 0.734 = 1.506$$

$$R_{\mu v} = 1.506 - 0.168\, p_{\mu v}$$

The slope β' is obtained according to

$$\beta' = \frac{0.168 \cdot k}{2} = \frac{0.168 \cdot 700}{2} = 60 \text{ kcal/mol Å}$$

It should be noted that the function $\beta = \beta(R)$ is negative for all values of R and asymptotically approaches zero:

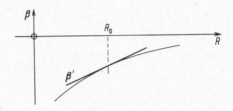

Consequently the slope β' is positive.

Problem 10.2: Substituting the corresponding bond orders $p_{\mu v}$ (HMO Table ⑥⑥⑥, Volume 3) into the regression (10/12), calculate the bond lengths for anthracene, and compare the results obtained with experimental values $R_{\mu v}^{\exp}$ listed below.

$\mu - v$	$R_{\mu v}^{\exp}$ [Å]
1– 2	1·370
1–12	1·423
2– 3	1·408
9–12	1·396
11–12	1·436

From the regression

$$R_{\mu v} = 1.506 - 0.1678\, p_{\mu v} \tag{10/12}$$

we obtain the following absolute bond lengths $R_{\mu\nu}^{calc}$ from the corresponding bond orders $p_{\mu\nu}$:

$\mu - \nu$	$p_{\mu\nu}$	$R_{\mu\nu}^{calc.}$ (Å)	$\Delta R_{\mu\nu}$
1 – 2	0.737	1.382	+0.012
1 – 12	0.535	1.416	−0.007
2 – 3	0.586	1.408	±0.000
9 – 12	0.606	1.404	+0.008
11 – 12	0.485	1.425	−0.011

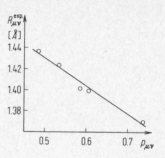

As can be seen, measured and calculated values are in satisfactory agreement. The graphical representation demonstrates that very good agreement exists between $p_{\mu\nu}$ and $R_{\mu\nu}^{exp.}$ for anthracene. Usually the deviations about the regression are greater.

Problem 10.3: Starting from the 10-centre perimeter (HMO Table ⑩, Volume 3) and using second order perturbation procedures, calculate the peripheral bond orders $p_{\mu\nu}$ of the tricyclodecapentaene

and discuss the interatomic distances $R_{\mu\nu}^{calc}$ obtained from (10/12).

The set of bond-bond polarizabilities $\pi_{\mu\nu, \rho\sigma}$ starting at center 1 is given in the HMO Table of the 10-perimeter (Vol. 3). The additional bonds in the system are therefore to be introduced between centers 1 and 4 and centers 6 and 9.

The list of perturbations reads

$$\langle \mu | h | \nu \rangle = 0; \text{except} \langle 1 | h | 4 \rangle = \langle 6 | h | 9 \rangle = \beta.$$

The bond orders of the peripheral bonds are obtained according to (7/91)

$$p'_{\mu\nu} = p^0_{\mu\nu} + \pi_{14,\mu\nu} + \pi_{69,\mu\nu}$$

with the values:

$\mu - \nu$	$p^0_{\mu\nu}$	$\pi_{14,\mu\nu}$	$\pi_{69,\mu\nu} = \pi_{14,\rho\sigma}$	$\rho - \sigma$	$p'_{\mu\nu}$
$1-2$	0.647	0.012	0.059	$6-7$	0.718
$2-3$	0.647	-0.117	-0.070	$7-8$	0.460
$4-5$	0.647	0.111	-0.089	$5-6$	0.669

The interatomic distances $R_{\mu\nu}$ are calculated according to (10/12) as

$$R_{12} = 1.386 \text{ Å}$$
$$R_{23} = 1.429 \text{ Å}$$
$$R_{45} = 1.394 \text{ Å}$$

The bond lengths $1-4$ and $6-9$ can only be calculated approximately using the values from the HMO Tables (Vol. 3), since the bond-bond polarizability $\pi_{14\ 69}$ between the two transannular bonds is not given there. Assuming that its magnitude is small and may therefore be neglected the bond order would be

$$p'_{14} = p^0_{14} + \pi_{14,14} = -0.247 + 0.365 = 0.118.$$

A complete calculation with $\pi_{14,69} = -0.035$ gives

$$p'_{14} = p^0_{14} + \pi_{14,14} + \pi_{14,69} = 0.083.$$

In the following molecular diagrams, the bond orders $p'_{\mu\nu}$ (I) obtained by perturbation calculations are compared with those from an exact HMO calculation (II), the bond characters from a resonance treatment involving superposition of the four Kekulé structures (III), and finally with the expectations of chemical intuition for a system of localized double bonds (IV).

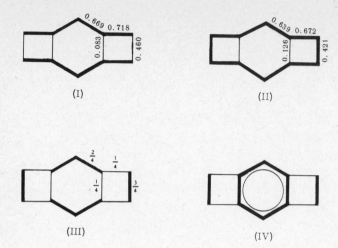

(I)   (II)

(III)   (IV)

As can be seen, the double bond localization predicted by HMO theory deviates noticeably from those of resonance theory and of chemical intuition. Unfortunately no experimental decision is possible in this case since the compound is unknown. For diphenylene, which is another example of a π-electron system composed of 4- and 6-membered rings the predictions of HMO theory are in better agreement with the results of X-ray structure analysis, especially regarding alternance in the six-membered rings, than are those of resonance theory or chemical intuition.

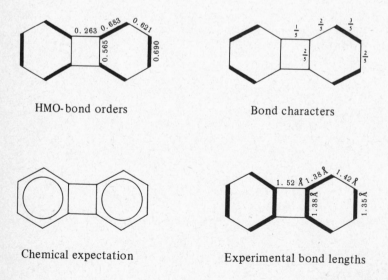

HMO-bond orders

Bond characters

Chemical expectation

Experimental bond lengths

Problem 10.4: In contrast to azulene, naphthalene displays a marked double bond fixation around its perimeter. How can this be rationalized in terms of the molecular orbitals of a 10-centre perimeter model (HMO Table ⑩, Volume 3)?

Introduction of a bond by perturbation of the 10-perimeter between centers 1 and 6 generates the alternant naphthalene π-system; joining centers 1 and 5 produces the nonalternant azulene π-system.

$$\pi_{\mu\nu,\,16} \neq 0$$

$$\pi_{\mu\nu,\,15} = 0$$
(except $\pi_{15.\,15} = 0.439$)

For ring closure to the nonalternant system, the bond-bond polarizabilities $\pi_{\mu\nu',15}$ are identically equal to zero (cf. Vol. 3) except for the self-polarizability $\pi_{15,15}$ of the newly formed bond. In contrast, the perturbation incurred by a bond between a starred and an unstarred center — as in the case of naphthalene — induces an alternance of the peripheral double bonds.

In particular we calculate according to (7/91)

$$p'_{\mu\nu} = p^0_{\mu\nu} + \pi_{\mu\nu,\rho\sigma}$$

and

$$R^{\text{calc.}}_{\mu\nu} = 1.506 - 0.1678\, p'_{\mu\nu} \tag{10/12}$$

the following values (cf. Problem 7.12):

a) Naphthalene:

List of perturbations:

$$<\mu|h|\nu> = 0;\ \text{except}\ <1|h|6> = \beta$$

$\mu - \nu$	$p^0_{\mu\nu}$	$\pi_{\mu\nu,\,16}$	$p'_{\mu\nu}$	$R^{calc.}_{\mu\nu}$ (Å)	$R^{exp.}_{\mu\nu}$ (Å)	$p^{HMO}_{\mu\nu}$	$R^{calc.}_{\mu\nu}$ (Å)
1 – 2	0.647	−0.063	0.584	1.408	1.422	0.555	1.413
1 – 6	0.200	+0.375	0.575	1.410	1.419	0.518	1.419
2 – 3	0.647	+0.085	0.732	1.383	1.368	0.725	1.384
3 – 4	0.647	−0.044	0.603	1.405	1.414	0.603	1.405

b) Azulene:

List of perturbations:

$<\mu|h|\nu> = 0$; except $<1|h|5> = \beta$

$\mu - \nu$	$p^0_{\mu\nu}$	$\pi_{\mu\nu,\,15}$	$p'_{\mu\nu}$	$R^{calc.}_{\mu\nu}$ (Å)	$R^{exp.}_{\mu\nu}$ (Å)	$p^{HMO}_{\mu\nu}$	$R^{calc.}_{\mu\nu}$ (Å)
1 – 2	0.647	0	0.647	1.397	1.413	0.596	1.406
1 – 5	0	+0.439	0.439	1.432	1.483	0.401	1.439
1 – 10	0.647	0	0.647	1.397	1.383	0.586	1.408
2 – 3	0.647	0	0.647	1.397	1.391	0.656	1.396
8 – 9	0.647	0	0.647	1.397	1.385	0.639	1.399
9 – 10	0.647	0	0.647	1.397	1.401	0.664	1.395

Comparison with the accompanying interatomic distances calculated from the HMO bond orders $p^{HMO}_{\mu\nu}$ shows that perturbation calculations can also give satisfactory results to within the limits of accuracy of the method.

Problem 10.5: For 2,3,4,5-dibenzocoronene, calculate the *Pauling* double bond characters $X_{\mu\nu}$ and show that they allow a satisfactory prediction of the relative bond lengths, when plotted against the measured interatomic distances $R^{exp}_{\mu\nu}$. (Note that the numbering of the atoms does not correspond to chemical convention.)

$\mu - \nu$	$R^{exp}_{\mu\nu}$ [Å]	$\mu - \nu$	$R^{exp}_{\mu\nu}$ [Å]
1–2	1·35	15–23	1·44
1–15	1·47	16–24	1·42
2–16	1·47	20–21	1·49
3– 4	1·40	21–29	1·42
3–16	1·39	22–29	1·42
11–12	1·43	23–24	1·43
11–21	1·36	23–30	1·41
12–13	1·37	24–25	1·44
13–22	1·43	27–30	1·47
14–15	1·37	29–30	1·40
14–22	1·40		

The *Pauling* bond characters $X_{\mu\nu}$ are obtained by dividing the number $Z_{\mu\nu}$ of the *Kekulé* structures in which the observed bond $\mu-\nu$ exists as a double bond by the total number Z of all the *Kekulé* structures. The latter is most conveniently determined for 2, 3, 4, 5-dibenzocoronene in the following manner (the enclosed partial systems are each varied separately):

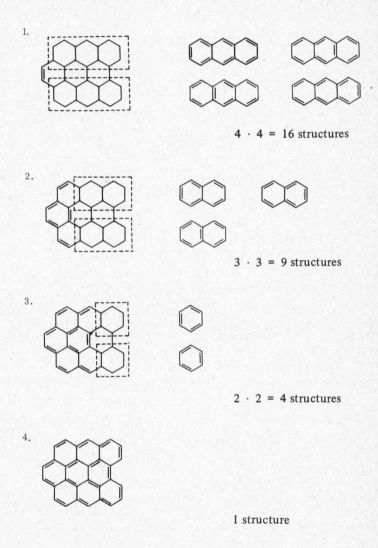

1.

$4 \cdot 4 = 16$ structures

2.

$3 \cdot 3 = 9$ structures

3.

$2 \cdot 2 = 4$ structures

4.

1 structure

The $Z_{\mu\nu}$ values obtained from the 30 possible *Kekulé* structures are listed along with the resulting *Pauling* bond characters $X_{\mu\nu}$ in the following table:

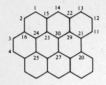

$\mu - \nu$	$Z_{\mu\nu}$	$X_{\mu\nu}$	$\mu - \nu$	$Z_{\mu\nu}$	$X_{\mu\nu}$
1 − 2	26	0.87	15 − 23	7	0.23
1 − 15	4	0.13	16 − 24	12	0.40
2 − 16	4	0.13	20 − 21	1	0.03
3 − 4	16	0.53	21 − 29	9	0.30
3 − 16	14	0.47	22 − 29	9	0.30
11 − 12	10	0.33	23 − 24	9	0.30
11 − 21	20	0.67	23 − 30	14	0.47
12 − 13	20	0.67	24 − 25	9	0.30
13 − 22	10	0.33	27 − 30	4	0.13
14 − 15	19	0.63	29 − 30	12	0.40
14 − 22	11	0.37			

A graphical representation of the pairs of values shows that the above crude approximation treatment, which is purely topological in nature, gives a satisfactory correlation between the measured interatomic distances $R_{\mu\nu}^{exp}$ and the estimated double bond characters $X_{\mu\nu}$ of 2, 3, 4, 5-dibenzocoronene.

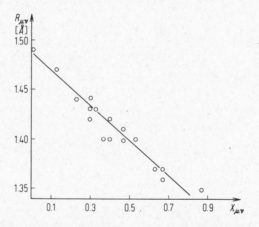

Problem 10.6: Calculate the bond lengths in 1-azaazulene using the values listed in HMO Table ⑤ ⑦, Volume 3.

According to Table (6/80) the parameters for aza-substitution in π-electron systems are

$$h_{N \cdot} = 0.5; \quad k_{C=N} = 1.0.$$

Hence the list of perturbations for azulene is

$$<\mu |h| \nu> = 0; \text{except} <1|h|1> = \delta\alpha_1 = h_N \cdot \beta = 0.5\,\beta.$$

According to (7/91)

$$p'_{\mu\nu} = p^0_{\mu\nu} + \pi_{\mu\nu,1} \cdot 0.5$$

and the regression (10/12), the values for 1-azaazulene are:

$\mu - \nu$	$p^0_{\mu\nu}$	$\pi_{\mu\nu,1}$	$p'_{\mu\nu}$	$R^{calc.}_{\mu\nu}$ (Å)
1 – 2	0.656	−0.064	0.624	1.401
1 – 9	0.596	−0.044	0.574	1.410
2 – 3	0.656	+0.075	0.694	1.390
3 – 10	0.596	−0.038	0.577	1.409
4 – 5	0.664	+0.010	0.669	1.394
4 – 10	0.586	−0.014	0.579	1.409
5 – 6	0.639	±0.000	0.639	1.399
6 – 7	0.639	+0.001	0.640	1.399
7 – 8	0.664	+0.008	0.668	1.394
8 – 9	0.586	−0.011	0.580	1.409
9 – 10	0.401	+0.075	0.439	1.432

A comparison of the values (Problem 10.4) calculated for azulene shows that the interatomic distances are predicted to remain constant on aza substitution within the limits of the approximation

Problem 10.7: Using the covalent atomic radii given below, calculate the interatomic distances for the C—O, C=O, C—N, and C=N bonds. Compare these values with the experimental data found for diketopiperazine

$\mu - \nu$	$R^{exp}_{\mu\nu}$ [Å]
1–2	1·33
1–6	1·47
1–7	1·25
2–3	1·41

Explain the differences, and attempt to calculate the bond lengths using the HMO bond orders of the systems C=O, C=Ṅ, and O=C—N and the relationship

$$R_{C \cdots X} = R_{C-X} - \frac{p_{C \cdots X}}{p_{C=X}}(R_{C-X} - R_{C=X}).$$

$(r_{C-(sp^3)} = 0.77 \text{ Å}; r_{C=(sp^2)} = 0.67 \text{ Å}; r_{-O} = 0.66 \text{ Å}; r_{=O} = 0.54 \text{ Å}; r_{=N} = 0.60 \text{ Å})$

The values $R_{\mu\nu}^{pred.}$ of the bond lengths predicted from the covalent atomic radii r_μ and r_ν are:

$\mu - \nu$	r_μ	r_ν	$R_{\mu\nu}^{pred.}$	$R_{\mu\nu}^{exp.}$	$\Delta R_{\mu\nu}(\text{Å})$
$1-2$	0.77	0.70	1.47	1.33	+0.14
$1-6$	0.77	0.77	1.54	1.47	+0.07
$1-7$	0.67	0.54	1.21	1.25	−0.04
$2-3$	0.77	0.70	1.47	1.41	+0.06

Thus, with the exception of the value for the $C=O$ double bond which is too small, the bond lengths are predicted to be too long, especially for the C—N single bond between the centers 1 and 2. This situation can be rationalized by the following resonan[t] formulae:

Within the framework of a simple HMO model, starting form the parameters (6/80)

$$h_{N^\oplus} = 2; \quad h_O = 1; \quad k_{C=N} = k_{C=O} = k_{C=C} = 1$$

the bond lengths 1−2 and 1−7 can be estimated as follows:

a) The bond order of an isolated $C = N^\oplus$ double bond is obtained from

$$\begin{Vmatrix} -x & 1 \\ 1 & -x+2 \end{Vmatrix} = 0 = x^2 - 2x - 1; \quad x_{1,2} = 1 \pm 1.414$$

by way of the normalized coefficients

$x_1 = 2.414:$ $\quad c_C'(-x_1) + c_{N^\oplus}' = 0;$ $\qquad c_C' = 1, c_{N^\oplus}' = 2.414$
$\quad\quad\quad\quad\quad\;\; c_C' + c_{N^\oplus}'(-x_1 + 2) = 0$

$$N = \frac{1}{\sqrt{1^2 + 2.414^2}} = 0.383$$

$$c_C = 0.383, \quad c_{N^\oplus} = 0.924$$

which lead to

$$p_{C=N}^{\;\oplus} = \sum_J b_J c_{JC}\, c_{JN^\oplus} = 2 \cdot 0.383 \cdot 0.924 = 0.708.$$

b) In like manner the $C=O$ bond order is found to be:

$$\begin{Vmatrix} -x & 1 \\ 1 & -x+1 \end{Vmatrix} = 0 = x^2 - x - 1; \quad x_{1,2} = 0.5 \pm 1.118$$

$x_1 = 1.618:$ $c'_C(-x_1) + c'_O = 0;$ $c'_C = 1, c'_O = 1.618$

$$c'_C + c'_O(-x + 1) = 0$$

$$N = \frac{1}{\sqrt{1^2 + 1.618^2}} = 0.526$$

$$c_C = 0.526, \quad c_O = 0.851$$

$$p_{C=O} = 2 \cdot 0.526 \cdot 0.851 = 0.894$$

c) For the system $\overset{\delta\oplus}{N}\text{---}C\text{---}\overset{\delta\ominus}{O}$ of interest, the *Hückel* determinant reads

$$\begin{Vmatrix} -x+2 & 1 & 0 \\ 1 & -x & 1 \\ 0 & 1 & -x+1 \end{Vmatrix} = 0 = x^3 - 3x^2 + 3$$

Inserting the energies of the two bonding molecular orbitals x_1 and x_2 into the secular equations yields the coefficients after normalization:

$$x_1 = 2.532; \quad c'_N = 1, \quad c'_C = 0.532, \quad c'_O = 0.347$$

$$N = 0.844$$

$$c_N = 0.844, \quad c_C = 0.449, \quad c_O = 0.293$$

$$x_2 = 1.347; \quad c'_N = 1, \quad c'_C = -0.653, \quad c'_O = -1.879$$

$$N = 0.449$$

$$c_N = 0.449, \quad c_C = -0.293, \quad c_O = -0.844$$

Hence the bond orders are

$$p_{N\text{---}C}^{\delta\oplus} = 2 \cdot (0.843 \cdot 0.449 + 0.449 \cdot (-0.293)) = 0.495$$

$$p_{C\text{---}O}^{\delta\ominus} = 2 \cdot (0.449 \cdot 0.293 + (-0.293) \cdot (-0.843)) = 0.758$$

d) With the values determined

$\mu - \nu$	$p_{\mu\nu}$	$\mu - \nu$	$R_{\mu\nu}^{\text{pred.}}$ (Å)
$C = N^{\oplus}$	0.71	$C - N$	1.47
$(O^{\delta\ominus}\cdots)\, C\cdots N^{\delta\oplus}$	0.49	$C = N$	1.27
$C = O$	0.89	$C - O$	1.43
$(N^{\delta\oplus}\cdots)\, C\cdots O^{\delta\ominus}$	0.76	$C = O$	1.21

the crude qualitative relationship

$$R_{C\cdots X}^{\text{calc.}} = R_{C-X}^{\text{pred.}} - \frac{p_{C\cdots X}}{p_{C=X}} (R_{C-X}^{\text{pred.}} - R_{C=X}^{\text{pred.}})$$

affords the following interatomic distances $R_{C=X}^{\text{calc.}}$ in the system $N^{\delta\oplus}\cdots C\cdots O^{\delta\ominus}$

$$R_{C\cdots N^{\delta\oplus}}^{\text{calc.}} = 1.47 - (1.47 - 1.27) \cdot \frac{0.49}{0.71} = 1.33$$

$$R_{C\cdots O^{\delta\ominus}}^{\text{calc.}} = 1.43 - (1.43 - 1.21) \cdot \frac{0.76}{0.89} = 1.24$$

The interatomic distances thus obtained are in very good agreement with those found experimentally.

Problem 10.8: How much will the individual bond lengths of fulvalene change if the central bond is twisted by 60°?

To calculate the differences $\Delta R_{\mu\nu}$ between the interatomic distances, the relation

$$R_{\mu\nu} = R_0 - k \cdot p_{\mu\nu} \tag{10/11}$$

is first expanded

$$R'_{\mu\nu} = R_0 - k(p_{\mu\nu} + \Delta p_{\mu\nu})$$

$$\Delta R_{\mu\nu} = R'_{\mu\nu} - R_{\mu\nu} = -k\Delta p_{\mu\nu}$$

Then using

$$\Delta p_{\mu\nu} = \pi_{\mu\nu,\rho\sigma} \cdot \Delta \beta_{\rho\sigma}$$

it follows that

$$\Delta R_{\mu\nu} = (-k \cdot \Delta\beta_{\rho\sigma})\,\pi_{\mu\nu,\rho\sigma}.$$

Substitution of $k = 0.1678$ and the perturbation $<9\,|\,h|\,10> = \Delta\beta = \beta' - \beta = (\cos 60° - 1)\,\beta = -0.5\,\beta$ which is obtained from $\beta' = (\cos 60°)\,\beta$, eventually affords from

$$\Delta R_{\mu\nu} = 0.0839\,\pi_{\mu\nu,9\ 10}$$

the desired values:

$\mu - \nu$	$\pi_{\mu\nu,9\ 10}$	$\Delta R_{\mu\nu}(\text{Å})$
$1 - 2$	0.045	+0.004
$1 - 10$	−0.104	−0.009
$2 - 3$	0.022	+0.002
$9 - 10$	0.191	+0.016

As expected, it is in particular the length of the central bond which increases. It becomes more and more like a single bond with increasing angle of twist, i.e. decreasing π-interaction.

Problem 10.9: Calculate approximately the bond order $p_{\rho\sigma}$, and thence the interatomic distance $R_{\rho\sigma}$, of bond $\rho - \sigma$ in each of the following π-electron systems, and compare the results with experimental values:

$R_{\rho\sigma}^{\text{exp}}$: 1·48   1·48   1·48   [Å]

From the empirical relation

$$p_{\rho\sigma} \approx 0.1 + 0.7\sqrt{\pi_{\rho\rho}\,\pi_{\sigma\sigma}} \tag{10/20}$$

and the regression

$$R_{\mu\nu} = 1.506 - 0.1678\,p_{\mu\nu} \tag{10/12}$$

we obtain the interatomic distances $\rho - \sigma$ of the given systems as:

$R + S$	$\rho - \sigma$	$\pi_{\rho\rho}$	$\pi_{\sigma\sigma}$	$p_{\rho\sigma}$	$R_{\rho\sigma}^{calc.}$(Å)	$p_{\rho\sigma}^{HMO}$	$R_{\rho\sigma}^{calc.}$(Å)
Ethylene	$2 - 3$	0.500	0.500	0.450	1.430	0.447	1.431
Ethylene + benzene	$1 - 7$	0.500	0.398	0.412	1.437	0.406	1.438
Benzene	$6 - 7$	0.398	0.398	0.379	1.442	0.370	1.444

Within the limits of the approximation, good agreement is obtained between the empirically determined interatomic distances $R_{\rho\sigma}^{calc.}$ and those from the HMO bond orders.

10.2. Force Constants and Stretching Frequencies

Problem 10.10: Replacement of the force constant k of the potential function $V = (k/2)(R - R_0)^2$ by $k = k_0 + k_1(R_0 - R)$ predicts that the frequency v depends on $R_{\mu\nu}$ for vibration about the equilibrium position $R_{\mu\nu}$. What approximate relationship between the frequency v and the HMO bond order $p_{\mu\nu}$ does this assumption imply?

For a quadratic potential

$$V(R) = \frac{k}{2}(R - R_0)^2 \tag{10/3}$$

the force constant has the value k. The frequency v of a vibrating system having reduced mass m_{red} is given by

$$v = \frac{1}{2\pi}\sqrt{\frac{k}{m_{red}}}. \tag{10/27}$$

If this quadratic potential is combined as in [10.4] with one which is linear in R, for example the total π-electron energy

$$E_\pi = A + B(R - R_0) \tag{10/22}$$

we obtain the total energy

$$E_G = V + E_\pi = \frac{k}{2}(R - R_0)^2 + A + B(R - R_0).$$

According to

$$\frac{dE_G}{dR} = 0 = k(R - R_0) + B$$

this possesses a minimum at

$$R_{\mu\nu} = R_0 - \frac{B}{k}$$

Considered near the equilibrium distance $R_{\mu\nu}$, the total energy takes the following form

$$E_G = \left(A - \frac{B^2}{2k}\right) + \frac{k}{2}(R - R_{\mu\nu})^2$$

Thus — considered relative to the equilibrium position $R_{\mu\nu}$ — we again find a quadratic potential with force constant k, so that the frequency ν is given independently of $R_{\mu\nu}$ by the above relationship (10/27).

However, the potential functions of σ-bonds in molecules are not quadratic functions of R, but rather *Morse* functions, which are steeper for $R < R_0$ and flatter for $R > R_0$.

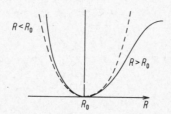

Such potentials are designated as anharmonic. The anharmonicity can be taken into account by the expression

$$k = k_0 + k_1(R_0 - R).$$

This leads to the potential

$$V = \frac{k_0 + k_1(R_0 - R)}{2}(R - R_0)^2 = \frac{k_0}{2}(R - R_0)^2 - \frac{k_1}{2}(R - R_0)^3,$$

which is identical with the harmonic potential (10/3) for $k_1 = 0$. The associated total energy

$$E_G = \frac{k_0}{2}(R - R_0)^2 - \frac{k_1}{2}(R - R_0)^3 + A + B(R - R_0)$$

possesses according to

$$\frac{dE_G}{dR} = 0 = k_0(R - R_0) - \frac{3k_1}{2}(R - R_0)^2 + B$$

a minimum at

$$(R - R_0)^2 - \frac{2k_0}{3k_1}(R - R_0) - \frac{2B}{3k_1} = 0$$

$$(R - R_0) = \frac{k_0}{3k_1} - \sqrt{\frac{k_0^2}{9k_1^2} + \frac{2B}{3k_1}}$$

$$= \frac{k_0}{3k_1} - \frac{k_0}{3k_1}\sqrt{1 + \frac{6k_1 B}{k_0^2}}.$$

From this we obtain

$$R_{\mu\nu} = R_0 + \frac{k_0}{3k_1}\left(1 - \sqrt{1 + \frac{6k_1 B}{k_0^2}}\right).$$

For the equilibrium distance $R_{\mu\nu}$, results by definition,

$$\left(\frac{dE_G}{dR}\right)_{R = R_{\mu\nu}} = 0.$$

The frequency of a vibration about the equilibrium position is determined by

$$\left(\frac{d^2 E_G}{dR^2}\right)_{R = R_{\mu\nu}},$$

i.e., by the quadratic component of the curvature of the total energy at position $R = R_{\mu\nu}$. This amounts to

$$\frac{d^2 E_G}{dR^2} = k_0 - 3k_1(R - R_0)$$

and for $R = R_{\mu\nu}$, substitution of the relation derived above leads to

$$\frac{d^2 E_G}{dR^2} = k_0 \sqrt{1 + \frac{6k_1 B}{k_0^2}} = k'.$$

In this case, k' is the force constant of a quadratic potential which for small displacements about the equilibrium position $R_{\mu\nu}$ approximates the curve of the total energy. Use of (10/11) leads to

$$R_0 - R_{\mu\nu} = \frac{B}{k} = \frac{2\beta'}{k}p_{\mu\nu} \; ; \; B = 2\beta' p_{\mu\nu},$$

which, on introduction into (10/27) with the above result affords the relation between the stretching frequency ν and the bond order $p_{\mu\nu}$ in the anharmonic model:

$$\nu = \frac{1}{2\pi} \sqrt{\frac{k'}{m_{red}}} = \frac{1}{2\pi} \sqrt{\frac{k_0}{m_{red}} \sqrt{1 + \frac{12 k_1 \beta' p_{\mu\nu}}{k_0^2}}}.$$

According to this equation, which embraces the harmonic case for $k_1 = 0$ and $k' = k_0$, the stretching frequency ν increases with increasing bond order $p_{\mu\nu}$. A greatly simplified approximation formula results if the root within the root is expanded in a series, all terms beyond the first being neglected, and the constants are collected together:

$$\nu^2 \cong \frac{1}{4\pi^2} \left(\frac{k_0}{m_{red}} + \frac{6 k_1 \beta' p_{\mu\nu}}{k_0^2 m_{red}} \right)$$

$$\nu^2 \cong \nu_0^2 + K p_{\mu\nu}$$

$$K = \frac{3}{2\pi^2} \frac{k_1 \beta'}{k_0^2 m_{red}}$$

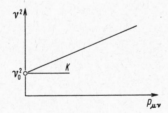

It becomes clear that the square of the stretching frequency is linearly dependent upon the bond order. For large values of ν and small interval $\Delta\nu$, however, no distinction between quadratic and simple linear dependency is possible.

10.3. Dipole Moments

Problem 10.11: Which of the following molecules (a)–(n) have no dipole moment on account of their symmetry?

(a)

H_3C-CH_3

(b)

ClH_2C-CH_2Cl

(c)

$N(SiH_3)_3$

(d)

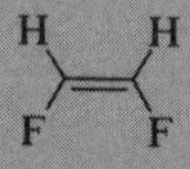

(e)

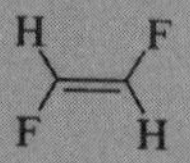

(f)

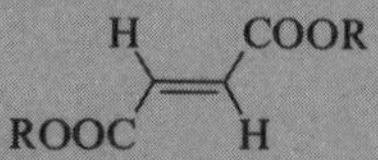

(g)

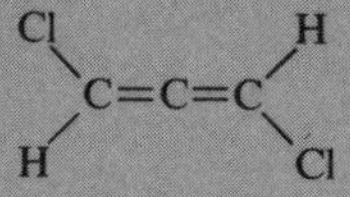

(h)

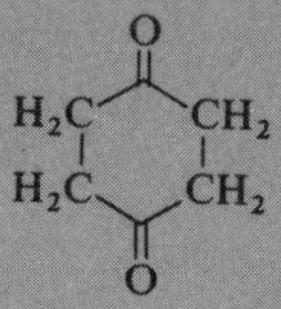

(i)

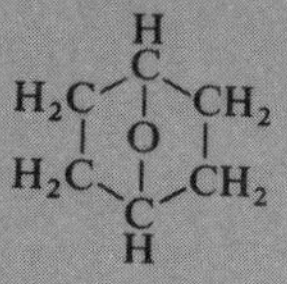

(j)

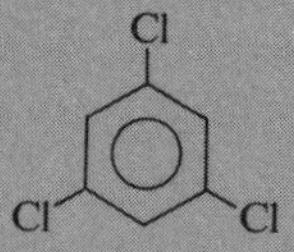

(k)

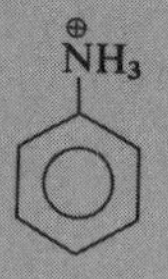

(l)

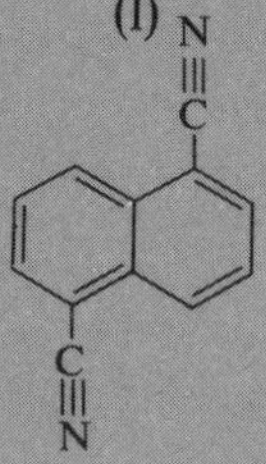

(m)

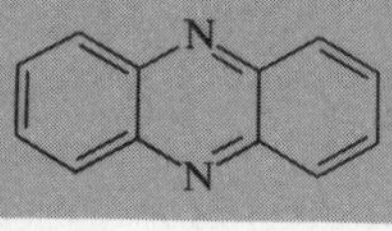

(n)

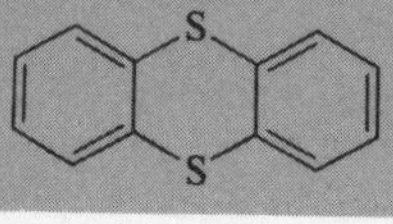

According to the symmetry rules, the compounds (a), (c), (e), (h), (j), (l), and (m) possess no dipole moment. For the individual cases:

(a) The staggered conformations II in ethane are energetically favored over the eclipsed (I), and have an inversion center for an angle of twist $\omega = 60°$, or three twofold axes at right angles to the threefold axis for $0° < \omega < 60°$.

(I)

D_{3h}

(II)

D_{3d}

D_3

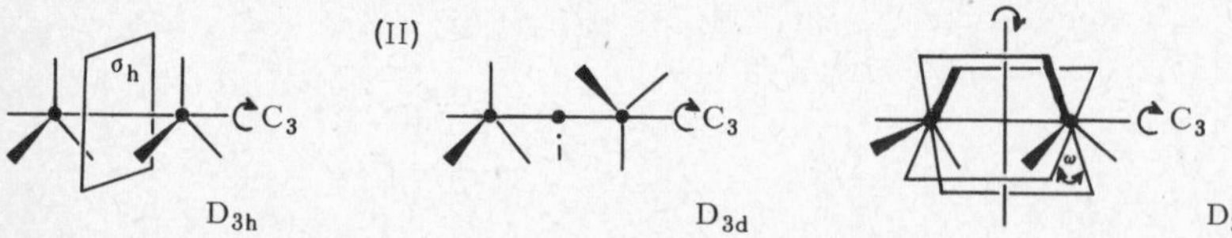

None of the conformations contributes to a finite moment.

(b) Of the energetically preferred staggered conformations of 1,2-dichloro-ethane, the antiplanar one (I) has no moment, while the gauche conformations (II) have measurable moments.

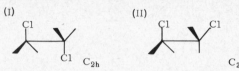

(I) C_{2h}

(II) C_2

(c) Trisilylamine is without dipole, because of its planar $N(Si)_3$ framework of D_{3h} symmetry which contrasts with that of trimethylamine.

(d) and (e) Trans-1,2-difluoroethylene (C_{2h}) displays no dipole moment because it possesses an inversion center, in contrast to the cis compound (C_{2v}).

(f) In fumaric ester, planar conformations of symmetry C_s are possible because of the unsymmetric carboxylic ester groups; these contribute to the experimentally determined dipole moment of 2.39 *Debye*.

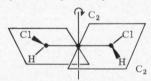

(g) 1,3-Dichloroallene has just one symmetry element, a twofold axis:

and should therefore have a finite moment.

(h) In 1,4-cyclohexanedione, the boat forms, of which I is energetically more favorable would contribute to a finite moment. However, the molecule prefers the twist form III (D_2) which is dipole-free:

(I)   (II)   (III)

(i) A three-dimensional representation of the tricyclic ether:

shows that a dipole moment is to be expected.

(j) 1,3,5-Trichlorobenzene has no dipole moment because of its D_{3h} symmetry.

(k) No coordinate-independent dipole moment can be defined for charged molecules.

(l) 1,5-Dicyanonaphthalene has an inversion center (C_{2h} symmetry) and consequently has no dipole moment.

(m) and (n) In contrast to planar phenazine (D_{2h}) which has no dipole, thianthrene

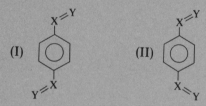

C_{2v}

is bent, and has a dipole moment of 1.5 *Debye*.

Problem 10.12: In 1,4-disubstituted benzene derivatives, the group X=Y possesses a dipole moment which does not coincide with the molecular axis:

(I)   X=Y   Y=X   (II)   X=Y   X=Y

Calculate the total dipole moment μ_G assuming both (a) that the two conformers are present in the mole fractions κ_I and $\kappa_{II} = 1 - \kappa_I$ and (b) that the groups X=Y can rotate freely.

(a) The moment perpendicular to the rotational axis amounts to $\mu_{xy}\cos\alpha$. For the total moment of a mixture of both conformers we obtain:

$$\mu_I = 0 \qquad\qquad \mu_{II} = 2\mu_{xy}\cos\alpha$$
$$P_I = 0 \qquad\qquad P_{II} = k \cdot \mu_{II}^2$$
$$P_G = \kappa_I P_I + \kappa_{II} P_{II} = k\,\kappa_{II}\mu_{II}^2 = k \cdot \mu_G^2$$
$$\mu_G = \sqrt{\kappa_{II}}\,\mu_{II} = 2 \cdot \sqrt{\kappa_{II}} \cdot \mu_{xy}\cos\alpha$$

For $\kappa_I = \kappa_{II} = \dfrac{1}{2}$, we find

$$\mu_G = \frac{1}{\sqrt{2}}\mu_{II} = \sqrt{2}\,\mu_{xy}\cos\alpha.$$

(b) Free rotation of both XY groups corresponds to the rotation of one group relative to the other, and the resultant dipole moment μ_R of a discrete conformation is:

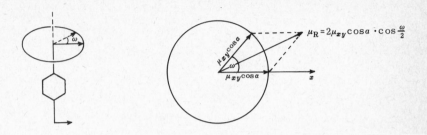

The total polarizability P_G is the sum of n different discrete conformations

$$P_G = \sum_n \kappa_n P_n = k \cdot \sum_n \kappa_n \mu_n^2 = k \cdot \mu_G^2.$$

For a continuous range of conformations summation is replaced by integration from o to π $(d\kappa = d\omega/\pi)$:

$$P_G = k \int_o^\pi \mu_R^2 (\omega) \frac{d\omega}{\pi} = k \int_o^\pi \left(2\mu_{xy} \cos\alpha \cdot \cos\frac{\omega}{2}\right)^2 \frac{d\omega}{\pi}$$

$$= k \cdot 4\mu_{xy}^2 \cos^2\alpha \cdot \frac{1}{\pi} \int_o^\pi \cos^2 \frac{\omega}{2} d\omega = k \cdot \mu_G^2$$

With

$$\int_o^\pi \cos^2 \frac{\omega}{2} d\omega = 2 \int_o^{\pi/2} \cos^2 x \, dx = \frac{\pi}{2}$$

we obtain

$$P_G = k \cdot 4\mu_{xy}^2 \cos^2\alpha \cdot \frac{1}{\pi} \cdot \frac{\pi}{2} = k \cdot 2\mu_{xy}^2 \cos^2\alpha,$$

$$\mu_G = \sqrt{2}\,\mu_{xy} \cdot \cos\alpha.$$

The result according to model (b) cannot be differentiated from that obtained by model (a) for free rotation of both groups and for $\kappa_I = \kappa_{II} = 1/2$. On the other hand, different results are to be expected when the energy of the conformations varies with the angle ω, and/or $\kappa_I \neq \kappa_{II}$.

Problem 10.13: Cis- and trans-1,2-dichlorocyclohexane (a, b). 1,2,3,4-tetra-chlorocyclohexane of unspecified configuration (c), and β-hexachlorocyclo-hexane (d) were found to possess the following moments:

(a)	(b)	(c)	(d)

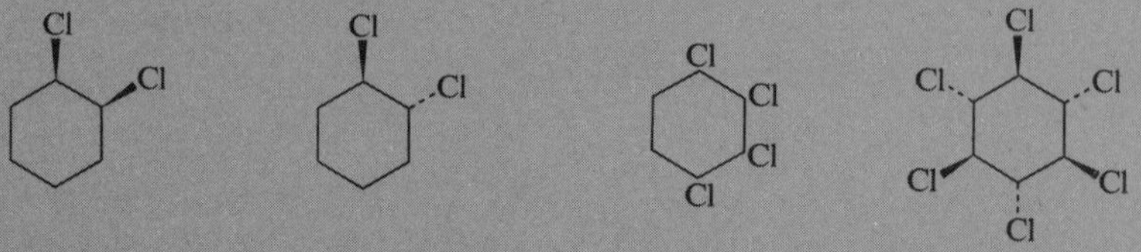

3·1 D	2·7 D	3·0 D	0 D

Calculate the dipole moments for (a) through (d), assuming an ideal chair form of the six-membered ring ($\measuredangle\,CCC=109\cdot5°$) and a bond moment $\mu_{C-Cl} = 1\cdot9$ D, and compare the results with the experimental values.

(a) Cis-1,2-dichlorocyclohexane:

Both the possible conformations I and II have one chlorine atom in an axial (a) position and one in an equatorial (e) position:

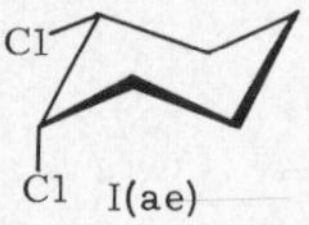

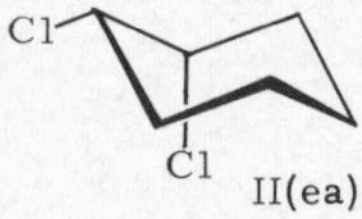

and therefore have the same dipole moment, which can be constructed in a vector diagram as follows:

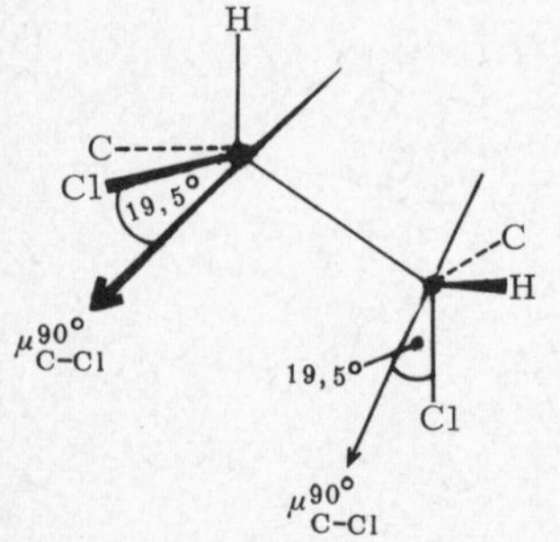

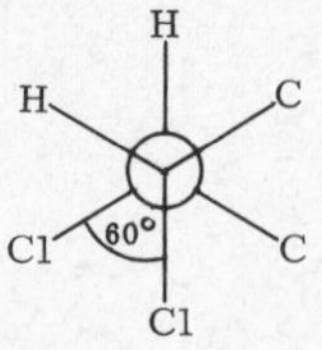

$$\mu_{C-Cl}^{90°} = \mu_{C-Cl} \cdot \cos 19.5° \qquad \mu_G = \sqrt{\mu_1^2 + \mu_2^2 + 2\mu_1\mu_2 \cos 60°}$$

$$= 1.9 \cdot 0.943 = 1.79\,D \qquad = \mu_{C-Cl}^{90°}\sqrt{3}$$

$$= 1.79 \cdot 1.732 = 3.1\,D$$

Calculated and experimental values are in good agreement.

(b) Trans-1,2-dichlorocyclohexane:
In the trans configuration, the two possible conformations I and II differ with respect to the positions of the chlorine atoms:

I(ee)   II(aa)

Of these, II obviously has a total dipole moment $\mu_{II} = 0\,D$ because of the equal and opposite bond moments. I has the same moment as the cis-isomer:

(trans)   (cis)

If both conformations with $\mu_I = 3.1\,D$ and $\mu_{II} = 0\,D$ coexist in equilibrium the total moment should be $\mu_G < 3.1\,D$. The experimental value $\mu_G = 2.7\,D$ indicates preponderance of conformation I.

(c) 1,2,3,4-Tetrachlorocyclohexane:
The 6 possible configurations (A) – (F) can always occur in the conformations I and II, which are related as object and mirror image only in cases (A) and (E). The following tabular survey also contains the calculated dipole moments of the individual conformations:

Configuration	Conformations I		II	μ_I [D]	μ_{II}
(A) cis cis cis	(eaea)	≡	(aeae)	5.3	5.3
(B) cis cis trans	(eaee)		(aeaa)	3.1	3.1
(C) cis trans cis	(eaae)		(aeea)	0.0	3.1
(D) cis trans trans	(eaaa)		(aeee)	3.1	4.4
(E) trans cis trans	(eeaa)	≡	(aaee)	3.1	3.1
(F) trans trans trans	(eeee)		(aaaa)	3.1	0.0

The two moments μ_A and $\mu_{D,II}$, which can neither be traced back to the moment of cis- or trans-1,2-dichlorocyclohexane nor be but equal to zero, can be expediently calculated as follows:

μ_A:

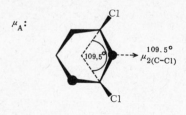

$$\mu_{2(C-Cl)}^{109.5°} = \sqrt{2\mu_{C-Cl}^2 + 2\mu_{C-Cl}^2 \cos 109.5°}$$

$$= \sqrt{7.22 - 2.41} = 2.2\,D$$

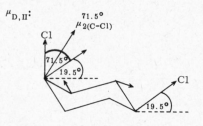

$$\mu_A = \sqrt{(2\mu_{C-Cl})^2 + (\mu_{2(C-Cl)}^{109.5°})^2 + 2 \cdot (2\mu_{C-Cl}) \cdot \mu_{2(C-Cl)}^{109.5°} \cdot \cos 60°}$$

$$= \sqrt{3.8^2 + 2.2^2 + 3.8 \cdot 2.2}$$

$$= 5.3\,D$$

$\mu_{D,II}$:

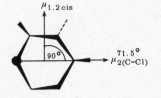

$$\mu_{2(C-Cl)}^{71.5°} = \sqrt{2\mu_{C-Cl}^2 + 2\mu_{C-Cl}^2 \cdot \cos 71.5°}$$

$$= 3.1\,D$$

$$\mu_{D,II} = \sqrt{(\mu_{2(C-Cl)}^{71.5°})^2 + (\mu_{1.2\,cis})^2}$$

$$= 3.1 \cdot \sqrt{2}$$

$$= 4.4\,D$$

This result can be obtained in a more elegant way by utilizing the following vector shift:

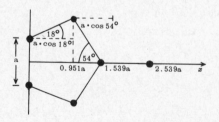

$$\mu_{D,II} = 2\,(\mu_{2\,(C-Cl)}^{109.5°})^2 = 2 \cdot 2.2\,D = 4.4\,D$$

The experimental value $\mu = 3.0\,D$ cannot be assigned to any definite configuration; presumably a mixture is present.

(d) β-Hexachlorocyclohexane:
Both conformations

possess a center of inversion, and consequently a dipole moment $\mu = 0$ in agreement with experiment.

Problem 10.14: Calculate the π-electron contribution to the dipole moment of fulvene and to that of heptafulvene (HMO Tables ⑤– and ⑦–, Volume 3) assuming regular rings with all C—C distances 1·4 Å.

(a)   (b)

With the CC distance $a = 1.4$ Å the coordinates of the fulvene centers in the x-direction are:

With the charge densities (Vol. 3) we deduce as the π_x contribution to the dipole moment

$$\mu_{\pi x} = e \cdot a \cdot \sum_\mu x_\mu (q_\mu - 1) \tag{10/42}$$

$$= 4.8 \cdot 1.4 \left[(2 \cdot 0 \cdot (0.073) + 2 \cdot 0.951(0.092) + 1.539(0.047) + 2.539(-0.378) \right]$$

$$= 6.72 \left[0.175 + 0.072 - 0.960 \right] = -4.79 \, D$$

The experimentally determined moment $\mu_G^{exp} = 1.3 \, Debye$ is smaller by a factor of 3.7, but nevertheless points in the direction from the side chain into the ring.

(b) Assuming a planar system with a CC distance $a = 1.4$ Å, we obtain the coordinates of the heptafulvene centers as:

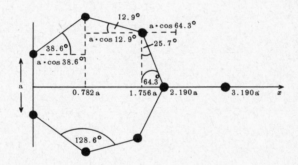

With the charge densities (Vol. 3), the π_x-component to the dipole moment is is

$$\mu_{\pi x} = e \cdot a \sum_\mu x_\mu (q_\mu - 1) \tag{10/42}$$

$$= 4.8 \cdot 1.4 \left[2 \cdot 0 \cdot (-0.047) + 2 \cdot 0.782(-0.038) + 2 \cdot 1.756(-0.058) + 2.190(-0.024) \right.$$
$$\left. + 3.190(+0.311) \right]$$

$$= 6.72 \left[-0.060 - 0.204 - 0.053 + 0.992 \right]$$

$$= +4.55 \, D$$

In view of its positive value the moment points in the direction of the x-axis; it is directed from the ring toward the side chain in contrast to fulvene.

Although the π_x-components of the dipole moments calculated for fulvene and heptafulvene are certainly too large because of the overemphasis on polar structures in the HMO theory, they do agree in their directions with chemical experience.

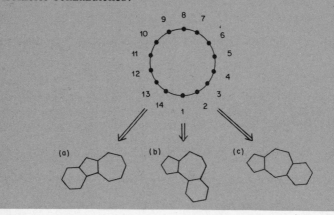

(a) $\mu_{\pi x} = -4.79\ D$

(b) $\mu_{\pi x} = 4.55\ D$

Problem 10.15: Starting from a perturbation of a 14-perimeter (HMO Table ⑭, Volume 3), what does HMO theory predict regarding the dipole moments of the isomeric benzazulenes?

The compounds are conveniently numbered as follows:

(a)   (b)   (c)

because the bond between starred and unstarred centers at the junction of the 6-membered ring then ensures that the bond-atom polarizabilities are identically equal to zero.

$$\pi_{*0,\mu} = 0$$

Thus only one new bond has to be introduced as a perturbation at the juncture point between the 5- and 7-membered ring. With $\delta\beta = \beta$ and according to

$$q'_\mu = q_\mu + 2\pi_{\rho\sigma,\mu}\frac{\delta\beta}{\beta} = 1 + 2\pi_{\rho\sigma,\mu} \quad,$$

$$q'_\mu - 1 = 2\pi_{\rho\sigma,\mu} = \delta q_\mu$$

we obtain the desired changes in the charge orders δq_μ directly from the bond-atom polarizabilities

$$\mu_x = e \cdot a \sum_\mu x_\mu \delta q_\mu \quad,$$

$$\mu_y = e \cdot a \sum_\mu y_\mu \delta q_\mu.$$

Vectorial addition of the partial moments in the x- and y-directions yields the π-component of the total dipole moment:

$$\mu_\pi = \sqrt{\mu_x^2 + \mu_y^2}$$

The coordinates are most easily determined graphically on millimeter paper; the accuracy is adequate in view of the approximation used. The molecular diagrams are conveniently constructed in the present case by drawing circumscribed circles whose radii have the following values for each individual ring:

$$r_a^{(5)} = 0,8507\,a; \; r_a^{(6)} = 1,0000\,a; \; r_a^{(7)} = 1.1523\,a$$

upon which the bond lengths $a = 1.4$ Å are marked off.

(a) 1,2-Benzoazulene:

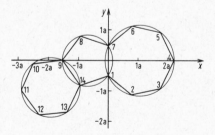

With the coordinates and the polarizabilities (Vol. 3) we obtain:

μ	$x_\mu\,[a]$	$y_\mu\,[a]$	$2\pi_{17,\mu}$	$x_\mu \cdot \delta q_\mu$	$y_\mu \cdot \delta q_\mu$
1	0	−0.50	−0.020	0	0.010
2	+0.78	−1.12	−0.133	−0.104	0.149
3	+1.76	−0.90	−0.035	−0.062	0.032
4	+2.19	0	−0.126	−0.276	0
5	+1.76	+0.90	−0.035	−0.062	−0.032
6	+0.78	+1.12	−0.133	−0.104	−0.149
7	0	+0.50	−0.020	0	−0.010
8	−0.95	+0.81	0.123	−0.117	0.100
9	−1.54	0	0.010	−0.115	0
10	−2.53	−0.10	0.108	−0.273	−0.011
11	−2.94	−1.02	0.017	−0.042	−0.017
12	−2.35	−1.83	0.108	−0.254	−0.200
13	−1.36	−1.72	0.010	−0.014	−0.017
14	−0.95	−0.81	0.123	−0.117	−0.100
				−1.440	−0.245

From the component moments μ_x and μ_y

$$\mu_x = e \cdot a \cdot (\Sigma\, x_\mu \cdot \delta q_\mu) = 4.8 \cdot 1.4 \cdot (-1.440) = -9.68\,D,$$

$$\mu_y = 6.72 \cdot (-0.245) = -1.65\,D$$

the π-contribution to the total dipole moment is

$$\mu_\pi = \sqrt{(-9.68)^2 + (-1.65)^2} = 9.82\,D,$$

which is oriented according to the signs of the component moments as follows:

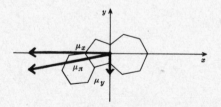

(b) 4,5-Benzoazulene:

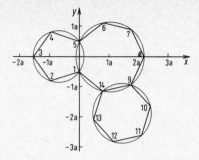

With the coordinates and the polarizabilities (Vol. 3) we obtain:

μ	$x_\mu[a]$	$y_\mu[a]$	$2\pi_{15,\mu}$	$x_\mu \cdot \delta q_\mu$	$y_\mu \cdot \delta q_\mu$
1	0	−0.50	+0.071	0	−0.036
2	−0.95	−0.81	+0.169	−0.161	−0.137
3	−1.54	0	+0.078	−0.120	0
4	−0.95	+0.81	+0.169	−0.161	+0.137
5	0	+0.50	+0.071	0	+0.036
6	+0.78	+1.12	−0.133	−0.104	−0.149
7	+1.76	+0.90	+0.010	+0.018	+0.009
8	+2.19	0	−0.103	−0.226	0
9	+1.76	−0.90	−0.005	−0.009	+0.005
10	+2.43	−1.65	−0.097	−0.237	+0.158
11	+2.12	−2.59	−0.005	−0.011	+0.013
12	+1.14	−2.81	−0.103	−0.120	+0.289
13	+0.47	−2.08	+0.010	+0.005	−0.021
14	+0.78	−1.12	−0.133	−0.104	+0.149
				−1.230	+0.453

From the component moments calculated as

$$\mu_x = 6.72 \cdot (-1.230) = -8.3\,D,$$

$$\mu_y = 6.72 \cdot 0.453 = +3.0\,D,$$

the π-contribution to the dipole moment is

$$\mu_\pi = \sqrt{(-8.3)^2 + (3.0)^2} = 8.8\,D.$$

Its orientation follows from the signs of the component moments

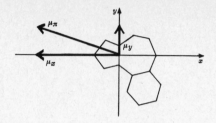

(c) 5,6-Benzoazulene:

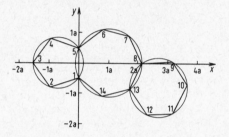

With the coordinates from the molecular diagram and the bond-atom polarizabilities (Vol. 3), the following values are found:

μ	$x_\mu[a]$	$y_\mu[a]$	$2\pi_{15,\mu}$	$x_\mu \cdot \delta q_\mu$	$y_\mu \cdot \delta q_\mu$
1				0	−0.036
2				−0.161	−0.137
3				−0.120	0
4	as under (b)			−0.161	+0.137
5				0	+0.036
6				−0.104	−0.149
7				+0.018	+0.009
8				−0.226	0
9	+3.19	+0.07	−0.005	−0.016	−0.000
10	+3.75	−0.75	−0.097	−0.364	+0.073
11	+3.32	−1.65	−0.005	−0.017	+0.008
12	+2.32	−1.73	−0.103	−0.239	+0.178
13	+1.76	−0.90	+0.010	+0.018	−0.009
14				−0.104	+0.149
				−1.476	+0.259

From the component moments μ_x and μ_y

$$\mu_x = 6.72 \cdot (-1.476) = -9.9\,D,$$

$$\mu_y = 6.72 \cdot 0.259 \quad = +1.7\,D$$

the π-contribution to the dipole moment is

$$\mu_\pi = \sqrt{(-9.9)^2 + (1.7)^2} = 10.0\,D,$$

which is oriented as follows corresponding to the signs of μ_x and μ_y:

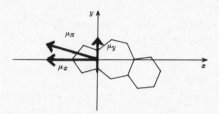

The result can be discussed as follows: the direction of the resulting dipole moment μ_π always agrees with the expected polarization of azulene — negative excess charge in the 5-membered ring (cyclopentadienyl anion) and a positive one in the 7-membered ring (tropylium cation). The magnitudes of the dipole moments on the other hand are basically too large, and can be corrected, e.g., in the following way:

From the experimentally determined dipole moment of azulene

$$\mu_{\text{exp.}} = \mu_\sigma + \mu_\pi = 1.0\,D$$

and from the π-contribution calculated by way of a perturbation treatment of the 10-perimeter to facilitate comparison,

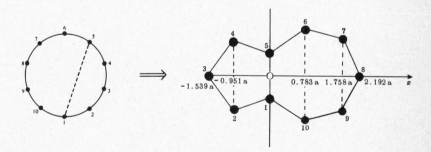

$$\mu_\pi = e \cdot a\,(2 \cdot 0 \cdot 0.037 + 2 \cdot (-0.951) \cdot 0.185 + (-1.539) \cdot 0.056 + 2 \cdot 0.783(-0.163)$$
$$+ 2 \cdot 1.758(-0.015) + 2.192(-0.144))$$
$$= 6.72 \cdot 1.062 = 7.1\,D$$

the factor

$$\frac{\mu_{\text{exp.}}}{\mu_{\text{calc.}}} = \frac{1.0}{7.1} = 0.141$$

is obtained, neglecting the μ_σ-component.

Applying this factor, the approximate values for the dipole moments of the benzazulenes become

(a) $9.8 \cdot 0.141 = 1.4\,D$
(b) $8.8 \cdot 0.141 = 1.2\,D$
(c) $10.1 \cdot 0.141 = 1.4\,D$

Problem 10.16:   Calculate the π-electron contributions to the dipole moments and their directions in each of the following heterocycles, and compare them with the measured total moments μ^{exp}:

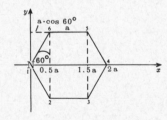

μ^{exp} 2·21   2·19   2·55   1·95 D

The nitrogen atom is introduced into the isoconjugate compounds according to (6/80) by applying the perturbation

$$<\mu_N|h|\mu_N> = h_N\beta = 0.5\,\beta$$

With the charge order $q_\mu = 1$ in alternant π-electron systems, and with (7/64) we find

$$q'_\mu = q_\mu + h_N\pi_{N,\mu} = 1 + 0.5\,\pi_{N,\mu}$$

$$\delta q_\mu = (q'_\mu - 1) = 0.5\,\pi_{N,\mu}$$

and obtain the following π-component of the dipole moments for the individual compounds:

(a)   Pyridine:
With the coordinates

y↑
a·cos 60°
6   a   5
60°
N   0.5a   1.5a   2a   x
2   3

and the atom-atom polarizabilities (Vol. 3) we obtain

$$\mu_\pi = e \cdot a \cdot \Sigma x_\mu \delta q_\mu = e \cdot a \cdot \Sigma x_\mu \cdot 0.5 \, \pi_{N,\mu}$$

$$= 6.72 \, [0 \cdot (0.199) + 2 \cdot 0.5(-0.079) + 2 \cdot 1.5(0.005) + 2(-0.051)]$$

$$= 6.72 \cdot (-0.166) = -1.1 \, D$$

(b) Quinoline:

With the coordinates

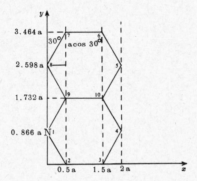

ant the atom-atom polarizabilities of naphthalene (Vol. 3), we find from the moments in the x- and y-directions the π-part of the dipole moment

$$\mu_\pi^x = 6.72 \, [0(0.222 + 0.014) + 0.5(-0.107 - 0.016 - 0.045)$$
$$+ 1.5(0.009 + 0.003 + 0.002) + 2.0(-0.070 - 0.012)]$$
$$= 6.72 \cdot (-0.227) = -1.53 \, D$$

$$\mu_\pi^y = 6.72 \, [0(-0.107 + 0.009) + 0.866 \, (0.221 - 0.070) + 1.732 \, (-0.045 + 0.002)$$
$$+ 2.598(-0.012 + 0.014) + 3.464(+0.003 - 0.016)]$$
$$= 6.72 \cdot (+0.016) = 0.11 \, D$$

$$\mu_\pi = \sqrt{(\mu_\pi^x)^2 + (\mu_\pi^y)^2} = 1.5 \, D$$

(c) Isoquinoline:

With the coordinates (b) which in this case have the nitrogen atom in position 2, and with the atom-atom polarizabilities (Vol. 3) the π-contribution to the dipole moment is

$$\mu_\pi^x = 6.72 \, [0(-0.107 - 0.016) + 0.5(0.203 + 0.000 + 0.004)$$
$$+ 1.5(-0.055 - 0.017 - 0.025) + 2.0(+0.009 + 0.003)]$$
$$= 6.72 \cdot (-0.016) = -0.11 \, D$$

$$\mu_\pi^y = 6.72\,[0(+0.203 - 0.055) + 0.866(-0.107 + 0.009) + 1.732(0.004 - 0.025)$$
$$+2.598(0.003 - 0.016) + 3.464(-0.017 - 0.000)]$$
$$= 6.72 \cdot (-0.212) = -1.42\,D$$

$$\mu_\pi = \sqrt{(\mu_\pi^x)^2 + (\mu_\pi^y)^2} = 1.4\,D$$

(d) Acridine:
With the coordinates

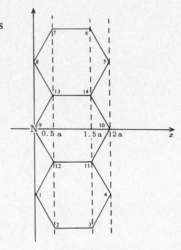

and with the atom-atom polarizabilities of anthracene (Vol. 3), the value of μ_π is

$$\mu_\pi = 6.72[0(2(0.022) + 0.263) + 0.5(2(-0.027) + 2(-0.063))$$
$$+ 1.5(2(0.007) + 2(0.005)) + 2.0(2(-0.020) + (-0.108))]$$
$$= 6.72(-0.350) = -2.4\,D$$

A comparison of calculated and experimental dipole moments yields:

$\mu_\pi^{calc.}$ 1.1 D	1.5 D	1.4 D	2.4 D
$(\mu_\pi + \mu_\sigma)^{exp.}$ 2.21 D	2.19 D	2.55 D	1.95 D

The poor agreement shows that in the present case other factors are obviously decisive in determining the magnitude of the dipole moment, e.g., the considerable contribution of the free electron pair on nitrogen, the interaction of these electrons with neighboring bonds, the changes in the partial moments of the C–N σ-bonds, and the mutual interaction of π- and σ-electrons.

10.4. Spin Populations

Problem 10.17: What ESR spectra would one expect for (a) the ethylene radical cation, (b) the cyclopropenyl radical, and (c) the benzene radical anion?

(a)   (b)   (c)

$[H_2C{=}CH_2]^{\oplus}$ (triangle with radical dot) $\left[\text{(hexagon)} \right]^{\ominus} \cdot$

The systems (a) through (c) have a set of 4,3 and 6 equivalent protons, respectively.

$$\left[\begin{array}{c} H \quad H \\ \diagup\diagdown \\ H \quad H \end{array}\right]^{\oplus} \cdot \qquad \overset{H}{\underset{H \diagup \quad \diagdown H}{\triangle}} \qquad \left[\begin{array}{c} H \\ H \diagup\diagdown H \\ H \diagdown\diagup H \\ H \end{array}\right]^{\ominus}$$

$$D_{2h} \qquad\qquad D_{3h} \qquad\qquad D_{6h}$$

For reasons of symmetry the spin populations in the $2p_z$-atomic orbitals of the carbon atoms are $\rho_C = \frac{1}{2}$, $\rho_C = \frac{1}{3}$, and $\rho_C = \frac{1}{6}$. With $|Q| = 23$ *Gauss* we thus obtain the ESR spectra:

(a)

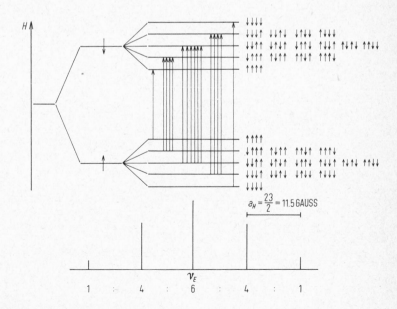

$$a_H = \frac{23}{2} = 11.5\,GAUSS$$

1 : 4 : 6 : 4 : 1

(b)

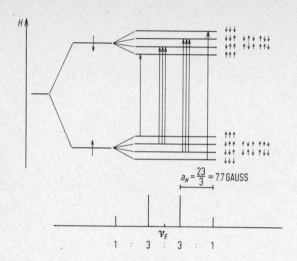

$$a_H = \frac{23}{3} = 7.7 \text{ GAUSS}$$

ν_E

1 : 3 : 3 : 1

(c) There are generally 2^n different possible arrangements of n spin moments. The number of those combinations in which r spin moments lie in the direction of the field, and $n-r$ in the opposite orientation is given by

$$\binom{n}{r} = \frac{n(n-1)(n-2) \dots (n-r)}{1 \cdot 2 \dots r} = \frac{n!}{(n-r)! \, r!}.$$

In the above case of six spin moments there are accordingly $2^6 = 64$ possible arrangements of which the following are equivalent:

$$\binom{6}{0} = \frac{1 \cdot 2 \cdot 3 \cdot 4 \cdot 5 \cdot 6}{1 \cdot 2 \cdot 3 \cdot 4 \cdot 5 \cdot 6} = 1 = \binom{6}{6}$$

$$\binom{6}{1} = \frac{1 \cdot 2 \cdot 3 \cdot 4 \cdot 5 \cdot 6}{1 \cdot 2 \cdot 3 \cdot 4 \cdot 5 \cdot 1} = 6 = \binom{6}{5}$$

$$\binom{6}{2} = \frac{1 \cdot 2 \cdot 3 \cdot 4 \cdot 5 \cdot 6}{1 \cdot 2 \cdot 3 \cdot 4 \cdot 1 \cdot 2} = 15 = \binom{6}{4}$$

$$\binom{6}{3} = \frac{1 \cdot 2 \cdot 3 \cdot 4 \cdot 5 \cdot 6}{1 \cdot 2 \cdot 3 \cdot 1 \cdot 2 \cdot 3} = 20$$

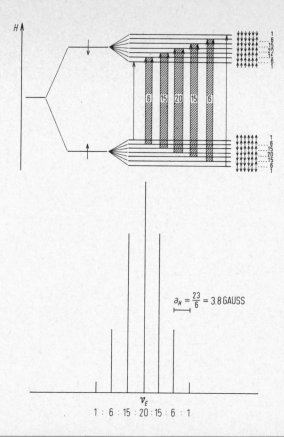

$$a_H = \frac{23}{6} = 3.8 \text{ GAUSS}$$

ν_E

1 : 6 : 15 : 20 : 15 : 6 : 1

Problem 10.18: How many lines are to be expected in the ESR spectrum of the hydrazine radical cation $[N_2H_2]^{\oplus}$ and what will the relative intensities be? Draw a scheme for the expected ESR spectrum.

In the hydrazine radical cation

$$\left[\begin{array}{c} H \\ H \end{array} \!\! N \cdots N \!\! \begin{array}{c} H \\ H \end{array} \right]^{\oplus}$$

with D_{2h} symmetry, there are two equivalent nitrogen atoms ($I_K^N = 1$) and four equivalent protons ($I_K^H = \frac{1}{2}$). The spin population in each of the nitrogen $2p_z$-atomic orbitals of the π-system which is occupied by 3 π-electrons amounts to $\rho = \frac{1}{2}$ for symmetry reasons. According to (10/47) and (10/48) the total number of hyperfine structure lines to be expected is

$$z_G = z_N \cdot z_H = (2 n_K^N I_K^N + 1)(2 n_K^H I_K^H + 1)$$

$$= 5 \cdot 5 = 25$$

The intensity ratio is taken from Table (10/49):

$$n_K^H = 4 \qquad 1:4:6:4:1$$
$$n_K^N = 2 \qquad 1:2:3:2:1$$

1 2 3 2 1   4 8 12 8 4   6 12 18 12 6   4 8 12 8 4   1 2 3 2 1

The scheme is conveniently drawn in the following way:

(a) Possible orientations of the two nitrogen moments

↑↑   ①

↑→ + →↑   ②

↑↓ + ↓↑ + $\overset{\rightarrow}{\rightarrow}$ ③

↓→ + →↓   ②

↓↓   ①

(b) Possible orientations of the four proton moments

↑↑↑↑   ①

↓↑↑↑ + ↑↓↑↑ + ↑↑↓↑ + ↑↑↑↓   ④

↓↓↑↑ + ↓↑↓↑ + ↓↑↑↓ + ↑↓↓↑ + ↑↓↑↓ + ↑↑↓↓   ⑥

↓↓↓↑ + ↓↓↑↓ + ↓↑↓↓ + ↑↓↓↓   ④

↓↓↓↓   ①

(c) Interaction with coupling constants $a_H = 26/2 = 13$ *Gauss* and $a_N = 20/2 = 10$ *Gauss* which follow from the spin density $\rho = \dfrac{1}{2}$ leads to

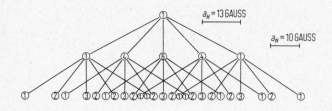

and thus to the intensities

1|2|4|3|8|6|2|12|12|4|1|8|18|8|1|4|12|12| 2|6|8|3|4|2|1

(d) We therefore obtain the following schematic ESR spectrum:

ν_E

10 GAUSS

Problem 10.19:   How many lines will appear in the ESR spectra of the anthracene and the azulene radical anion?

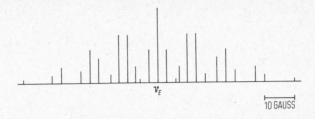

(a)   (b)

What values for the coupling constants of the equivalent sets of protons are predicted by HMO theory?

(a) Anthracene radical anion:

The protons within the three sets $(1, 4, 5, 8)$, $(2, 3, 6, 7)$, and $(9, 10)$ are equivalent. According to (10/47) and (10/48) there are thus $5 \cdot 5 \cdot 3 = 75$ lines to be expected. The spin densities $c_{8\mu}^2$ are obtained from the coefficients $c_{8\mu}$ (Vol. 3), and the coupling constants a_μ according to (10/50) with $|Q| = 23$ *Gauss*. The proportionality factors $|Q_\mu|$ for the measured values a_μ^{exp} are given by the expression

$$\frac{a_\mu^{exp.}}{c_{8\mu}^2} = |Q_\mu| . \tag{10/50}$$

μ	$c_{8\mu}$	$c_{8\mu}^2$	a_μ	$a_\mu^{exp.}$	$|Q_\mu|$	a_μ'
1,4,5,8	−0.311	0.097	2.23	2.74	28.2	2.77
2,3,6,7	0.220	0.048	1.10	1.10	31.5	1.37
9,10	0.440	0.194	4.46	5.34	27.5	5.55

The improved coupling constants a'_μ were calculated with the corrected average value:

$$\frac{\sum\limits_{\mu=1}^{10} a_\mu^{\text{exp.}}}{\sum\limits_{\mu=1}^{10} c_{8\mu}^2} = \frac{27.68}{0.968} = 28.6 \text{ Gauss} = \overline{|Q_\mu|}$$

and are in good agreement with the measured values $a_\mu^{\text{exp.}}$.

(b) Azulene radical anion:

To five sets of equivalent protons $(1, 3), (2), (4, 8), (5, 7)$, and (6) there correspond $3 \cdot 2 \cdot 3 \cdot 3 \cdot 2 = 108$ lines according to (10/47) and (10/48). Using the coefficients $c_{6\mu}$ (Vol. 3) we obtain as spin densities $c_{6\mu}^2$, with $|Q| = 23$ *Gauss*, as coupling constants a_μ and from the measured values $a_\mu^{\text{exp.}}$ the proportionality factors $|Q_\mu|$

μ	$c_{6\mu}$	$c_{6\mu}^2$	a_μ	$a_\mu^{\text{exp.}}$	$|Q_\mu|$	a'_μ
1,3	0.063	0.004	0.09	0.28	(70.0)	0.14
2	−0.316	0.100	2.30	3.95	39.5	3.42
4,8	−0.470	0.221	5.08	6.22	28.1	7.56
5,7	−0.103	0.011	0.24	1.34	(121.8)	0.38
6	0.510	0.260	5.98	8.83	34.0	8.89

The improved coupling constants a'_μ were again calculated with the corrected average value (with the omission of the bracketed values)

$$\frac{\sum\limits_{\mu=1}^{8} a_\mu^{\text{exp.}}}{\sum\limits_{\mu=1}^{8} c_{6\mu}^2} = \frac{28.46}{0.832} = 34.2 \text{ Gauss} = \overline{|Q_\mu|}$$

and show considerably greater deviations from the measured values in contrast to the anthracene radical anion.

The proportionality factor $|Q|$ from (10/50) is thus generally to be regarded as a variable, and the commonly used value $|Q| = 23$ *Gauss*, which stems from the benzene radical anion, is only an indication of the magnitude for alternant radical anions. The assumption that $|Q|$ should be constant within a system to a first approximation receives some degree of confirmation from the above examples.

Problem 10.20: Determine the coupling constants a_μ from the ESR spectrum of the 1,3-butadiene radical anion

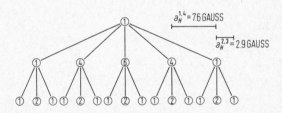

and use the values found and the HMO coefficients $c_{J\mu}$ (HMO Table K_4, Volume 3) to calculate the proportionality factor $|Q|$ of equation (10/46).

For the two sets of 2 and 4 magnetically equivalent protons of the 1, 3-butadiene radical anion, a total of 15 lines ($= 3 \cdot 5$) are to be expected according to (10/47) and (10/48) in the intensity ratio (10/49)

$$n_2 \quad 1 \quad 2 \quad 1$$

$$n_4 \quad 1 \quad 4 \quad 6 \quad 4 \quad 1$$

$$1 \quad 2 \quad 1 \qquad 4 \quad 8 \quad 4 \qquad 6 \quad 12 \quad 6 \qquad 4 \quad 8 \quad 4 \qquad 1 \quad 2 \quad 1$$

According to the scheme

we can deduce from the given spectrum

$$a_H^{14} = 7.6 \; Gauss$$

$$a_H^{23} = 2.9 \; Gauss$$

The HMO coefficients $c_{3\mu}$ (Vol. 3) for the molecular orbital Ψ_3 furnish the proportionality factors $|Q_\mu|$ according to (10/50):

μ	$c_{3\mu}$	$c_{3\mu}^2$	$\dfrac{a_\mu}{c_{3\mu}^2} = |Q_\mu|$
1.4	0.602	0.362	21.1 *Gauss*
2.3	−0.372	0.138	21.0 *Gauss*

As can be seen, the values $|Q_\mu|$ obtained agree well with each other, and deviate in this case by only about 9 % from the average value $|Q| = 23$ *Gauss*, most commonly used.

Problem 10.21: The acenaphthalene radical anion was found to have the following coupling constants:

$$a_H^a = 5\!\cdot\!72 \; Gauss$$
$$a_H^b = 4\!\cdot\!57 \; Gauss$$
$$a_H^c = 3\!\cdot\!12 \; Gauss$$
$$a_H^d = 0\!\cdot\!45 \; Gauss$$

The coefficients $c_{7\mu}$ of the molecular orbital Ψ_7 read:

μ	1	2	3	4	5	6	7	8
	0·32	−0·32	0·39	0·12	−0·42	0·42	−0·12	−0·39

Assign the coupling constants a_H^n to the sets of equivalent protons.

The equivalent protons are in positions

(1 + 2)
(3 + 8)
(4 + 7)
(5 + 6)

Using relation (10/50) $a_\mu = |Q| c_{7\mu}^2$ it can be shown that the coupling constants should be assigned as follows:

μ	$c_{7\mu}^2$	a_H^n [*Gauss*]	$|Q_\mu|$ [*Gauss*]
5.6	0.176	5.72	32.5
3.8	0.152	4.57	30.1
1.2	0.102	3.12	30.6
4.7	0.014	0.45	32.1

Because the values of $|Q_\mu|$ differ only slightly ($|\bar{Q}| = 31.3$ *Gauss*) we may confidently expect that the ESR spectrum of the acenaphthalene radical anion composed of $3^4 = 81$ lines can be satisfactorily interpreted within the framework of HMO theory.

Problem 10.22: The ESR spectra of the radical anion and the radical cation are almost identical in the case of pyrene (a), whereas they differ considerably from each other in acenaphth[1,2-a]acenaphthylene (b):

(a)   (b)

How can this observation be understood within the framework of the HMO theory?

Pyrene (a) is an alternant hydrocarbon having an even number (16) of centers. The general properties of such π-electron systems (Vol. 1, 5.3) lead to the following HMO orbital energy schemes for the two radical ions:

Because in this case the coefficients of the corresponding molecular orbitals $\Psi_{(x_J)}$ and $\Psi_{(-x_J)}$ differ only in sign according to (5/25) and (5/26), the squares of the coefficients $c_{J\mu}^2$ and the spin densities ρ_μ and therefore also the copling constants a_μ are always equally large for the three sets of 2,4, and 4 protons in the radical cation and the radical anion. Consequently the ESR spectra of both radical ions are predicted by HMO theory to be identical. The experimental observation that the coupling constants in the radical cation are slightly larger than in the radical anion can be attributed to the differing charge:

μ	$a_\mu\,(R^\oplus)$	$a_\mu\,(R^\ominus)$
1,3,6,8	5.38	4.75
2,7	1.18	1.09
4,5,9,10	2.12	2.08

Acenaphthacenaphthylene (b), on the other hand, represents a nonalternant π-electron system and HMO theory predicts, applying the above argument in reverse, for radical cation and radical anion,

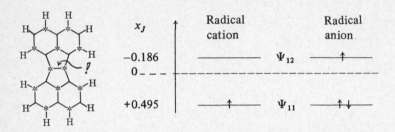

differing coupling constants a_μ for the 3 sets of 4 equivalent protons. The ESR spectra should therefore differ in both their hyperfine structure and their width. This expectation coincides with the experimental observation, as seen from the figure below. The width of the radical anion spectrum amounts to 29.4 *Gauss,* i.e. about two and a half times that of the radical cation spectrum (12.0 *Gauss*)!

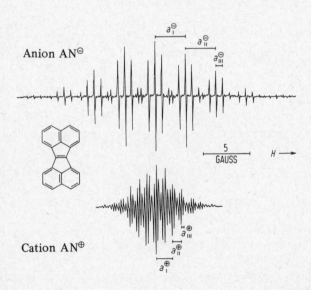

The situation described above is generally valid. The ESR spectra of radical cations and radical anions differ only slightly from each other as a result of pairwise correspondence between molecular orbitals in even alternant π-electron systems, whereas they differ considerably for most nonalternant systems.

Let us interpret the different behavior for the compounds pyrene (a) and acenaphth-acenaphthylene (b) chosen as examples on the basis of the relevant molecular orbitals, whose squares represent the spin density according to (10/43). The indentical HMO diagrams for the radical cation of pyrene and radical anion — except for signs — show that the unpaired electron is always located at the peripheral centers

In contrast, the HMO diagrams of acenaphthacenaphthylene (b) only show relatively large values of the coefficients for the peripheral centers in Ψ_{12}, while in Ψ_{11} the coefficients of the 'inner' centers tend to predominate. The unpaired electron is accordingly distributed relatively evenly over the whole system in the radical anion, whereas in the radical cation it is preferentially located in the region of the central five-membered rings.

Problem 10.23: Derive the predictions of HMO theory for the ESR spectra of the pentadienyl radical (a), the benzyl radical (b), and the perinaphthenyl radical (c):

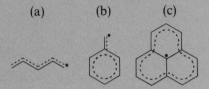

(a)   (b)   (c)

Radicals (a) through (c) are odd alternant π-electron systems in which the unpaired electron occupies the nonbonding molecular orbital Ψ_{nb}. In such systems the coefficients of the smaller unstarred set have the value zero for Ψ_{nb} according to (5/31), and therefore only coupling with the protons of the starred set is to be expected. Furthermore, geometrically nonequivalent centers may exhibit equivalent spin populations, although in general only geometrically equivalent centers have equal spin populations. For the systems (a) through (c) the HMO predictions agree only crudely with the measured spectra because small (negative) spin populations occur at the centers predicted to have a zero spin population.

(a) Pentadienyl radical:

Three sets of 1, 2, and 4 equivalent protons occur, and $2 \cdot 3 \cdot 5 = 30$ lines are to be expected according to (10/48). In contrast, HMO theory gives the nonbonding molecular orbital as

$$\Psi_3 = \frac{1}{\sqrt{3}} (\Phi_1 - \Phi_3 + \Phi_5).$$

according to (5/30) through (5/33). The resulting spin densities are

$$\rho_1 = \rho_3 = \rho_5 = \frac{1}{3}; \quad \rho_2 = \rho_4 = 0.$$

Thus six equally spaced lines $a_\mu = |Q|/3$ are predicted by HMO theory to arise from the interaction of the unpaired electron with the 5 populationally equivalent protons. Of the 10 lines (= 2 · 5) to be expected for the two sets of 1 and 4 geometrically equivalent protons, 4 are degenerate.

(b) Benzyl radical:

Four sets of 1, 2, 2, and 2 geometrically equivalent protons are present, and according to (10/48) $2 \cdot 3 \cdot 3 \cdot 3 = 54$ lines result. According to (5/30) through (5/33) the nonbonding molecular orbital is

$$\Psi_4 = \frac{1}{\sqrt{7}}(2\Phi_1 - \Phi_3 + \Phi_5 - \Phi_7)$$

and the spin densities are

$$\rho_1 = \frac{4}{7}; \; \rho_3 = \rho_5 = \rho_7 = \frac{1}{7}; \; \rho_2 = \rho_4 = \rho_6 = 0.$$

According to HMO theory only $3 \cdot 4 = 12$ lines are to be expected in the ESR spectrum corresponding to 2 sets with 2 and 3 protons of equivalent population density. The coupling constants are

$$a_1 = \frac{4|Q|}{7}; \; a_3 = a_5 = a_7 = \frac{|Q|}{7}.$$

Of the original 18 lines $(2 \cdot 3 \cdot 3)$ stemming from 3 sets of 1, 2, and 2 protons, 6 are degenerate.

(c) Perinaphthenyl radical:
Two sets of 3 and 6 geometrically equivalent protons are present, and according to (10/48) $4 \cdot 7 = 28$ lines are to be expected.

According to (5/30) through (5/33) the nonbonding molecular orbital is

$$\Psi_7 = \frac{1}{\sqrt{6}}(\Phi_1 - \Phi_3 + \Phi_4 - \Phi_6 + \Phi_7 - \Phi_9)$$

and the spin densities are therefore

$$\rho_1 = \rho_3 = \rho_4 = \rho_6 = \rho_7 = \rho_9 = \frac{1}{6},$$

$$\rho_2 = \rho_5 = \rho_8 = \rho_{10} = \rho_{11} = \rho_{12} = \rho_{13} = 0.$$

Corresponding to 6 protons of equivalent population, only 7 equally spaced lines $a_\mu = |Q|/6$ are predicted.

In practice the protons at the unstarred centers are also found to couple with the unpaired electron. Calculation according to many-electron models accounting for electronic interaction leads to 'negative' spin populations for such centers. This indicates that the π-electrons of the radicals or radical ions at such centers contribute a resultant spin which is opposite to that at the starred centers. The 'spin deficiency' must of course be compensated for by a 'spin excess'. For the allyl radical such calculations afford, in contrast to the HMO prediction

$$\frac{1}{2} \underline{\qquad} \quad 0 \underline{\qquad} \frac{1}{2}$$

a distribution according to

$$\frac{2}{3} \underline{\qquad} -\frac{1}{3} \underline{\qquad} \frac{2}{3}.$$

Problem 10.24: Within the LCMO approximation (cf. Section 7.5), calculate the effect of a methyl group on the energy levels of benzene by introducing the resonance integral $\beta_{C_\mu - C_M} = 0.8\beta$ as a perturbation. How large is the spin population at the 'atomic orbital' Φ_{H_3} if the unpaired electron is inserted into the antibonding molecular orbital Ψ_5 or Ψ_6 of the toluene radical anion?

In addition to hyperconjugation, the inductive electron donating effect of the methyl group also plays an important role. This can be simulated within the model developed by increasing the *Coulomb* integral α_{C_μ} by a positive perturbation $\delta\alpha_\mu = -0.2\beta$ through -0.3β, remembering that β is negative.

In analogy to (7/43) the differences in the orbital energies are obtained according to

$$\Delta x_j^B = \sum_K \frac{<\Psi_j^B|h|\Psi_K^M>^2}{x_j^B - x_K^M}.$$

With the perturbation

$< \mu^B |h| \nu^M > = 0$, exception $< 1^B |h| 1^M > = < 1^M |h| 1^B > = 0.8 \, \beta$

and the orbital energies and the orbitals of the isolated methyl group $C \equiv H_3$

$$x_2^M = -3.260 \qquad \Psi_2^M = 0.677 \, \Phi_C - 0.736 \, \Phi_{H_3}$$

$$x_1^M = +2.760 \qquad \Psi_1^M = 0.736 \, \Phi_C + 0.677 \, \Phi_{H_3}$$

we obtain the relation

$$\Delta x_j^B \qquad \frac{J_1 \cdot 0.8 \cdot c_{11}^M)^2}{x_J^B - x_1^M} + \frac{(c_{J_1}^B \cdot 0.8 \cdot c_{21}^M)^2}{x_J^B - x_2^M}$$

$$= \frac{0.347 \cdot (c_{J_1}^B)^2}{x_J^B - 2.76} + \frac{0.293 \cdot (c_{J_1}^B)^2}{x_J^B + 3.26}.$$

Substitution of the value for benzene (Vol. 3) gives

J^B	$c_{J_1}^B$	x_J^B	Δx_J^B	x_J^T	J^T
6	−0.408	−2.000	−0.012 + 0.039 = +0.027	−1.973	7
4	−0.577	−1.000	−0.031 + 0.043 = +0.012	−0.988	5
3	+0.577	+1.000	−0.066 + 0.023 = −0.043	+0.957	4
1	+0.408	+2.000	−0.076 + 0.009 = −0.067	+1.933	2
			−0.185 + 0.114		

The orbital energies x_2^B and x_4^B of benzene remain unchanged because $c_{21}^B = c_{41}^B = 0$, i.e. the molecular orbitals of the methyl group do not combine with the benzene molecular orbitals Ψ_2^B and Ψ_4^B which are antisymmetric with respect to the plane passing through 1 and 4. The changes in the orbital energies of the methyl group on admixture of the benzene molecular orbitals Ψ_1^B, Ψ_3^B, Ψ_5^B, and Ψ_6^B amount to $x_1^M = +0.185$ and $x_2^M = -0.114$, corresponding to the sums of the columns with reversed signs. The results are represented in the following energy level scheme:

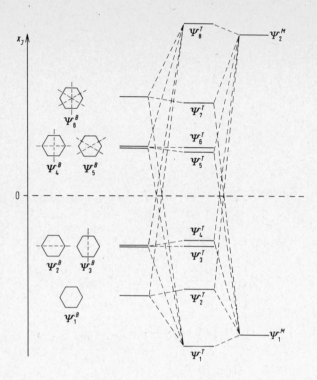

Approximate values of the coefficients $c_{JH_3}^T$ are obtained, neglecting normalization, from the perturbed eigenfunction

$$\Psi_5^T \cong \Psi_5^B + \frac{<\Psi_5^B|h|\Psi_1^M>}{x_5^B - x_1^M}\Psi_1^M + \frac{<\Psi_5^B|h|\Psi_2^M>}{x_5^B - x_2^M}\Psi_2^M$$

in analogy to (7/48) according to:

$$c_{5H_3}^T \cong \frac{c_{51}^B \cdot 0,8 \cdot c_{11}^M}{x_5^B - x_1^M}c_{12}^M + \frac{c_{51}^B \cdot 0.8 \cdot c_{21}^M}{x_5^B - x_2^M}c_{22}^M$$

$$\cong \frac{(-0.577) \cdot 0.8 \cdot 0.736}{-1.000 - 2.76} \cdot 0.677 + \frac{(-0.577) \cdot 0.8 \cdot 0.677}{-1.000 - (-3.26)}(-0.736)$$

$$\cong +0.061 + 0.102 \cong +0.163$$

Because $c_{41}^B = 0$, the coefficient $c_{6H_3}^T = 0$, i.e. as already predicted on the basis of symmetry, no conjugation occurs. Therefore the spin density at the 'atomic orbital' Φ_{H_3} is

$$\rho_{5H_3}^T = 0.0266, \quad \rho_{6H_3}^T = 0.$$

With the proportionality factor for the splitting between the proton and the nuclear spin $a = 504$ *Gauss* [10.7], much too large a coupling constant is obtained for the unpaired electron in the toluene molecular orbital Ψ_5^T compared with the experimental value $a_{5H_3}^T = 0.8$ *Gauss* (10/57). This is so even if we take into account that the calculated spin population is distributed over three protons. The coupling constant resulting on occupation of Ψ_6^T by the single electron would, however, also permit a negative spin density at this center according to the results of Problem 10.23. Thus on the basis of the measured coupling constant (10/57) for the methyl group, no decision can be reached about which of the two lowest antibonding molecular orbitals of toluene the unpaired electron resides in, although the low coupling constant favors the latter possibility (Problem 10.25).

Problem 10.25: How does the sequence of molecular orbitals of toluene calculated in Problem 10.24 change on introduction of the inductive effect of the methyl group?

In the LCMO approximation (Problem 10.24) hyperconjugation of the $C\equiv H_3$ group leads to the orbital energies x_J^T for toluene recorded in the following table. Introduction of an inductive effect $\delta\alpha_\mu = -0.3\,\beta$ of the $C\equiv H_3$ group via the perturbation

$\langle\mu|h_{\text{ind}}|\mu\rangle = 0$; except $\langle 1|h_{\text{ind}}|1\rangle = \delta\alpha_1 = h_{\text{ind}}\beta = -0.3\,\beta$

yields, according to (6/12)

$$\delta x_J = c_{J_1}^2\, h_{\text{ind.}} = -0.3\, c_{J_1}^2$$

the perturbed orbital energy coefficients x_J' of toluene.

J	x_J^T	c_{J1}	δx_J	x_J'
8	−3.374	---	-----	−3.374
7	−1.973	$-\dfrac{1}{\sqrt{6}}$	−0.05	−2.023
6	−1.000	0	0	−1.000
5	−0.988	$-\dfrac{1}{\sqrt{3}}$	−0.10	−1.088
4	+0.957	$\dfrac{1}{\sqrt{3}}$	−0.10	+0.857
3	+1.000	0	0	+1.000
2	+1.933	$\dfrac{1}{\sqrt{6}}$	−0.05	+1.883
1	+2.945	---	-----	+2.945

From the adjoining energy level scheme, which summarizes the results of the Problems 10.24 and 10.25, it is obvious that the inductive effect of the $C{\equiv}H_3$ group exceeds that of hyperconjugation. As a result Ψ_6^T will become the lowest antibonding molecular orbital Ψ_5'. Since the coefficient is $c_{51} = 0$, no interaction should occur with the $C{\equiv}H_3$ group and the spin density at the methyl carbon atom of the toluene radical anion is therefore predicted to be $\rho_M = 0$. As given in (10/57) a small interaction is nevertheless recorded which can be attributed, e.g. to a small negative spin density at the H_3 'center'.

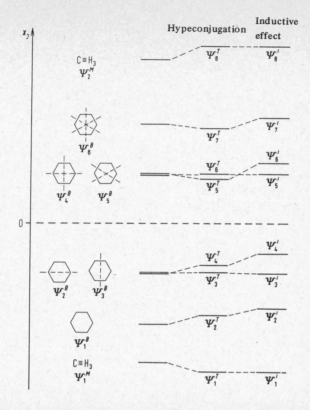

Problem 10.26: Predict the values of the coupling constants at the unsubstituted centres of o-, m-, and p-xylene radical anions.

In Problem 10.25 it was shown that the inductive effect of the $C{\equiv}H_3$ group exceeds that of hyperconjugation. Thus of the degenerate antibonding molecular orbitals of benzene

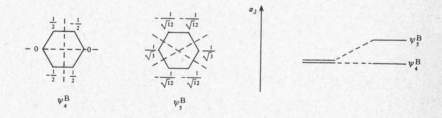

Ψ_4^B is the lowest antibonding molecular orbital of the toluene radical anion which is occupied by the unpaired electron. For o-, m-, and p-xylene, we obtain the following results:

(a) *p*-Xylene:

The splitting induced by the inductive effect at positions 1 and 4 is

$$\Delta x_5 = -0.3 \cdot 2 \cdot \left(\frac{1}{\sqrt{3}}\right)^2 = -0.2\beta$$

and the unpaired electron goes into Ψ_4^B. The calculated spin densities and coupling constants are in good agreement with experimental values.

(b) *m*-Xylene:

The perturbations are to be introduced in a symmetry correct fashion, i.e. the orbital symmetries of Ψ_4^B and Ψ_5^B must also be retained in the perturbed system

The splitting induced by the inductive effect then amounts to:

$$\Delta x_4 = -0.3 \cdot 2 \cdot \left(\frac{1}{2}\right)^2 = -0.15\beta$$

$$\Delta x_5 = -0.3 \cdot 2 \left(\frac{1}{\sqrt{12}}\right)^2 = -0.05\beta$$

The single electron occupies Ψ_5^B. In agreement with the experimental values, the coupling constants obtained are:

$|Q|_C = 23$ GAUSS
$|Q|_{H_3} = 27$ GAUSS

ϱ_μ

$\alpha_\mu^{\text{calc.}}$

$\alpha_\mu^{\text{exp.}}$

The spin density on the pseudocenter H_3 is seen to be proportional to that at the substituent carbon atom to a first approximation. The proportionality factor between the observed coupling constants of the methyl protons and the spin density at the C center amounts to about 27 *Gauss*.

(c) *o*-Xylene:

On symmetry-correct perturbation

as a result of the splitting of the degenerate levels induced by the inductive effect of the methyl groups

$\Delta x_4 = -0.3 \cdot 2 \left(\frac{1}{2}\right)^2 = -0.15\beta$

ψ_4^B

ψ_5^B

$\Delta x_5 = -0.3 \cdot 2 \left(\frac{1}{\sqrt{12}}\right)^2 = -0.05\beta$

Ψ_5^B becomes the lowest antibonding molecular orbital, and the spin densities and coupling constants are found to be:

$|Q|_C = 23$ GAUSS
$|Q|_{H_3} = 27$ GAUSS

ϱ_μ

$\alpha_\mu^{\text{calc.}}$

$\alpha_\mu^{\text{exp.}}$

As can be seen, satisfactory agreement is again obtained with experimental values.

282

10.5 Enthalpies of Formation

Problem 10.27: Using the enthalpies of formation ΔHf^0_{298} (X, g) of methane and ethane, and of the atoms concerned,

CH_4	H_3CCH_3	H	C	
-17.9	-20.2	52.1	171.7	[kcal/mol]

calculate the bond enthalpies of the C—H and C—C bonds.

Some values needed for bond enthalpies and for enthalpies of formation which are tabulated together with their sources in Vol. 3 of the German edition (but not in this English one) are given in abbreviated form here:

Bond enthalpies of formation $\Delta Hb_{298,2}$ in kcal/mol, single bonds

$A-B$	C	N	O	Cl
H	-98.8	-93.4	-110.6	-103.2
C	-83.1	-69.7	-84.0	-78.5
N		-38.4		
O			-33.2	

Bond enthalpies of formation $\Delta Hb_{298,2}$ in kcal/mol, multiple bonds

A	B	$A-B$	$A=B$	$A\equiv B$
C	C	-83.1	-147	-194
C	N	-69.7	-147	-213
C	O	-84.0	-171	

Enthalpy of formation $\Delta Hf^0_{298,2}$ of the atoms

H	C	N	O	Cl
52.09	171.70	113.0	59.16	29.01

Enthalpies of formation $\Delta Hf^0_{298,2}$ of hydrocarbons H-$(CH_2)_n$-H

$n =$	1	2	3	4	5	6
$Hf^0_{298,2}$	-17.9	-20.2	-24.8	-30.2	-35.0	-40.0

Corresponding to the scheme [10.15], substitution of the appropriate values affords:

$$4\,\Delta Hb^0_{298}(C-H) = -\Sigma\,\Delta Hf^0_{298}(Atoms) + \Delta Hf^0_{298}(CH_4, g)$$

$$= -(4\,\Delta Hf^0_{298}(H, {}^2S, g) + \Delta Hf^0_{298}(C, {}^3P, g)) + \Delta Hf^0_{298}(CH_4, g)$$

$$= -(4 \cdot 52.09 + 171.70) - 17.9 = -398.0 \text{ kcal/mol.}$$

$$\Delta Hb^0_{298}(C-H) = -\frac{398.0}{4} = -99.5 \text{ kcal/mol.}$$

From the C−H bond enthalpy thus calculated, and from the known enthalpy of formation of ethane, the C−C bond enthalpy can be determined as follows:

$$\Delta Hb^0_{298}(C-C) = -\Sigma\,\Delta Hf^0_{298}(Atoms) + \Delta Hf^0_{298}(C_2H_6, g) - 6\,\Delta Hb^0_{298}(C-H)$$

$$= -(6 \cdot 52.09 + 2 \cdot 171.70) - 20.2 - 6(-99.5)$$

$$= -79.1 \text{ kcal/mol.}$$

The calculated value deviates from the value ΔHb^0_{298} (C−C) = −83.1 kcal/mol tabulated above because the latter is an average value from a larger number of analogous determinations.

Problem 10.28: Calculate the bond enthalpies ΔHb^0_{298} of S−H and C−S bonds from the following enthalpies of formation $\Delta Hf^0_{298}(X, g)$:

H_2S	CH_4	CH_3SH	CH_3SCH_3	H	C	S	
−4.8	−17.9	−3.0	−6.9	52.1	171.7	53.3	[kcal/mol]

Corresponding to the additive scheme

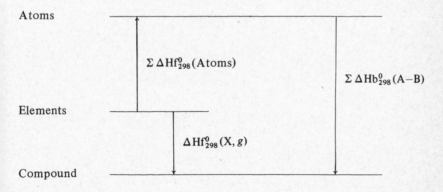

we obtain values of the bond enthalpies for the individual compounds in kcal/mol:

Compound X:	$-\underset{\text{Atoms}}{\Sigma}\,\Delta Hf^0_{208}(\text{Atoms})$	$+\,\Delta Hf^0_{298}(X, g)=$	$\underset{\text{Bonds}}{\Sigma}\,\Delta Hb^0_{298}(A-B)$	$(A-B)$
H_2S	2 H 104.2			
	1 S 53.3			
	$\overline{-157.5}$	-4.8	-162.3	2 (S–H)
CH_4	4 H 208.4			
	1 C 171.7			
	$\overline{-380.1}$	-17.9	-398.0	4 (C–H)
CH_3SH	4 H 208.4			
	1 C 171.7			
	1 S 53.3	-3.0	-436.4	3 (C–H)
	$\overline{-433.4}$			1 (S–H)
				1 (C–S)
$CH_3\,S\,CH_3$	6 H 312.6			
	2 C 343.4			
	1 S 53.3	-6.9	-716.2	6 (C–H)
	$\overline{-709.3}$			2 (C–S)

Introduction of the abbreviations

$$\Delta Hb^0_{298}(S-H) = a$$
$$\Delta Hb^0_{298}(C-H) = b$$
$$\Delta Hb^0_{298}(C-S) = c$$

affords the following system of equations with four equations and only three unknowns. However, in order to completely exploit the experimental data, a least squares treatment is carried out with all four equations:

$$
\begin{aligned}
2a &\quad\quad\quad + 162.3 = R_1 \\
4b &\quad\quad + 398.0 = R_2 \\
a + 3b &+ c + 436.4 = R_3 \\
6b &+ 2c + 716.2 = R_4
\end{aligned}
$$

The errors should be as small as possible

$$\sum_{i=1}^{4} R_i^2 = 0$$

and according to

$$\frac{\partial}{\partial a} \sum_{i=1}^{4} R_i^2 = 0,$$

$$\frac{\partial}{\partial b} \sum_{i=1}^{4} R_i^2 = 0,$$

$$\frac{\partial}{\partial c} \sum_{i=1}^{4} R_i^2 = 0,$$

we thus obtain the following three equations with three unknowns:

$$2\,[(2a + 162.3) \cdot 2 + (a + 3b + c + 436.4)] = 0$$
$$2\,[(4b + 398.0) \cdot 4 + (a + 3b + c + 436.4) \cdot 3 + (6b + 2c + 716.2) \cdot 6] = 0$$
$$2\,[(a + 3b + c + 436.4) + (6b + 2c + 716.2) \cdot 2] = 0$$

Rearranging the equations

$$5a + 3b + c + 761.0 = 0,$$
$$3a + 61b + 15c + 7198.4 = 0,$$
$$a + 15b + 5c + 1868.8 = 0,$$

and elimination of a

$$72b + 24c + 8583.0 = 0,$$
$$16b + 1592.0 = 0,$$
$$b = -99.5; \quad \Delta Hb_{298}^0 (C - H) = -99.5 \ \text{kcal/mol}$$

leads to the desired bond enthalpies of the S–H and C–S bonds

$$a = \Delta Hb_{298}^0 (S–H) = -80.8 \ \text{kcal/mol},$$
$$c = \Delta Hb_{298}^0 (C–S) = -59.1 \ \text{kcal/mol}.$$

Problem 10.29: Calculate the enthalpies of formation $\Delta Hf_{298}^0 (X, g)_{calc}$ of the following compounds

(a) $CH_3-C\equiv C-CH_3$

    (35·0)

(b) $CH_2=CH-CH_2-CH=CH_2$

    (25·2)

(c) $CH_2=CH-CH=CH-CH_3$

    (trans: 18·6)

(d) $H-C\underset{OH}{\overset{O}{\diagup\diagdown}}$

    (−86·7)

from the corresponding bond enthalpies

C−C	C=C	C≡C	C−H	C−O	C=O	O−H
−83·1	−147	−194	−98·8	−84	−171	−110·6 [kcal/mol]

and compare the results with the experimental values ($\Delta Hf^0_{298,\exp}$) [kcal/mol] given above.

The relation

$$\Delta Hf^0_{298}(X, g)_{\text{calc.}} = \sum_{\text{Atoms}} \Delta Hf^0_{298}(\text{Atoms}) + \sum_{\text{Bonds}} \Delta Hb^0_{298}(A-B) \qquad (10/60)$$

together with the tabulated enthalpies of formation and the bond enthalpies (see Problem 10.27: p. 282) gives the following values [kcal/mol]:

Compound X:	$\sum_{\text{Atoms}} \Delta Hf^0_{298}(\text{Atoms}) +$		$\sum_{\text{Bonds}} \Delta Hb^0_{298}(A-B) =$		$\Delta Hf^0_{298}(X, g)$ calc.	exp.	Error
(a)	4 C	686.8	2 C−C	−166.2			
	6 H	312.5	1 C≡C	−194			
$H_3C-C\equiv C-CH_3$			6 C−H	−592.8			
		999.3		−953.0	46.3	35.0	+11.3
(b)	5 C	858.5	2 C−C	−166.2			
	8 H	416.7	2 C=C	−294			
$H_2C=CH-CH_2-CH=CH_2$			8 C−H	−790.4			
		1275.2		−1250.6	24.6	25.2	−0.6
(c)							
$H_2C=CH-CH=CH-CH_3$		1275.2		−1250.6	24.6	18.6	+6.0
(d)	1 C	171.7	1 C−H	−98.8			
	2 H	104.2	1 C−O	−84			
	2 O	118.3	1 C=O	−171			
$HC\underset{OH}{\overset{O}{\diagdown}}$			1 O−H	−110.6			
		394.2		−464.4	−70.2	−86.7	+16.5

The discrepancies between calculated and experimental enthalpies of formation can be interpreted as follows:

The deviation (b) = −0.6 kcal/mol lies within the 'normal' limits of error for the assumption of competely localized two-center bonds (cf. (10/61) for instance). The large positive deviations (c) = + 6.0 kcal/mol and (d) = +16.5 kcal/mol are customarily explained as 'resonance energies'— arising from π-electron delocalization.

However, the positive error (a) = + 11.3 kcal/mol shows that such an explanation is questionable, at least for compound (c). The bond increment for the C≡C bond was derived from the enthalpy of formation of acetylene using the 'normal' value for the C−H bond (cf. Problem 10.27). Furthermore, in calculation of the bond enthalpy of (a), we have used the 'normal' value for the $C(sp^3)$−$C(sp^3)$ single bond which apparently leads to an underestimate of the $C(sp^3)$−$C(sp)$ single bond by about 5 kcal/mol relative to the difference between the bond enthalpies of $C(sp^3)$−$H(1s)$ and $C(sp)$−$H(1s)$. Analogous errors can also be shown to apply to the error in (c), and once again demonstrate that the 'resonance energy', which is inaccessible to direct measurement, is often attributable to origins having nothing to do with the 'definition' of this quantity.

Problem 10.30: Calculate the eigenvalues E_1 through E_7 of ethane, starting from the C−H two-centre orbitals φ_1 through φ_6 having the energies E_{C-H}, and the C−C two-centre orbital φ_7 with energy E_{C-C}. The resonance integral between two of the equivalent C−H bonds originating from the same C atom is B. Use B' for the interaction between C−C and C−H orbitals at the same centre C. The secular determinants should be factorized in the usual way. Show that the additivity rule is also satisfied if one assumes complete electron delocalization over the entire system. (Hint: Start from an eclipsed conformation.)

The expression

$$\Psi = \sum_{j=1}^{7} c_j \varphi_j$$

leads, in analogy to (10/67), to the secular determinant

$$\begin{vmatrix}
E_{CH}-E & B & B & & & & B' \\
B & E_{CH}-E & B & & & & B' \\
B & B & E_{CH}-E & & & & B' \\
& & & E_{CH}-E & B & B & B' \\
& & & B & E_{CH}-E & B & B' \\
& & & B & B & E_{CH}-E & B' \\
B' & B' & B' & B' & B' & B' & E_{CC}-E
\end{vmatrix} = 0$$

It is convenient to adopt the abbreviations

$$\frac{E_{CH}-E}{B} = -x; \quad E_{CC} = E_{CH} + HB \quad \therefore \frac{E_{CC}-E}{B} = -x + H, \quad \text{also} \quad \frac{B'}{B} = K$$

whence we obtain

$$\begin{vmatrix}
-x & 1 & 1 & & & & K \\
1 & -x & 1 & & & & K \\
1 & 1 & -x & & & & K \\
& & & -x & 1 & 1 & K \\
& & & 1 & -x & 1 & K \\
& & & 1 & 1 & -x & K \\
K & K & K & K & K & K & -x+H
\end{vmatrix} = 0$$

Arbitrarily assuming an eclipsed conformation

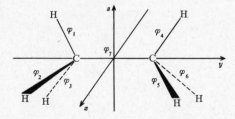

the secular determinant can be factorized by utilizing the reflection in the planes $\sigma(xz)$ and $\sigma(yz)$ according to the rules (4/98).

$$
\begin{array}{c|ccc|ccc|c|}
\sigma(xz) & & & & & & & \\
1+4 & -2x & 2 & 2 & & & & 2K \\
2+5 & 2 & -2x & 2 & & & & 2K \\
3+6 & 2 & 2 & -2x & & & & 2K \\
\hline
\Longrightarrow & & & & & & & \\
1-4 & & & & -2x & 2 & 2 & \\
2-5 & & & & 2 & -2x & 2 & \\
3-6 & & & & 2 & 2 & -2x & \\
\hline
7 & 2K & 2K & 2K & & & & -x+H \\
\end{array} = 0
$$

Factorization by reflection in $\sigma(xz)$ next leads to a subdeterminant which is formally identical with that of the cyclopropenyl radical

$$
\begin{vmatrix}
-x & 1 & 1 \\
1 & -x & 1 \\
1 & 1 & -x
\end{vmatrix} = 0
$$

and accordingly yields the following orbital energies:

$$
\begin{aligned}
x_1 &= 2; & E_1 &= E_{CH} + 2B, \\
x_2 &= x_3 = -1; & E_2 &= E_3 = E_{CH} - B.
\end{aligned}
$$

Factorization of the remaining determinant by reflection in $\sigma(yz)$ splits it into one determinant of the first order and one of the third order.

$$
\begin{vmatrix}
-2x & 2 & 2 & 2K \\
2 & -2x & 2 & 2K \\
2 & 2 & -2x & 2K \\
2K & 2K & 2K & -x+H
\end{vmatrix}
\quad
\begin{array}{c}
\sigma(yz) \\
1 \\
2+3 \\
\Longrightarrow \\
2-3 \\
\\
1
\end{array}
\quad
\begin{array}{|cc|c|c|}
-2x & 4 & & 2K \\
4 & -4x+4 & & 4K \\
\hline
 & & -4x-4 & \\
\hline
2K & 4K & & -x+H
\end{array} = 0
$$

From the first order determinant one gets the orbital energy

$$
x_4 = -1; \quad E_4 = E_{CH} - B.
$$

Solution of the third order determinant leads to

$$
\begin{vmatrix}
-x & 2 & K \\
1 & -x+1 & K \\
2K & 4K & -x+H
\end{vmatrix} = 0
$$

$$0 = x^3 - x^2(H+1) - x(2 - H + 6K^2) - 6K^2 + 2H$$
$$0 = (x+1)(-x^2 + x(H+2) + 6K^2 - 2H) ,$$

i.e., one root must have the value -1, and yields the orbital energy

$$x_5 = -1 \quad ; \quad E_5 = E_{CH} - B .$$

Finally, the orbital energies x_6 and x_7 are:

$$x^2 - x(H+2) - 6K^2 + 2H = 0$$

$$
x_{6,7} = \frac{H+2}{2} \pm \sqrt{\left(\frac{H+2}{2}\right)^2 + 6K^2 - 2H}
$$

$$
= \frac{H+2}{2} \pm \sqrt{\left(\frac{H-2}{2}\right)^2 + 6K^2}
$$

$$
E_{6,7} = \left(\frac{E_{CC} - E_{CH}}{2B} + 1 \pm \sqrt{\left(\frac{E_{CC} - E_{CH}}{2B} - 1\right)^2 + 6\frac{B'}{B}} \right) B + E_{CH}
$$

$$
= \frac{E_{CC} + E_{CH}}{2} + \left(1 \pm \sqrt{\left(\frac{E_{CC} - E_{CH}}{2B} - 1\right)^2 + 6\frac{B'}{B}} \right) B
$$

The result for the sum over all orbital energies of ethylene is

$$
\sum_{J=1}^{7} E_3 = (E_{CH} + 2B) + 4(E_{CH} - B) + \left(\frac{E_{CC} + E_{CH}}{2} + B + B \cdot \sqrt{} \right)
$$

$$
+ \left(\frac{E_{CC} + E_{CH}}{2} + B - B\sqrt{} \right)
$$

$$
= 6E_{CH} + E_{CC}
$$

As can be seen, in spite of the splitting of the molecular orbitals as a result of the assumed electron delocalization over the whole system, the sum of the orbital energies is again equal to the sum which results from the additivity scheme with strict localization of the electrons in the individual two-center bonds.

The result corresponds to the known rule that the sum of the eigenvalues must equal the trace, i.e. the sum of the main diagonal elements of the underlying matrix.

Problem 10.31: Calculate the delocalization energies of naphthalene, azulene, anthracene, and phenanthrene, and compare the results with the associated combustion enthalpies [kcal/mol] of each compound:

(a)	(b)	(c)	(d)
−1249·7	−1282·3	−1712·1	−1705·0

From the relations (10/72) and (10/73), the delocalization energy $DE(X)$ of a compound X with k localized double bonds in a *Kekulé* structure is calculated according to

$$DE(X)^{HMO} = E_\pi(X) - 2k\,(\alpha + \beta)$$
$$= X_\pi(X) - 2k\,\beta = (X_\pi(X) - 2k)\,(-20)\,[kcal/mol]$$

and for compounds (a) through (d) we obtain

Kekulé -Structure	k	$X_\pi(X)$	$DE(X)^{HMO}[kcal/mol]$
(a)	5	13.683	−73.7
(b)	5	13.364	−67.3
(c)	7	19.314	−106.3
(d)	7	19.448	−109.0

Comparison with the enthalpies of combustion deduced from the additivity scheme

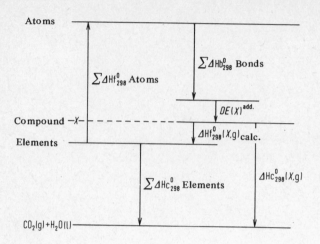

is possible in the following way:

$$DE(X)^{\text{add.}} = \underset{\text{Atoms}}{\Sigma} \Delta Hf^0_{298}(\text{Atoms}) + \underset{\text{Bonds}}{\Sigma} \Delta Hb^0_{298}(\text{Bonds}) + \Delta Hf^0_{298}(X, g)_{\text{calc.}}$$

The enthalpies of formation $\Delta Hf^0_{298}(X, g)_{\text{calc}}$ are obtained from the difference in the enthalpies of combustion

$$\Delta Hf^0_{298}(X, g)_{\text{calc.}} = \Delta Hc^0_{298}(X, g) - \Sigma \Delta Hc^0_{298}(\text{Elements}),$$

of which $\Delta Hc^0_{298}(X,g)$ is given, and $\Sigma \Delta Hc^0_{298}$ (Elements) are to be calculated from standard values of the reactions given here

$$H_2(g) + \frac{1}{2} O_2(g) \rightarrow H_2O(l) \; ; \; \Delta Hf^0_{298}(H_2O, l) = -68.32 \text{ kcal/mol,}$$

$$C(\text{Graphit}) + O_2(g) \rightarrow CO_2(g) \; ; \; \Delta Hf^0_{298}(CO_2, g) = -94.05 \text{ kcal/mol,}$$

Using again the tabulated enthalpies of formation and the bond enthalpies tabulated in the explanation of Problem 10.27: p. 282, altogether the following values [kcal/mol] result:

| Compound X: | | $\Sigma\ \Delta Hf^0_{298}$ (Atoms) $+$ | | $\Sigma\ \Delta Hb^0_{298}$(Bonds) $+ \Delta Hc^0_{298}(X, g) - \Sigma\Delta Hc^0_{298}$(Elements)$= -DE(X)^{add.}$ | | | |
		Atoms		Bonds			
(a)	C₁₀H₈	10 C	1717.0	6 C–C	−498.6	10 CO₂	−940.5
		8 H	416.7	5 C=C	−735.0	4 H₂O	−273.3
				8 C–H	−790.4		
			+2133.7		−2024.0	−1249.7	−(−1213.8) 73.8
(b)	C₁₀H₈		+2133.7		−2024.0	−1282.3	+1213.8 41.2
(c)	C₁₄H₁₀	14 C	2403.8	9 C–C	−747.9	14 CO₂	−1316.7
		10 H	520.9	7 C=C	−1029.0	5 H₂O	−341.6
				10 C–H	−988.0		
			+2924.7		−2764.9	−1712.1	−(−1658.3) 106.0
(d)	C₁₄H₁₀		+2924.7		−2764.9	−1705.1	+1658.3 113,0

	$-DE(X)^{HMO}$	$-DE(X)^{add.}$	Δ
(a)	73.7	73.8	+0.1
(b)	67.3	41.2	−26.1
(c)	106.3	106.0	−0.3
(d)	109.0	113.3	+4.3

The deviation of -26.1 kcal/mol in the case of azulene can be attributed inter alia to the considerable strain energy in a five membered ring, whose CCC angle deviates greatly from the unstressed angle

With the exception of azulene (b) good agreement within the limits of error is obtained as shown in the comparison of the delocalization energies [kcal/mol] calculated according to both treatments:

and to overemphasis of the central π-bond between centers 9 and 10 in the HMO model which leads to too high an HMO delocalization energy. In conclusion, it should be mentioned that the delocalization energy in the 10-membered ring amounts to only

$$DE(\text{10-ring})^{HMO} = (12.944 - 10)\,\beta$$

$$= 2.944\,(-20) = -58.9 \text{ kcal/mol.}$$

Problem 10.32: From values given for the 18-perimeter (HMO Table ⑱, Volume 3), and from the following bond-bond polarizabilities $\pi_{\rho\sigma,\mu\nu}$, calculate the differences in delocalization energies of the five isomeric tetracyclic aromatic compounds below, and compare these with the experimentally determined differences in the enthalpies of combustion listed, $\Delta\Delta Hc^0_{298}(X, g)_{exp}$ [kcal/mol]:

$$\Delta\Delta Hc^0_{298}(X, g)_{exp}$$

$\Longrightarrow$ (a) Triphenylene   0

$\pi_{7/12,1/6} = +0.056$

$\pi_{9/18,1/6} = +0.080$

$\pi_{10/15,1/6} = -0.022$

$\pi_{7/16,1/6} = +0.080$ (b) Chrysene   1·32

$\pi_{8/13,1/6} = -0.025$

$\pi_{9/14,1/6} = +0.049$

$\pi_{7/16,9/14} = +0.009$

$\pi_{8/17,1/6} = +0.009$

(c) Benzophenanthrene   8·04

(d) Tetraphene   5·37

(e) Tetracene   6·16

According to (7/96) first and second order perturbation calculations yield

$$E''_\pi = E_\pi + \frac{\partial E_\pi}{\partial \beta_{\rho\sigma}} \delta\beta_{\rho\sigma} + \frac{1}{2} \frac{\partial^2 E_\pi}{\partial \beta^2_{\rho\sigma}} \delta\beta^2_{\rho\sigma}$$

for the total π-electron energy. With

$$\frac{\partial E_\pi}{\partial \beta_{\rho\sigma}} = 2P_{\rho\sigma} \tag{6/55}$$

and

$$\frac{\partial^2 E_\pi}{\partial \beta^2_{\rho\sigma}} = \frac{2}{\beta} \pi_{\rho\sigma,\rho\sigma} \tag{7/97}$$

the expression

$$X''_\pi = X_\pi + 2 \sum_\rho \sum_\sigma P_{\rho\sigma} + \sum_{\rho\sigma} \sum_{\mu\nu} \pi_{\rho\sigma,\mu\nu}.$$

results for the perturbations $\delta\beta = \beta$ caused by introduction of several bonds.

Starting with the tabulated values of the 18-perimeter (Vol. 3) and considering bonds of the same type we find for the isomers (a) − (e):

(a) Triphenylene:

$$X''_\pi = X_\pi + 2(P_{1\,6} + P_{7\,12} + P_{13\,18}) + 3\,\pi_{1\,6,1\,6} + 6\,\pi_{1\,6,7\,12}$$

$$= 23.035 + 2(3 \cdot 0.145) + 3 \cdot 0.422 + 6 \cdot 0.056$$

$$= 25.507$$

(b) Chrysene:

$$X''_\pi = X_\pi + 2(P_{1\,6} + P_{9\,18} + P_{10\,15}) + 2\pi_{1\,6,1\,6} + \pi_{1\,10,1\,10} + 4\pi_{1\,6,9\,18} + 2\pi_{1\,6,10\,15}$$

$$= 23.035 + 2(2 \cdot 0.145 + 0.111) + 2 \cdot 0.422 + 0.430 + 4 \cdot 0.080 + 2(-0.022)$$

$$= 25.387$$

(c) 3,4-Benzophenanthrene:

$$X''_\pi = X_\pi + 2(P_{1\,6} + P_{7\,16} + P_{8\,13}) + 2\pi_{1\,6,1\,6} + \pi_{1\,10,1\,10} + 4\pi_{1\,6,7\,16} + 2\pi_{1\,6,8\,13}$$

$$= 23.035 + 2(2 \cdot 0.145 + 0.111) + 2 \cdot 0.422 + 0.430 + 4 \cdot 0.080 + 2(-0.025)$$

$$= 25.381$$

(d) Tetraphene:

$$X''_\pi = X_\pi + 2(P_{1\,6} + P_{7\,16} + P_{9\,14}) + 2\pi_{1\,6,1\,6} + \pi_{1\,10,1\,10} + 2\pi_{1\,6,7\,16} + 2\pi_{1\,6,9\,14} + 2\pi_{7\,16,9\,14}$$

$$= 23.035 + 2(2 \cdot 0.145 + 0.111) + 2 \cdot 0.422 + 0.430 + 2 \cdot 0.080 + 2(-0.049) + 2 \cdot 0.00$$

$$= 25.191$$

(e) Tetracene:

$$X''_\pi = X_\pi + 2(P_{1\,6} + P_{8\,7} + P_{10\,15}) + 2\pi_{1\,6,1\,6} + \pi_{1\,10,1\,10} + 4\pi_{1\,6,8\,17} + 2\pi_{1\,6,10\,15}$$

$$= 23.035 + 2(2 \cdot 0.145 + 0.111) + 2 \cdot 0.422 + 0.430 + 4 \cdot 0.009 + 2(-0.022)$$

$$= 25.103$$

The delocalization energies $DE(X)''$ can be obtained according to

$$DE(X)'' = (X''_\pi - 2k)\beta \qquad\qquad (10/73)$$
$$= (X''_\pi - 18)(-20) \text{ [kcal/mol]}$$

from the X''_π values with $k = 9$ double bonds in a *Kekulé* structure. These delocalization energies are compared in the following table with the values $DE(X)^{HMO}$ from the exact HMO π-electron energies X^{HMO}_π also listed for the isomers (a) $-$ (e). In the last three columns of this table, the differences in the calculated delocalization energies relative to isomer (a) are compared with the differences in the experimentally determined enthalpies of combustion $\Delta\Delta Hc^0_{298}$ (X,g) for the structures considered, again relative to isomer (a).

Compound	X''_π	X^{HMO}_π	$DE(X)''$	$DE(X)^{HMO}$	$\Delta DE(X)''$	$\Delta DE(X)^{HMO}$	$\Delta\Delta Hc^0_{298}$ (
						[kcal/mol]	
(a)	25.507	25.274	−150.14	−145.48	0	0	0
(b)	25.387	25.192	−147.74	−143.84	2.40	1.64	1.32
(c)	25.381	25.187	−147.62	−143.74	2.54	1.74	8.04
(d)	25.191	25.101	−143.82	−142.02	6.32	3.46	5.37
(e)	25.103	24.931	−142.06	−138.62	8.08	6.86	6.16

Attention should be directed to the satisfactory agreement between the values obtained from perturbation of the 18-perimeter and the HMO values X_π although the difference between the individual isomers is revealed only by second perturbation. Furthermore, the following plot

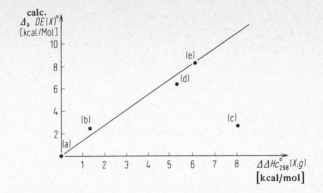

shows the greatest deviation to occur for compound (c). The excessive difference in the experimentally determined enthalpies of combustion corresponding to an insufficient delocalization energy can be largely attributed to destabilization of the system by the steric interaction between the hydrogen atoms at centers 5 and 9.

Problem 10.33: Calculate the delocalization energies of 9,10-diphenylanthracene as a function of angles ω_9 and ω_{10} for 0°, 30°, 45°, 60°, and 90°.

According to (10/73), the partial systems of 9,10-diphenylanthracene with $k = 3$ and $k = 7$ double bonds in the *Kekulé* structures have the delocalization energies

$$\text{DE}\left(\bigcirc\right) = E_\pi \left(\bigcirc\right) - 2k(\alpha+\beta) = (8.000 - 6)(-20) = -40.0 \text{ kcal/mol}$$

$$\text{DE}\left(\bigcirc\bigcirc\bigcirc\right) = (19.314 - 14)\beta = 5.314(-20) = -106.3 \text{ kcal/mol}$$

Twisting can be taken into account via a perturbation by the amount $\beta \cos \omega$. Using the tabulated atom-atom self-polarizabilities for anthracene and benzene

$$\pi_{9\,9} = \pi_{10\,10} = 0.526,$$

$$\pi_{1\,1} = 0.398$$

we obtain the difference in the delocalization energies from the approximation formula (10/74) as a function of the angle of twist $\omega_9 = \omega_{10} = \omega$:

$$\Delta DE = (0.811\sqrt{\pi_{\rho\rho} \cdot \pi_{\sigma\sigma}} + 0.062)\beta \cdot 2\cos\omega$$

$$= 2(0.811\sqrt{0.526 \cdot 0.398} + 0.062)(-20)\cos\omega$$

$$= -17.32 \cdot \cos\omega \ [\text{kcal/mol}]$$

According to the relation

$$DE(\omega) = DE\left(\text{⬡⬡⬡}\right) + 2\ DE\left(\text{⬡}\right) + \Delta DE(\omega)$$

$$= -186.3 - 17.32\cos\omega \ [\text{kcal/mol}]$$

the delocalization energies are finally obtained as [kcal/mol]:

ω	0°	30°	45°	60°	90°
ΔDE	−17.3	−15.0	−12.2	−8.7	0
$DE(\omega)$	−203.6	−201.3	−198.5	−195.0	−186.3

As can be seen, the additional delocalization energy ΔDE is relatively small even for complete coplanarity, which is typical for aromatic π-electron systems formally linked via single bonds. In the present approximation $\beta = \beta(\omega)$, a twist of 60° merely leads to loss of half of the additional delocalization energy ΔDE. Since experience shows the actual loss to exceed the value thus calculated, another approximation

$$\beta_{\mu\nu} = \beta\cos^2\omega_{\mu\nu}$$

has been proposed as an improvement.

Problem 10.34: Show how the delocalization energy of butadiene depends on the localization of the double bonds. Here, the parameter k of the resonance integrals for the bond between centres 2 and 3 is to be varied over the interval from 0 to 1.

$$C\overset{\beta}{=\!=}C\overset{k\beta}{-\!\!-}C\overset{\beta}{=\!=}C$$

In the present case, the Hückel determinant of the butadiene system reads

$$\begin{vmatrix} -x & 1 & & \\ 1 & -x & k & \\ & k & -x & 1 \\ & & 1 & -x \end{vmatrix} = 0$$

and can be factorized with respect to reflection in the symmetry plane between centers 2 and 3 according to the rules (4/98) as follows:

$$
\begin{matrix} 1+4 \\ 2+3 \\ \Longrightarrow \\ 2-3 \\ 1-4 \end{matrix}
\left\|
\begin{array}{cc|cc}
-2x & & & \\
2 & -2x+2k & & \\
\hline
& & -2x-2k & 2 \\
& & 2 & -2x
\end{array}
\right\| = 0
$$

Solution of the subdeterminants leads to the orbital energies

$$
\left\|
\begin{matrix}
-x & 1 \\
1 & -x+k
\end{matrix}
\right\| = 0 = x^2 - kx - 1
$$

$$
x_{1,3} = \frac{k}{2} \pm \frac{1}{2}\sqrt{k^2+4}
$$

$$
\left\|
\begin{matrix}
-x-k & 1 \\
1 & -x
\end{matrix}
\right\| = 0 = x^2 + kx - 1
$$

$$
x_{2,4} = -\frac{k}{2} \pm \frac{1}{2}\sqrt{k^2+4}
$$

and we obtain e.g. for

$$k = 0 \quad x_{1,2} = x_{3,4} = \pm 1\beta \quad \text{(2 isolated double bonds)}$$

$$
k = 1 \quad
\begin{aligned}
x_1 &= +1.618\,\beta \\
x_2 &= +0.618\,\beta \\
x_3 &= -0.618\,\beta \\
x_4 &= -1.618\,\beta
\end{aligned}
\quad \text{(butadiene)}
$$

The total π-electron energy X_π is given for occupation of the two bonding molecular orbitals by two electrons each by

$$
X_\pi = \sum_{J=1}^{4} b_J x_J = 2(x_1 + x_2) = 2\left(\frac{k}{2} + \frac{1}{2}\sqrt{k^2+4} - \frac{k}{2} + \frac{1}{2}\sqrt{k^2+4} \right)
$$

$$
= 2\sqrt{k^2+4}
$$

and we obtain e.g. for

$$k = 0 \quad X_\pi = 4 \quad \text{(isolated double bonds)}$$

$$k = 1 \quad X_\pi = 2\sqrt{5} = 4.472 \quad \text{(butadiene)}$$

According to (10/73) the resulting delocalization energy DE for two double bonds in the *Kekulé* structure is

$$DE = (X_\pi - 2 \cdot 2)\beta = (2\sqrt{k^2 + 4} - 4)\beta$$

for the parameter k in the interval of 0 to 1:

k	1.0	0.8	0.6	0.4	0.2	0.0
DE/β	0.472	0.308	0.176	0.079	0.020	0.000

When plotted versus the parameter k, the delocalization energies are seen to fall off fairly steeply to small values, i.e. if the resonance integral is reduced to an appropriate value for the 2−3 bond of butadiene:

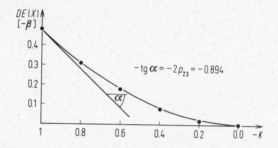

The slope of the tangent at point $k = 1$ is given by the bond order p_{23}:

$$\frac{\partial E_\pi}{\partial \beta_{23}} = 2 p_{23} = \frac{\partial DE}{\partial k} \cdot \frac{1}{\beta} = \frac{2k}{\sqrt{k^2 + 4}}$$

$$\frac{1}{\beta} \left(\frac{\partial DE}{\partial k} \right)_{k=1} = \frac{2}{\sqrt{5}} = 0.894$$

The deviation from the linear relation for $k < 1$ occurs largely at the expense of the second order perturbation, and corresponds at the point $k = 1$ to the bond-bond self-polarizability $\pi_{23,23}$.

$$\frac{\partial^2 E_\pi}{\partial \beta^2} = \frac{2}{\beta} \pi_{23,23} = \frac{\partial^2 DE}{\partial k^2} \cdot \frac{1}{\beta} = \left(\frac{2\sqrt{k^2 + 4} - 2k^2/\sqrt{k^2 + 4}}{k^2 + 4} \right) \frac{1}{\beta}$$

$$\frac{1}{\beta} \left(\frac{\partial^2 DE}{\partial k^2} \right)_{k=1} = \left(\frac{(2\sqrt{5}) - (2/\sqrt{5})}{5} \right) \frac{1}{\beta} = 0.716/\beta$$

From HMO Tables (Vol. 3), we obtain the values

$$p_{23} = 0.447 \, ,$$

$$\pi_{23,23} = 0.358 \, ,$$

which are identical with those derived above.

10.6. σ-Systems

Problem 10.35: Use the above procedure to determine which of the two structures is to be assigned to the anion $I_3^{\ominus}$ and which to the cation $I_3^{\oplus}$

$$\text{(a)} \quad \begin{matrix} I-I \\ | \\ I \end{matrix} \qquad \text{(b)} \quad I-I-I$$

By analogy with [10.20] the molecular orbitals are defined as follows:

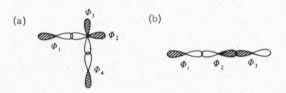

and are consequently composed of the σ-systems

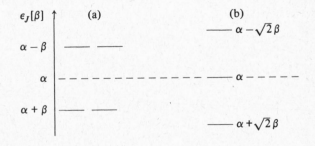

whose orbital energy schemes have the appearance:

(a) and (b) orbital energy diagram with $\epsilon_J[\beta]$ axis showing levels at $\alpha - \beta$, α, $\alpha + \beta$ for (a) and $\alpha - \sqrt{2}\beta$, α, $\alpha + \sqrt{2}\beta$ for (b).

The total energy is made up of the energy of the delocalized σ-system and that of the free electron pairs

$$E_G = E_\sigma + E_n.$$

The energy of a free electron pair amounts to

$$2\epsilon_n = 2\alpha.$$

On exclusion of the $5s$-electrons, the system contains

$$I_3^\oplus : \ 3 \cdot 7 - 6 - 1 = 14 \text{ Electrons,}$$
$$I_3^\ominus : \ 3 \cdot 7 - 6 + 1 = 16 \text{ Electrons.}$$

The numbers of electrons belonging to free electron pairs are

$$\text{(a)}: \ 5 \cdot 2 \ = 10 \text{ Electrons,}$$
$$\text{(b)}: \ 6 \cdot 2 \ = 12 \text{ Electrons.}$$

Hence, the ground state configurations are

$$I_3^\oplus \ \text{(a)} : (\sigma_y)^2 (\sigma_z)^2 (n)^{10}$$
$$\text{(b)} : (\sigma_z)^2 (n)^{12}$$
$$I_3^\ominus \ \text{(a)} : (\sigma_y)^2 (\sigma_z)^2 (n)^{10} (\sigma_y^*)^1 (\sigma_z^*)^1$$
$$\text{(b)} : (\sigma_z)^2 (\sigma_{z,nb})^2 (n)^{12}$$

and the resultant total energies are

System	E_n	E_σ	E_G
$I_3^\oplus$ (a)	10α	$4\alpha + 4\beta$	$14\alpha + 4\beta$
(b)	12α	$2\alpha + 2\sqrt{2}\beta$	$14\alpha + 2\sqrt{2}\beta$
$I_3^\ominus$ (a)	10α	$6\alpha + 2\beta$	$16\alpha + 2\beta$
(b)	12α	$4\alpha + 2\sqrt{2}\beta$	$16\alpha + 2\sqrt{2}\beta$

From the table it is seen that even in the first order approximation $I_3^\oplus$ is bent and $I_3^\ominus$ must be linear. According to (10/84) the populations are calculated as:

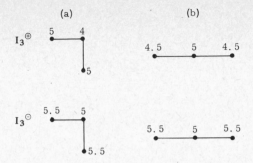

Based on these populations, a perturbation calculation according to (10/87) would lead to a reduction in the difference found for the energies between the structures (a) and (b) of the $I_3^\oplus$ cation, while leaving that for the $I_3^\ominus$ anion unchanged.

The geometry just derived for the $I_3^\oplus$ cation and for the $I_3^\ominus$ anion is in each case in agreement with experimental observation.

Problem 10.36: Starting from the HMO values tabulated for $K_3^\ominus$ (Volume 3), and using a second order perturbation procedure, calculate which of the following isomeric anions

    (a) $[Br{-}I{-}Cl]^\ominus$ (b) $[I{-}Br{-}Cl]^\ominus$ (c) $[I{-}Cl{-}Br]^\ominus$.

is the most stable. Employ the *Coulomb* integrals $\alpha_{Cl} = \alpha_I + 0.4\beta$ and $\alpha_{Br} = \alpha_I + 0.2\beta$.

This problem derives from Problem 10.35. The arguments used in the previous problem would require a linear structure in all three systems. We therefore have to consider the extent to which a perturbation $\delta\alpha_\mu$ at the individual centers μ influences the energy of the free electron pairs and the energy of the σ-system. Since the number of free electron pairs at each center is 2, obviously the change

$$\delta E_n = 4\,\delta\alpha_{Cl} + 4\,\delta\alpha_{Br}$$

is equally large for all three arrangements. Discrimination between the various structures is possible by a second order perturbation of the energy E_σ, starting as usual from the charge order contributions at the various centers due to the four σ-electrons in the delocalized σ-system:

$$q_{\sigma_1} = 1.5 \qquad q_{\sigma_2} = 1 \qquad q_{\sigma_3} = 1.5$$

The required atom-atom polarizabilities are taken form the HMO Table K_3^- (Vol. 3):

$$\pi_{11} = \pi_{33} = \quad 0.442$$
$$\pi_{12} = \pi_{23} = \quad -0.177$$
$$\pi_{22} = \quad\quad 0.354$$
$$\pi_{13} = \quad\quad -0.265$$

The corresponding perturbations of the energy of the σ-system

$$E_\sigma = 4\alpha + X_\sigma \beta$$

amount to

$$\delta E_\sigma = \sum_\mu q_{\sigma\,\mu}\, \delta \alpha_\mu + \frac{1}{2} \sum_\mu \sum_\nu \pi_{\mu\nu}\, \delta \alpha_\mu\, \delta \alpha_\nu$$

$$= 1.5(\delta \alpha_1 + \delta \alpha_3) + \delta \alpha_2 + 0.221(\delta \alpha_1^2 + \delta \alpha_3^2) + 0.177\, \delta \alpha_2^2$$
$$- 0.177\, \delta \alpha_2 (\delta \alpha_1 + \delta \alpha_3) - 0.265\, \delta \alpha_1\, \delta \alpha_3$$

Hence for the various structural possibilities we obtain

Unperturbed $XYZ^\ominus$		δE_n	δE_σ	E'_G
(a)			$0.923\,\beta$	$16\alpha + 6.151\,\beta$
(b)	$16\alpha + 2.828\,\beta$	$2.400\,\beta$	$0.828\,\beta$	$16\alpha + 6.056\,\beta$
(c)			$0.723\,\beta$	$16\alpha + 5.951\,\beta$

It can be seen that the most favorable arrangement is that in which the two most electronegative atoms occupy the chain termini, i.e. (a).

Problem 10.37: Discuss the bonding in square planar xenon tetrafluoride (D_{4h}).

By analogy with [10.26], the atomic p-orbitals are chosen as basis functions:

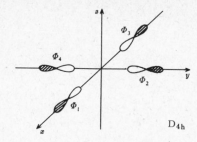

$$D_{4h}$$

The desired linear combinations

$$\varphi_j = \sum_{\mu=1}^{4} c_{j\mu} \Phi_\mu$$

correspond to the molecular orbitals of a 4-perimeter (Vol. 3).

$$\varphi_1 = \frac{1}{2}(\Phi_1 + \Phi_2 + \Phi_3 + \Phi_4)$$

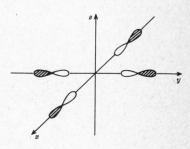

$$\varphi_2 = \frac{1}{2}(\Phi_1 - \Phi_2 - \Phi_3 + \Phi_4)$$

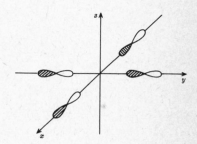

$$\varphi_3 = \frac{1}{2}(\Phi_1 + \Phi_2 - \Phi_3 - \Phi_4)$$

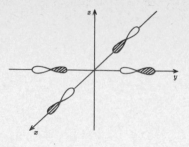

$$\varphi_4 = \frac{1}{2}(\Phi_1 - \Phi_2 + \Phi_3 - \Phi_4)$$

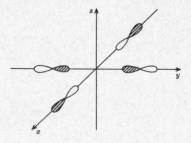

From Table [10.30] we conclude that the linear combinations can combine with the following atomic orbitals of the central xenon atom, with inclusion of the atomic $4d$-orbitals:

$$\varphi_1 ----- 5_s, 4\,d_{z^2}$$
$$\varphi_2 ----$$
$$\qquad\qquad >> 5\,p_x, 5\,p_y$$
$$\varphi_3 ----$$
$$\varphi_4 ----- 4\,d_{x^2-y^2}$$

No linear combination with the atomic $5p_z$-orbital can be given, since this function is antisymmetric with respect to the plane of the molecule. The energy level scheme analogous to [10.31] has the following appearance:

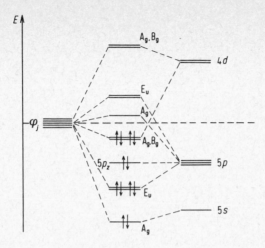

In the above scheme, it is assumed that the molecular orbitals A_g and B_g resulting from the interaction with the atomic $4d$-orbitals are practically degenerate. Apart from the free electron pair in the atomic $5p_z$-orbital, the lowest occupied molecular orbital A_g is also an atomic $5s$-orbital essentially localized on the xenon atom, whose electrons may be considered as a free electron pair.

Problem 10.38: With the aid of character Table D_{2h} (see e.g. Cotton, Reference, Ch 4, p. 130), show that the molecular orbitals in [10.31] are distributed as specified among the irreducible representations of this group.

The basis orbitals used for ethylene (10/97) are interconverted by the symmetry operations contained in D_{2h}, only E, $\sigma(xy)$ and $\sigma(yz)$ transforming basis orbitals into themselves.

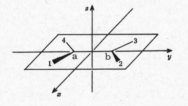

$$
\begin{array}{llll}
\sigma(xy): & 1s_\mu \circlearrowleft & \mu = 1,2,3,4 & 4 \\
 & 2s_\nu \circlearrowleft & \nu = a,b & 2 \\
 & 2p_{x\nu} \circlearrowleft & \nu = a,b & 2 \\
 & 2p_{y,\nu} \circlearrowleft & \nu = a,b & 2 \\
 & 2p_{z\nu} \rightarrow -2p_{z\nu} & \nu = a,b & \underline{-2} \\
 & & & 8 \\[6pt]
\sigma(yz): & 1s_1 \rightleftarrows 1s_4 & & 0 \\
 & 1s_2 \rightleftarrows 1s_3 & & 0 \\
 & 2s_\nu \circlearrowleft & \nu = a,b & 2 \\
 & 2p_{x\nu} \rightarrow -2p_{x\nu} & \nu = a,b & -2 \\
 & 2p_{y\nu} \circlearrowleft & \nu = a,b & 2 \\
 & 2p_{z\nu} \circlearrowleft & \nu = a,b & \underline{2} \\
 & & & 4
\end{array}
$$

This generates the reducible representation Γ.

D_{2h}	E	$C_2(z)$	$C_2(y)$	$C_2(x)$	i	$\sigma(xy)$	$\sigma(xz)$	$\sigma(yz)$	
A_g	1	1	1	1	1	1	1	1	3
B_{1g}	1	1	-1	-1	1	1	-1	-1	2
B_{2g}	1	-1	1	-1	1	-1	1	-1	0
B_{3g}	1	-1	-1	1	1	-1	-1	1	1
A_u	1	1	1	1	-1	-1	-1	-1	0
B_{1u}	1	1	-1	-1	-1	-1	1	1	1
B_{2u}	1	-1	1	-1	-1	1	-1	1	3
B_{3u}	1	-1	-1	1	-1	1	1	-1	2
Γ	12	0	0	0	0	8	0	4	12

Multiplication by rows and summation of the characters of the irreducible representations with those of the reducible representations and subsequent division by the number of symmetry elements (8) yields:

$$\Gamma \doteq 3 \times A_g + 2 \times B_{1g} + B_{3g} + B_{1u} + 3 \times B_{2u} + 2B_{3u}$$

11. Molecules in Electronically Excited States

11.1. Electronic Excitation

Problem 11.1: Compare the position of the longest wavelength maxima of the polyenes $H(HC=CH)_nH$

n	2	3	4	5	6	7	8	10
λ [nm]	217	268	304	334	364	390	410	447

with the predictions from HMO theory for the transitions $\Gamma \to \chi_b^a$ for the chains of $N = 2n$ carbons. Use these data to determine a value for the resonance integral β and explain why this differs from that calculated according to (10/72).

The orbital energies of unbranched polyenes with an even number N of centers are given by the previously derived relation

$$x_J = 2 \cos \left(\frac{\pi}{N+1} J \right); J = 1,2,3,....N \qquad (5/4)$$

Hence, with $J=N/2$ and $J=(N/2)+1$, we obtain for the highest bonding (Ψ_b) and the lowest antibonding (Ψ_a) molecular orbitals

$$x_b = 2 \cos \left(\frac{\pi}{N+1} \cdot \frac{N}{2} \right),$$

$$x_a = 2 \cos \left(\frac{\pi}{N+1} \left(\frac{N}{2} + 1 \right) \right) = -2 \cos \left(\frac{\pi}{N+1} \cdot \frac{N}{2} \right) = -x_b.$$

According to (11/7) the excitation energy ΔE_π ($\Psi_b \to \Psi_a$) is

$$x_a - x_b = -4 \cos \left(\frac{\pi}{2} \left(\frac{N}{N+1} \right) \right)$$

which gives the following values

n	2	3	4	5	6	7	8	10
N	4	6	8	10	12	14	16	20
$x_a - x_b$	−1.236	−0.888	−0.696	−0.580	−0.480	−0.420	−0.368	−0.300
$\tilde{\nu}_{exp.}$ [cm⁻¹]	46100	37300	32900	29900	27500	25600	24390	22400

A plot of the excitation energy $(x_b - x_a)$ versus the experimental absorption maxima in wavenumbers $\tilde{\nu}_{exp}$ [cm⁻¹]

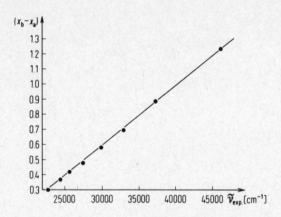

shows that a difference $\Delta (x_b - x_a) = 1$, i.e. $\Delta (\epsilon_b - \epsilon_a) = \beta$, corresponds to a wave-number difference $\Delta \tilde{\nu}_{exp} = 47800 - 22400 = 25400$ cm⁻¹, so that $\beta = -25400$ cm⁻¹. This difference corresponds to 71.4 kcal/mol and is thus about 2.5 times greater than the value of β from the delocalization energy (10/72) of benzene ($\beta = -20$ kcal/mol).

It should also be noted that the regression line in the graphic representation

$$\tilde{\nu}_{exp.} = 14800 + 25400(x_b - x_a) \text{ [cm⁻¹]}$$

does not pass through the origin, but reaches the point $\tilde{\nu}_{exp} = 14800$ cm⁻¹ for $(x_b - x_a) = 0$, i.e. $x_a = x_b = 0$. This can be interpreted as meaning that even in an infinitely long polyene a finite energy difference will still exist between the highest occupied bonding and lowest unoccupied antibonding molecular orbitals, in contrast to the predictions of HMO theory. This is a consequence of alternance of the bond lengths. In the HMO approach the effect of bond alternation is absorbed in the parameter β together with the neglected electron interaction whose effect is especially important in excited states. The calibration value obtained from the electronic spectra cannot therefore be expected to agree with that calculated from calorimetric data from the so-called 'delocalization energies'.

11.2. Electronic Excitation Energy

Problem 11.2: With the aid of the regression [11.9] and tabulated HMO values (Volume 3), calculate for the following π-electron systems the position $\tilde{\nu}^{HMO}$ of those absorption maxima which correspond to the ^1L_a band in the spectra of the benzenoid hydrocarbons:

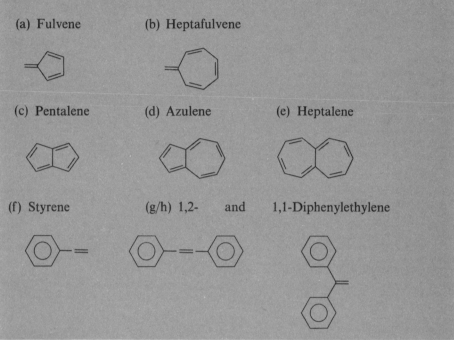

(a) Fulvene　　　(b) Heptafulvene

(c) Pentalene　　(d) Azulene　　　(e) Heptalene

(f) Styrene　　　(g/h) 1,2-　and　1,1-Diphenylethylene

It should be noted that, for nonalternant π-electron systems, the regression

$$\tilde{\nu}^{HMO} = 8200 - 22000(2x_a) \ [cm^{-1}] \tag{11/18}$$

has to be corrected thus

$$2x_a \neq x_a - x_b$$

because

$$\tilde{\nu}^{HMO} = 8200 - 22000(x_a - x_b) \ [cm^{-1}]$$

The results $\tilde{\nu}^{HMO}$ obtained on substituting the HMO values tabulated in Vol. 3 for the individual compounds are compared with the observed longest wavelength absorption maxima $\tilde{\nu}_{(^1L_a)}^{exp}$ in the following table:

Com-pound	x_a	x_b	$x_a - x_b$	$\tilde{\nu}^{HMO}$ [cm^{-1}]	$\tilde{\nu}^{exp.}$ (^1L_a) [cm^{-1}]	$\tilde{\nu}^{HMO} - \tilde{\nu}^{exp.}_{(^1L_a)}$ [cm^{-1}]
(a)	−0.254	+0.618	−0.872	27400	27600	− 200
(b)	−0.445	+0.216	−0.661	22700	23450	− 750
(c)	0.000	+0.471	−0.471	18700	(29762)*	(−11062)
(d)	−0.400	+0.477	−0.877	27500	17300	+10200
(e)	−0.311	0.000	−0.311	15000	(28400)	(−13400)
(f)	−0.662	+0.662	−1.324	37300	40300	− 3000
(g)	−0.504	+0.504	−1.008	30400	32700	− 2300
(h)	−0.565	+0.565	−1.130	33100	39700	− 6600

* This frequency really relates to the 1,3-dimethyl derivate of pentalene.

Although the regression used was set up considering alternant systems, it also gives pleasing agreement for the nonalternant compounds (a) and (b), provided of course that the regression line refers to the ^1L_a band of benzenoid systems, and that also with nonalternant systems the excitation ($\Psi_b \rightarrow \Psi_a$) does not necessarily correspond to the longest wavelength absorption. The considerable deviation for azulene (d) can be attributed inter alia to calibration of the regression as mentioned above for systems with distinct bond alternance, while the perimeter of azulene has practically equal bond lengths. In the case of heptalene (e), *Franck-Condon* broadening of the long wave length absorption band leads to a continuous fall-off in intensity over the whole visible spectral region in which no definite maximum can be located. Finally the difference in the case of 1,1-diphenylethylene (h) is attributable to the inability of the two phenyl moities to assume a coplanar arrangement when attached to the same sp^2 carbon center instead they adopt a propeller-like orientation.

Problem 11.3: The "inner" eigenvalues ε_b and ε_a of alternant benzenoid hydrocarbons can be evaluated according to the LCMO approximation (Section 7.5) from those of the odd-numbered partial systems (Problem 7.22). Use the regression [11.9] to calculate the position of the ^1L_a band of the following hydrocarbons, and compare the results with the electronic spectroscopic values $\tilde{\nu}^{exp}$ [cm^{-1}] given:

(a) Chrysene (b) 3,4-Benzophenanthrene (c) 3,4-Benzotetraphene

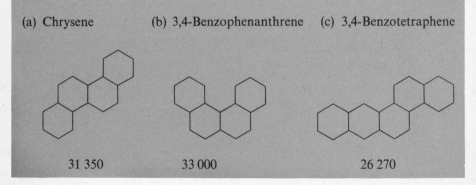

31 350   33 000   26 270

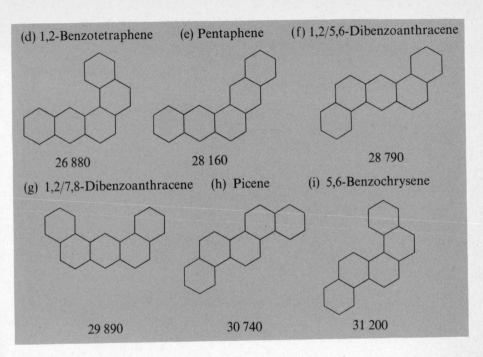

(d) 1,2-Benzotetraphene   (e) Pentaphene   (f) 1,2/5,6-Dibenzoanthracene

26 880   28 160   28 790

(g) 1,2/7,8-Dibenzoanthracene   (h) Picene   (i) 5,6-Benzochrysene

29 890   30 740   31 200

With the approximate orbital energies $0.8\,x_a^{\mathrm{LCMO}}$ from Problem 7.22, the regression

$$\tilde{\nu}^{\mathrm{HMO}} = 8200 - 22000\,(2x_a)\,[\mathrm{cm}^{-1}] \tag{11/18}$$

affords the results assembled in the table below:

Compound	$2 \cdot 0.8 x_a^{\mathrm{LCMO}}$	$\tilde{\nu}^{\mathrm{LCMO}}[\mathrm{cm}^{-1}]$	$\tilde{\nu}^{\mathrm{exp.}}_{(^1L_a)}[\mathrm{cm}^{-1}]$	$\Delta\,[\mathrm{cm}^{-1}]$
(a)	−1.082	32000	31350	− 650
(b)	−1.174	34000	33000	−1000
(c)	−0.956	29200	26270	−2930
(d)	−1.036	31000	26880	−4120
(e)	−0.940	28900	28160	− 740
(f)	−0.960	29300	28790	− 510
(g)	−1.042	31100	29890	−1210
(h)	−1.040	31100	30740	− 360
(i)	−1.128	33000	31200	−1800

The deviations Δ are generally small and are negative in each case so that a slight lowering of the empirical factor $f = 0.8$, should further enhance the agreement. The relatively large difference for compounds (c), (d), and (i) can be reduced by calculating the inner orbital energies — as for e.g. (e) and (g) — by choosing other combinations of partial systems (Problem 7.22: 2 naphthylmethyl units):

Compound	Combination	Cross Terms	$-x_a$	$-0.8\,x_a$
(c) I:		$\dfrac{4}{\sqrt{42}}\cdot\dfrac{2}{\sqrt{7}}+\dfrac{3}{\sqrt{42}}\cdot\dfrac{1}{\sqrt{7}}$	0.642	0.513
II:		$\dfrac{5}{\sqrt{46}}\cdot\dfrac{1}{\sqrt{7}}+\dfrac{3}{\sqrt{46}}\cdot\dfrac{2}{\sqrt{7}}$	0.613	0.491
III:		$\dfrac{5}{\sqrt{54}}\cdot\dfrac{1}{\sqrt{7}}+\dfrac{3}{\sqrt{54}}\cdot\dfrac{2}{\sqrt{7}}$	0.566	0.453

Compound	Combination	Cross Terms	$-x_a$	$-0.8\,x_a$

(d) I:

$-\dfrac{1}{\sqrt{7}}$ $+\dfrac{2}{\sqrt{7}}$

$-\dfrac{1}{\sqrt{34}}$ $+\dfrac{2}{\sqrt{34}}$ $-\dfrac{3}{\sqrt{34}}$ $+\dfrac{4}{\sqrt{34}}$

$+\dfrac{1}{\sqrt{34}}$ $-\dfrac{1}{\sqrt{34}}$ $+\dfrac{1}{\sqrt{34}}$ $-\dfrac{1}{\sqrt{34}}$

$$\frac{4}{\sqrt{34}}\cdot\frac{2}{\sqrt{7}}+\frac{3}{\sqrt{34}}\cdot\frac{1}{\sqrt{7}}$$

0.713   0.571

II:

$-\dfrac{1}{\sqrt{49}}$ $+\dfrac{1}{\sqrt{49}}$

$\dfrac{2}{\sqrt{7}}$ $+\dfrac{1}{\sqrt{49}}$ $-\dfrac{2}{\sqrt{49}}$

$-\dfrac{1}{\sqrt{7}}$ $\dfrac{3}{\sqrt{49}}$ $+\dfrac{2}{\sqrt{49}}$

$+\dfrac{5}{\sqrt{49}}$ $-\dfrac{2}{\sqrt{49}}$

$$\frac{5}{\sqrt{49}}\cdot\frac{1}{\sqrt{7}}+\frac{2}{\sqrt{7}}\cdot\frac{3}{\sqrt{49}}$$

0.594   0.476

III:

$-\dfrac{1}{\sqrt{51}}$

$+\dfrac{1}{\sqrt{51}}$ $+\dfrac{1}{\sqrt{51}}$

$+\dfrac{5}{\sqrt{51}}$ $-\dfrac{2}{\sqrt{51}}$ $-\dfrac{1}{\sqrt{51}}$

$-\dfrac{1}{\sqrt{7}}$ $-\dfrac{3}{\sqrt{51}}$ $+\dfrac{3}{\sqrt{51}}$

$+\dfrac{2}{\sqrt{7}}$

$$\frac{5}{\sqrt{51}}\cdot\frac{1}{\sqrt{7}}+\frac{3}{\sqrt{51}}\cdot\frac{2}{\sqrt{7}}$$

0.582   0.466

Compound	Combination	Cross Terms	$-x_a$	$-0.8\,x_a$
(e)	I(cf. d/I):	$\dfrac{4}{\sqrt{34}}\cdot\dfrac{1}{\sqrt{7}}+\dfrac{3}{\sqrt{34}}\cdot\dfrac{2}{\sqrt{7}}$	0.648	0.509
	II(cf. c/I):	$\dfrac{4}{\sqrt{42}}\cdot\dfrac{1}{\sqrt{7}}+\dfrac{3}{\sqrt{42}}\cdot\dfrac{2}{\sqrt{7}}$	0.583	0.466
(g)	(cf. c/II):	$\dfrac{5}{\sqrt{46}}\cdot\dfrac{2}{\sqrt{7}}+\dfrac{2}{\sqrt{46}}\cdot\dfrac{1}{\sqrt{7}}$	0.669	0.535
(i)	I(cf. c/II):	$\dfrac{5}{\sqrt{46}}\cdot\dfrac{2}{\sqrt{7}}+\dfrac{3}{\sqrt{46}}\cdot\dfrac{1}{\sqrt{7}}$	0.722	0.580

Com- pound	Combination	Cross Terms	$-x_a$	$-0.8\,x_a$
II(cf. d/III):		$\dfrac{5}{\sqrt{51}}\cdot\dfrac{2}{\sqrt{7}}+\dfrac{3}{\sqrt{51}}\cdot\dfrac{1}{\sqrt{7}}$	0.688	0.550

Since the LCMO treatment corresponds to a first order perturbation, and because inclusion of second order perturbations by the higher and lower lying molecular orbitals necessarily leads to a reduction in the energy values, the smallest of the 'inner' orbital energies $0.8\,x_a^{\mathrm{LCMO}}$ obtained according to the above combinations must always be adopted. Substitution in the regression leads to the following results:

Combina- tion	$2\cdot0.8\,x_a^{\mathrm{LCMO}}$	$\bar{\nu}^{\mathrm{LCMO}}\,[\mathrm{cm}^{-1}]$	$\bar{\nu}^{\mathrm{exp.}}_{(^1L_a)}\,[\mathrm{cm}^{-1}]$	$\Delta\,[\mathrm{cm}^{-1}]$
c/III	−0.906	28100	26270	−1830
d/III	−0.932	28700	26880	−1820
e/II	−0.932	28700	28160	− 540
g/0	−1.042	31100	29890	−1210
i/II	−1.100	32400	31200	−1200

As can be seen, better agreement results in all cases exept (g).

318

Problem 11.4: Attempt to estimate the relative positions of the longest wavelength electronic transitions of fulvene (a) and calicene (b) with aid of qualitative molecular orbitals (Chapter 8):

(a)   (b)

(a) Fulvene:

Starting from qualitative molecular orbitals, improved orbital energy coefficients x'_J were calculated for fulvene in Problem 8.12 by a perturbation calculation according to Section 8.3. These coefficients displayed good agreement with the exact HMO values. For the excitation

the resulting energy difference is

$$\Delta E'_\pi = (x'_4 - x'_3)\beta = (-0.222 - 0.625)\beta = -0.847\beta.$$

Comparsion with the exact HMO values [Section 4.4]:

$$\Delta E_\pi^{HMO} = (x_4^{HMO} - x_3^{HMO})\beta = (-0.254 - 0.618)\beta = -0.872\beta$$

shows a deviation of only 0.025 β-units.

(b) Calicene:

The starting point is the set of qualitative molecular orbitals established according to Section 8.2 from the irreducible representations for C_{2v} symmetry.

$$\Gamma \doteq 3 \overset{\times}{\times} A_2 \overset{.}{+} 5 \overset{\times}{\times} B_1$$

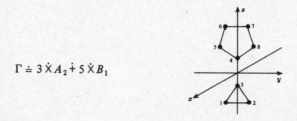

The five molecular orbitals (B_1) antisymmetric to rotation about $C_2(z)$ are conveniently chosen according to increasing numbers of nodes as follows:

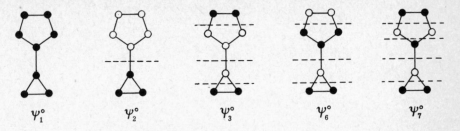

For the three molecular orbitals (A_2) symmetric with respect to rotation about $C_2(z)$ let us initially choose the following qualitative starting orbitals with increasing numbers of nodes:

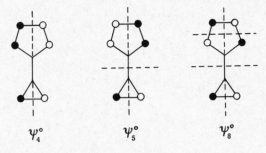

According to rules (8/16) and (8/19)

$$x_J^0 = 2 \cdot \left(\frac{1}{\sqrt{Z}}\right)^2 (Z_{BJ} - Z_{AJ})$$

the orbital energy coefficients x_J^0 for the above qualitative molecular orbitals Ψ_J^0 are:

J	Z	Z_{BJ}	Z_{AJ}	x_J^0	Irreducible representation
8	6	0	4	−1.33	A_2
7	8	2	7	−1.25	B_1
6	8	4	5	−0.25	B_1
5	6	2	2	0.00	A_2
4	6	2	2	0.00	A_2
3	8	5	4	+0.25	B_1
2	8	8	1	+1.75	B_1
1	8	9	0	+2.25	B_1

The qualitative molecular orbitals Ψ_4^0 and Ψ_5^0 belonging to the orbital energy $x_J^0 = 0$ are not interaction-free; their overlap integral S_{45} has the finite value

$$S_{45} = <\Psi_4^0|\Psi_5^0> = <\frac{1}{\sqrt{6}}(\Phi_1 - \Phi_2 + \Phi_5 + \Phi_6 - \Phi_7 - \Phi_8)|\frac{1}{\sqrt{6}}(\Phi_1 - \Phi_2 - \Phi_5 - \Phi_6 + \Phi_7 + \Phi_8).$$

$$= \frac{1}{6}(<\Phi_1|\Phi_1> + <\Phi_2|\Phi_2> - <\Phi_5|\Phi_5> - <\Phi_6|\Phi_6> - <\Phi_7|\Phi_7> - <\Phi_8|\Phi_8>)$$

$$= \frac{1}{6}(1 + 1 - 1 - 1 - 1 - 1) = -\frac{1}{3}.$$

Their degeneracy is accidental. Formation of linear combinations with $S_{45} = 0$ leads to the improved qualitative molecular orbitals:

$$\Psi_s = N(a\,\Psi_4^0 + b\,\Psi_5^0) = N \qquad + \qquad = N$$

$$\Psi_a = N(a\,\Psi_4^0 - b\,\Psi_5^0) = N \qquad - \qquad = N$$

The associated improved orbital energies x_J' read:

J	Z	Z_{BJ}	Z_{AJ}	x_J'	Irreducible representation
5	2	0	1	-1.00	A_2
4	4	2	1	$+0.50$	A_2

This result is of course identical with that of a perturbation calculation according to $(8/61)-(8/70)$.

$$S_{45} = \langle \Psi_4^0 | \Psi_5^0 \rangle = -\frac{1}{3}$$

$$H_{45} = \langle \Psi_4^0 | \mathcal{H} | \Psi_5^0 \rangle = \frac{1}{6}(\langle \Phi_1 | \mathcal{H} | \Phi_1 \rangle + \langle \Phi_2 | \mathcal{H} | \Phi_2 \rangle - \langle \Phi_5 | \mathcal{H} | \Phi_5 \rangle -$$

$$- \langle \Phi_6 | \mathcal{H} | \Phi_6 \rangle - \langle \Phi_7 | \mathcal{H} | \Phi_7 \rangle - \langle \Phi_8 | \mathcal{H} | \Phi_8 \rangle -$$

$$- 2 \langle \Phi_1 | \mathcal{H} | \Phi_2 \rangle - 2 \langle \Phi_5 | \mathcal{H} | \Phi_6 \rangle + 2 \langle \Phi_5 | \mathcal{H} | \Phi_7 \rangle -$$

$$- 2 \langle \Phi_7 | \mathcal{H} | \Phi_8 \rangle)$$

$$= -\frac{1}{3}\alpha - \frac{2}{3}\beta$$

$$\begin{Vmatrix} \alpha - \epsilon & -\frac{1}{3}\alpha - \frac{2}{3}\beta + \frac{1}{3}\epsilon \\ -\frac{1}{3}\alpha - \frac{2}{3}\beta + \frac{1}{3}\epsilon & \alpha - \epsilon \end{Vmatrix} = \begin{Vmatrix} -x & +\frac{x}{3} - \frac{2}{3} \\ +\frac{x}{3} - \frac{2}{3} & -x \end{Vmatrix} = 2x^2 + x - 1 = 0$$

$$x_{1,2} = -\frac{1}{4} \pm \sqrt{\frac{1}{16} + \frac{1}{2}}$$

$$= -\frac{1}{4} \pm \frac{3}{4}$$

$$x_1 = +0.500$$

$$x_2 = -1.000$$

From the coefficients

$$-(-1)c_4 + \left(+\frac{1}{3}(-1) - \frac{2}{3}\right) c_5 = 0; \ c_4 = c_5,$$

$$-\left(+\frac{1}{2}\right)c_4 + \left(+\frac{1}{3}\left(+\frac{1}{2}\right) - \frac{2}{3}\right)c_5 = 0; \ c_4 = -c_5$$

it is immediately apparent that in the linear combinations used

$$\Psi = N(a\Psi_4^0 \pm b\Psi_5^0)$$

a must equal b, as already assumed implicitly.

This preliminary result leads to the energy level scheme:

322

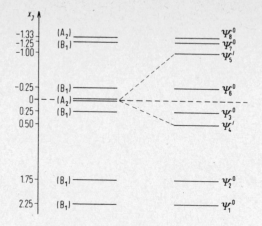

The diagram immediately reveals that an evaluation of the longest wavelength excitation energy of calicene, will also require improvement of the 'inner' orbital energies x_3^0 and x_6^0 belonging to the irreducible representation B_1.

Taking account of all orbital energies belonging to B_1, the expression

$$x_J' = x_J^0 + \sum_{I \neq J} \frac{(H_{JI} - S_{JI} x_J^0)^2}{x_J^0 - x_I^0} \tag{8/71}$$

yields

$$x_6' - x_6^0 = \Delta x_6 = \frac{(H_{61} - S_{61} x_6^0)^2}{x_6^0 - x_1^0} + \frac{(H_{62} - S_{62} x_6^0)^2}{x_6^0 - x_2^0} + \frac{(H_{63} - S_{63} x_6^0)^2}{x_6^0 - x_3^0} + \frac{(H_{67} - S_{67} x_6^0)^2}{x_6^0 - x_7^0}$$

$$= \frac{\left(\frac{1}{8} \cdot 4 - \frac{1}{8} \cdot 2 \left(-\frac{1}{4}\right)\right)^2}{-\frac{1}{4} - \frac{9}{4}} + \frac{\left(\frac{1}{8} \cdot 2 - 0\right)^2}{-\frac{1}{4} - \frac{7}{4}} +$$

$$+ \frac{\left(\frac{1}{8}(-4) - \frac{1}{8}(-2)\left(-\frac{1}{4}\right)\right)^2}{-\frac{1}{4} - \frac{1}{4}} + \frac{\left(\frac{1}{8}(-2) - 0\right)^2}{-\frac{1}{4} - \left(-\frac{5}{4}\right)}$$

$$= -0.127 - 0.031 - 0.633 + 0.063 = -0.728$$

$$x_6' = -0.978$$

$$x_3' - x_3^0 = \Delta x_3 = \frac{(H_{31} - S_{31}x_3^0)^2}{x_3^0 - x_1^0} + \frac{(H_{32} - S_{32}x_3^0)^2}{x_3^0 - x_2^0} + \frac{(H_{36} - S_{36}x_3^0)^2}{x_3^0 - x_6^0} + \frac{(H_{37} - S_{37}x_3^0)^2}{x_3^0 - x_7^0}$$

$$= \frac{\left(\frac{1}{8}(-2) - 0\right)^2}{\frac{1}{4} - \frac{9}{4}} + \frac{\left(\frac{1}{8} \cdot 4 - \frac{1}{8} \cdot 2 \cdot \frac{1}{4}\right)^2}{\frac{1}{4} - \frac{7}{4}} + \frac{\left(\frac{1}{8}(-4) - \frac{1}{8}(-2)\frac{1}{4}\right)^2}{\frac{1}{4} - \left(-\frac{1}{4}\right)} +$$

$$+ \frac{\left(\frac{1}{8}(-4) - \frac{1}{8} \cdot 6 \cdot \frac{1}{4}\right)^2}{\frac{1}{4} - \left(-\frac{5}{4}\right)}$$

$$= -0.031 - 0.128 + 0.383 + 0.315 = +0.539$$

$$x_3' = +0.789$$

The 'inner' molecular orbitals of calicene responsible for the excitation $\Psi_a \rightarrow \Psi_b$ are now in the right sequence, as will be shown by comparison with the exact HMO orbital energies $x_{J'}^{HMO}$:

J	x_J^0	$\rightarrow$	$x_{J'}'$	$x_{J'}^{HMO}$	J'
6	-0.25		-1.000	-1.000	6
5	0.00		-0.978	-0.871	5
4	0.00	$\longrightarrow$	+0.500	+0.618	4
3	0.25	$\longrightarrow$	+0.789	+0.677	3

The resulting excitation energy is

$$\Delta E_\pi' = (x_5' - x_4')\beta = -1.478\,\beta$$
$$\Delta E_\pi^{HMO} = (x_5 - x_4)\beta = -1.489\,\beta$$

Summarizing, the above estimate indicates that calicene (b), in spite of its containing one more double bond than fulvene (a), should nevertheless absorb at shorter wavelength.

Problem 11.5: With the aid of an isoconjugate model show that the π-electron systems of the cyanine type with $n = 2N + 1$ centres

$$[R_2\overline{N}-(CH=CH)_{N-1}-CH=\overset{\oplus}{N}R_2] \leftrightarrow [R_2\overset{\oplus}{N}=CH-(CH=CH)_{N-1}-\overline{N}R_2]$$

absorb at considerably longer wavelengths than polyenes with $2N$ centres. Compare the HMO predictions with the band positions observed for the given azacyanines

N	1	2	3	4	5
λ_{max}	224	310	412	510	660 [nm]

and also with approximation values calculated for the polyenes in Problem 11.1.

In contrast to the polyenes $H(CH=CH)_NH$ with an even number of $n = 2N$ centers, the isoconjugate models with $n = 2N + 1$ centers corresponding to the cyanine type always have an occupied nonbonding molecular orbital $x_{(n+1)/2} = 0$.

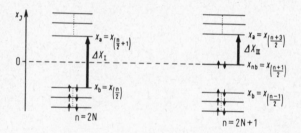

From the general formula for the orbital energies x_J of linear π-systems with n centers

$$x_J = 2\cos\left(\frac{\pi}{n+1}J\right) \;;\; J = 1,2,3\ldots n \tag{5/4}$$

the resulting excitation energies are (cf. Problem 11.1):

$$\Delta X_I = x_a - x_b = -4\cos\frac{\pi}{2}\left(\frac{n}{n+1}\right)$$

$$\Delta X_{II} = x_a - x_{nb} = +2\cos\frac{\pi}{2}\left(\frac{n+3}{n+1}\right)$$

For $N = 1$ this means

$$\left.\begin{array}{l} \Delta X_I = -4\cos\frac{\pi}{3} = -2 \\[2ex] \Delta X_{II} = +2\cos\frac{3\pi}{4} = -\sqrt{2} \end{array}\right\} \quad \Delta X_I = \sqrt{2}\ \Delta X_{II}$$

and for large values of n it follows that

$$\Delta X_1 > \Delta X_{II},$$

i.e. the excitation energy for even polyenes with $n = 2\,N$ centers is always greater than that for odd ones with $n = 2\,N + 1$ centers.

In particular, the isoconjugate models afford the following values for azacyanines in which the nitrogen always contributes two electrons to the π-system — cf. the energy level scheme:

N	1	2	3	4	5
n	3	5	7	9	11
$x_a - x_{nb}$	−1.414	−1.000	−0.766	−0.618	−0.518
$\nu_{max}^{exp.}$ [cm^{-1}]	44600	32300	24300	19600	15200

Comparison with the corresponding values for the polyenes (Problem 11.1) shows that they expectedly absorb at shorter wavelengths. Moreover, a plot of these results shows that the regression on the experimental band frequencies of azacyanines practically passes through the origin in contrast to the polyenes.

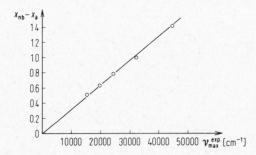

This can be attributed to the absence of bond alternance such as occurs in the polyenes, as already suggested by the resonance formulation given in the statement of this problem.

The perturbation $\delta\alpha_N$ incurred by aza substitution has been neglected in the above discussion. According to Section 5.3 the following coefficients at the ends of the chains are obtained for the molecular orbitals participating in the electronic transition:

$$\Psi_{nb}: \quad \underset{+\xi}{*} - \text{o} - \underset{-\xi}{*} - \text{o} - \underset{+\xi}{*} - \text{o} \cdots \underset{\pm\xi}{*} \; ; \; \xi^2 = \frac{1}{N+1} \; ; \; c^2_{nb,1} = \frac{1}{N+1} = \frac{2}{n+1}$$

$$\Psi_a: \quad c_{\frac{n+3}{2},1} = \sqrt{\frac{2}{n+1}} \sin\left(\frac{\pi}{2}\left(\frac{n+3}{n+1}\right)\right) \; ; \; \text{for large values of } n : c^2_{a,1} \approx \frac{2}{n+1}$$

The two energy levels are shifted in the same direction, by amounts that become equal and very small for large values of n so that they may be neglected to a first approximation.

Problem 11.6: Protonation of aromatic compounds produces carbonium ions. Utilizing HMO values (Volume 3), show that the addition of a proton to the benzenoid systems (a) → (b) and (c) → (d) is associated with a longer wavelength (bathochromic) shift, whereas on the other hand in the nonalternant azulene protonation (e) → (f) it is associated with a shorter wavelength (hypsochromic) shift of the $\Psi_b \rightarrow \Psi_a$ transition in the HMO scheme.

Comparison of the differences $(x_a - x_b)$ taken from the HMO Tables (Vol. 3) of the π-electron systems (a), (c), and (e) and of the residual systems (b), (d), and (f) gives:

Com-pound	x_a	x_b	$(x_a - x_b)$	Com-pound	x_a	x_b	$(x_a - x_b)$	Δ
(a)	−0.618	+0.618	−1.236	(b)	0.000	+1.000	−1.000	−0.236
(c)	−0.414	+0.414	−0.828	(d)	0.000	+1.000	−1.000	+0.172
(e)	−0.400	+0.477	−0.877	(f)	−0.338	+0.807	−1.145	+0.268

Hence the bands corresponding to the transitions $(\Psi_b \rightarrow \Psi_a)$ should experience a bathochromic shift on protonation of naphthalene (a), and a hypsochromic shift in the case of azulene (c). This differing behavior is qualitatively explained as follows: protonation corresponds to removal of a center ρ with two electrons. Reintroduction of this doubly occupied nonbonding atomic orbital leads to a first order splitting for alternant π-systems because of interaction with the nonbonding molecular orbital of the cationic fragment.

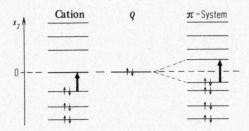

As shown in the scheme, a bathochromic shift of the longest wavelength band occurs on protonation of benzene or naphthalene (a). In the case of nonalternant azulene, the case of azulene (c). This differing behavior is qualitatively explained as follows: arises only from second order perturbation. This would appear to indicate a fundamental difference between alternant and nonalternant π-electron systems. However, the values in the adjoining table

	Benzene	Naphthalene	Anthracene	Tetracene	Azulene
$\tilde{\nu}_{max}$ [cm^{-1}]	50000	36400	26700	21200	17200
$\tilde{\nu}_{max}^{(H^{\oplus})}$ [cm^{-1}]	30000	25000	24000	22000	28000

show that this is not necessarily always the case. As the size of the π-electron system increases, a hypsochromic shift of $-0.172\,\beta$ is already predicted on reaching alternant anthracene, while experimentally a slight bathochromic shift is still found. The reason is to be sought in the energy level scheme of the anthracene residual system 2, i.e. the diphenylmethyl cation (cf. Vol. 3), which has three highest occupied molecular orbitals, so that the longest wavelength absorption band should correspond to a triply degenerate excited state. The splitting of such levels under the influence of electron interaction discussed in [11.6] – [11.8] leads to a corresponding bathochromic shift. Finally, for tetracene a hypsochromic shift is also observed experimentally.

Problem 11.7: Methyl substitution of azulene at various centres μ leads to hypsochromic or bathochromic displacements $\delta\tilde{v}_{max}$ of the longest wavelength absorption:

$\tilde{v}_{max} = 17\,240 \text{ cm}^{-1}$.

μ_{CH_3}	1	2	4	5	6
$\delta\tilde{v}_{max}$ [cm^{-1}]	-790	$+430$	$+370$	-350	$+460$

Interpret these shifts as influences of an inductive effect on the electronic transition $\Psi_b \rightarrow \Psi_a$.

For methyl substitution of azulene the positive perturbation $\delta\alpha_\mu > 0$ at the individual centers μ

$$\delta\alpha_\mu = \alpha'_\mu - \alpha_\mu = h_X\beta \qquad (6/78)$$
$$h_X = -\frac{1}{3}$$

affords the difference in excitation energies as

$$\delta\Delta E_\pi(b \rightarrow a) = \delta\epsilon_a - \delta\epsilon_b = (c_{a\mu}^2 - c_{b\mu}^2)\delta\alpha_\mu. \qquad (11/20)$$

Insertion of the HMO values (Vol. 3) yields:

μ	$c_{a\mu}$	$c_{a\mu}^2$	δx_a	$c_{b\mu}$	$c_{b\mu}^2$	δx_b	$\delta\Delta E_\pi[\beta]$	$\tilde{\nu}_{max}^{exp.}[cm^{-1}]$
1	+0.063	0.004	−0.001	+0.543	0.295	−0.098	+0.097	−790
2	−0.316	0.100	−0.033	0			−0.033	+430
4	−0.470	0.221	−0.074	+0.160	0.026	−0.009	−0.065	+370
5	−0.102	0.010	−0.003	+0.335	0.112	−0.037	+0.034	−350
6	+0.511	0.261	−0.087	0			−0.087	+460

The HMO predictions which agree in part satisfactorily (1, 2, 5) and in part just qualitatively (4, 6) with experimental data are summarized schematically in the following energy level diagram:

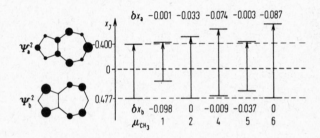

A graphic representation

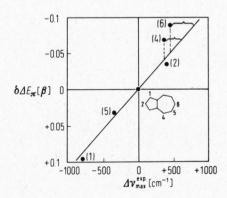

again confirms the good agreement of the HMO predictions with respect to the band shift caused by methyl substitution at centers 1, 2, and 5, while the calculated hypsochromic shifts for the centers 4 and 6 are apparently too large. The observed bathochromic components (——) in these compounds can be attributed, e.g., to a particularly large hyperconjugation effect at the relevant centers. This could be characterized in a resonance formulation by the particularly favorable structures (B) and (D):

Problem 11.8: Show that replacement of a carbon centre in an isoconjugate alternant system by a hetero atom induces no shift in the ^1L_a band.

For corresponding molecular orbitals $\Psi_{(x_j)}$ and $\Psi_{(-x_j)}$ the coefficients of the starred ($*$) set merely differ in sign, but not in magnitude, from those of the unstarred ($°$) set in an isoconjugate alternant π-electron system:

$$\Psi_{(-x_j)} = \sum_{\mu=1}^{m} c_{j_\mu}^* \Phi_\mu - \sum_{\nu=m+1}^{n} c_{j_\nu}^0 \Phi_\nu \tag{5/26}$$

$$\Psi_{(x_j)} = \sum_{\mu=1}^{m} c_{j_\mu}^* \Phi_\mu + \sum_{\nu=m+1}^{n} c_{j_\nu}^0 \Phi_\nu \tag{5/25}$$

Because of

$$c_{a\mu}^2 - c_{b\mu}^2 = 0$$

we have in a first order perturbation treatment

$$(c_{a\mu}^2 - c_{b\mu}^2)\delta\alpha_\mu = \delta\Delta E_\pi = 0 .$$

For the sake of illustration the excitation energies of aza- and diazanaphthalenes are compared with that of naphthalene.

$\lambda_{(^1L_a)} = 286$ nm

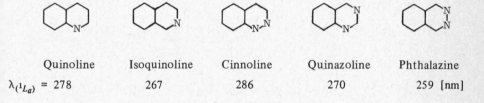

Quinoline	Isoquinoline	Cinnoline	Quinazoline	Phthalazine
$\lambda_{(^1L_a)} = 278$	267	286	270	259 [nm]

Provided that the ^1L_a band has been correctly assigned, aza substitution is seen to exert only the expectedly small effect on the relevant excitation energy. The largest difference amounts to 3600 cm^{-1} = 10 kcal/mol.

The above situation can be illustrated graphically as follows:

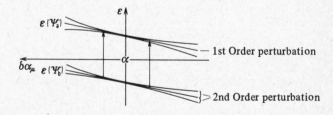

Deviations from the excitation energies, which are constant according to first order perturbation, are only to be expected from higher order perturbations.

The above prediction no longer applies to nonalternant systems because the orbital energies $\epsilon(\Psi_a)$ and $\epsilon(\Psi_b)$ depend differently on $\delta\alpha_\mu$. Thus for instance in the following case

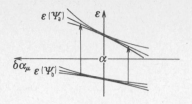

the excitation energy of the pertinent electronic transition will be raised or lowered, depending on the sign of the perturbation $\delta\alpha_\mu$, due to the different tangents at $\delta\alpha_\mu = $ •
The associated absorption bands are accordingly shifted hypsochromically or bathochromically.

Problem 11.9: In the series of ω methyl polyenaldehydes, a weak intensity $n \to \pi^*$ band extending beyond the longest wavelength $\pi \to \pi^*$ transition is observed only for $n = 0$ and $n = 1$:

$$CH_3-(CH\!=\!CH)_n-CHO$$

n	0	1	2	3	4
$\lambda_{max}^{\pi\to\pi^*}$ [nm]	185	225	270	312	343
$\lambda_{max}^{n\to\pi^*}$ [nm]	290	≈ 320	—	—	—

Explain these experimental results using HMO data.

The influence of a methyl group at centre μ on the HMO excitation energy of a π-electron system cannot always be simulated by inductive effects only (Problem 11.7). As has already been shown in the discussion of ESR spectra (10/55), the so-called hyperconjugation also has to be considered in this case; for electronic transitions the effect can most easily be estimated by a perturbation calculation.

The wave number maxima for $n\to\pi^*$ and $\pi\to\pi^*$ of the polyenealdehydes are listed together with the HMO excitation energies of corresponding isoconjugate chains (Vol. 3) in the table below.

n	0	1	2	3	4
$\tilde{\nu}_{max}^{n\to\pi^*}$ [cm^{-1}]	34500	31300	- - -	- - -	- - -
$\tilde{\nu}_{max}^{\pi\to\pi^*}$ [cm^{-1}]	54100	45500	37000	32100	29200
$-2x_a[\beta]$	2.000	1.236	0.890	0.694	0.570

From a graphic representation

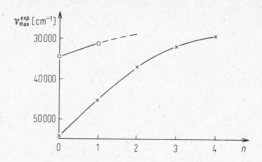

it can be deduced that the wavenumbers of the $n{\to}\pi^*$ maxima increase less steeply with increasing chain length than the $\pi{\to}\pi^*$ transitions since the n-level remains constant to a first approximation.

$$\Delta E_{\pi{\to}\pi^*} \cong 2x_a\beta$$

$$\Delta E_{n{\to}\pi^*} \approx (K + x_a)\beta$$

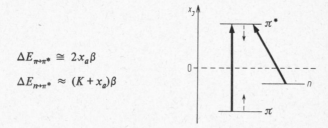

As a result, for $n = 2$ the weak ($\epsilon \sim 10-30$) $n{\to}\pi^*$ transition disappears beneath the tail of the intense $\pi{\to}\pi^*$ band ($\epsilon \sim 20000-60000$) which has a halfwidth of approximately 6000 cm^{-1}.

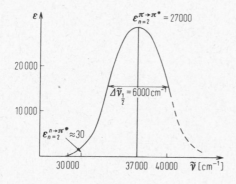

Problem 11.10: Show that the hyperconjugation effect of a methyl group on the HMO excitation $\Psi_b \rightarrow \Psi_a$ always leads to a bathochromic shift of the band for both alternant and nonalternant π-electron systems.

The orbital energies and orbitals of an isolated methyl group are given in Problem 10.24 as

$$x_2^M = -3.260 \; ; \; \Psi_2^M = 0.677 \, \Phi_C - 0.736 \, \Phi_{H_3} \, ,$$
$$x_1^M = +2.760 \; ; \; \Psi_1^M = 0.736 \, \Phi_C - 0.677 \, \Phi_{H_3} \, .$$

In the LCMO approximation the perturbation of the 'inner' orbital energies

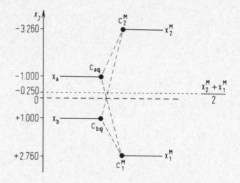

is given, in analogy to (7/43), by the relations

$$\delta x_a = \frac{(c_{a\rho} \cdot k \cdot c_1^M)^2}{x_a - x_1^M} + \frac{(c_{a\rho} \cdot k \cdot c_2^M)^2}{x_a - x_2^M} \, ,$$

$$\delta x_b = \frac{(c_{b\rho} \cdot k \cdot c_1^M)^2}{x_b - x_1^M} + \frac{(c_{b\rho} \cdot k \cdot c_2^M)^2}{x_b - x_2^M}$$

in which k is the coefficient of the resonance integral $k\beta$ between the methyl group and the substitution site.

For the special case of an alternant π-system

$$x_a = -x_b \; ; \; c_{a\rho}^2 = c_{b\rho}^2$$

and the simplifying assumption $c_1^M \sim c_2^M$, we obtain

$$\delta x_a - \delta x_b = k^2 c_M^2 c_\rho^2 \left(\frac{1}{x_a - 2.76} - \frac{1}{-x_a - 2.76} + \frac{1}{x_a + 3.26} - \frac{1}{-x_a + 3.26} \right)$$

$$= -k^2 c_M^2 c_\rho^2 \cdot 2x_a \left(\frac{1}{2.76^2 - x_a^2} + \frac{1}{3.26^2 - x_a^2} \right).$$

Since x_a is negative, the difference $\delta x_a - \delta x_b$ becomes positive, corresponding to a bathochromic shift of the longest wavelength band because $\delta(\Delta E_\pi) = (\delta x_a - \delta x_b)\beta$.

If x_a is located in the interval $-0.25 > x_a > -1$ and x_b likewise in the interval $1 > x_b > 0$, then because of the orbital energies of the isolated methyl group lying outside these intervals, the result obtained should be generally valid

$$\delta x_a - \delta x_b = k^2 c_M^2 \left[c_{a\rho}^2 \left(\frac{1}{x_a - 2.76} + \frac{1}{x_a + 3.26} \right) - c_{b\rho}^2 \left(\frac{1}{x_b - 2.76} + \frac{1}{x_b + 3.26} \right) \right],$$

I.e., with

$$\left| \frac{1}{x_a - 2.76} \right| < \left| \frac{1}{x_a + 3.26} \right| ; \quad \delta x_a \text{ positive}$$

and

$$\left| \frac{1}{x_b - 2.76} \right| > \left| \frac{1}{x_b + 3.26} \right| ; \quad \delta x_b \text{ negative}$$

we always observe a diminution of the excitation energy. A special case occurs when the antibonding molecular orbital lies below the mean of the methyl group orbital energies $(0 > x_a > -0.25)$; however, because $|\delta x_a| < |\delta x_b|$ the excitation energies will show an overall decrease in this case too.

Problem 11.11: Discuss the dependence of the HMO excitation energy ΔE_π $(b \to a)$ upon the twist angle ω in the LCMO approximation for an alternant π-electron system $R - S$.

In the LCMO approximation, the partial systems R and S are joined by a bond between the centers ρ and σ. In general, several cases need to be discussed, depending upon the positions of the inner molecular orbitals, the values of the coefficients c_ρ and c_σ, and also the angle of twist $\omega_{\rho\sigma}$.

In the special case of alternant partial systems R and S

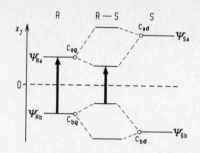

the longest wavelength transition for $\omega_{\rho\sigma} = 90°$ corresponds to a local excitation. In the following we assume that the energy difference $\Delta E\,(b \to a)$ in the partial system R is smaller than, or equal to that in the partial system S. On decreasing the angle of twist $\omega_{\rho\sigma}$, a cross term appears between the partial systems which has the value $c_\rho c_\sigma \cos \omega_{\rho\sigma}$ with respect to the dimensionless orbital energy coefficients x_b and x_a. We shall now consider three possibile cases:

(a) If the bonding and antibonding molecular orbitals of the two partial systems are degenerate

$$x_{Ra} = -x_{Rb} = x_{Sa} = -x_{Sb}$$

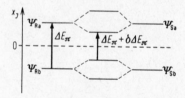

the first order perturbation due to coupling amounts to

$$\delta \Delta E_\pi = (\delta x_{Ra} - \delta x_{Rb})\beta = 2\,\delta x_{Ra}\beta = 2\left|c_{a\rho}c_{a\sigma}\right|\beta \cdot \cos \omega_{\rho\sigma}.$$

Accordingly, ΔE_π assumes a minimum for $\omega_{\rho\sigma} = 0$, i.e. for a coplanar orientation of the two partial systems R and S.

(b) For unequal orbital energies of the two partial systems

$$\left|x_{Ra}\right| = \left|x_{Rb}\right| < \left|x_{Sa}\right| = \left|x_{Sb}\right|,$$

provided that the coupling term between the bonding and antibonding molecular orbitals is small compared to the differences $x_{Ra} - x_{Sa} = -x_{Rb} + x_{Sb}$, the mutual interaction can be obtained by second order perturbation calculation ($c_{a\sigma}^2 = c_{b\sigma}^2$)

$$\delta x_{Ra} = -\delta x_{Rb} = \frac{(c_{a\rho} \cdot \cos \omega_{\rho\sigma} \cdot c_{b\sigma})^2}{x_{Ra} - x_{Sb}} + \frac{(c_{a\rho} \cdot \cos \omega_{\rho\sigma} \cdot c_{a\sigma})^2}{x_{Ra} - x_{Sa}}$$

$$= c_{a\rho}^2 \, c_{a\sigma}^2 \left(\frac{1}{x_{Ra} - x_{Sb}} + \frac{1}{x_{Ra} - x_{Sa}} \right) \cos^2 \omega_{\rho\sigma} \, .$$

Since the expression in parentheses is positive because of

$$\left| \frac{1}{x_{Ra} - x_{Sb}} \right| < \left| \frac{1}{x_{Ra} - x_{Sa}} \right|$$

we have $\delta \Delta E_\pi \sim \cos^2 \omega_{\rho\sigma} \beta$. For $\omega_{\rho\sigma} \to 0$ a slight bathochromic shift results from a second order perturbation.

(c) For the general case, the problem can be solved by way of a secular determinant of the fourth degree.

$$0 = \begin{vmatrix} \epsilon_{Ra} - \epsilon & 0 & c_{a\rho} c_{a\sigma} \beta \cos \omega_{\rho\sigma} & c_{a\rho} c_{b\sigma} \beta \cos \omega_{\rho\sigma} \\ 0 & \epsilon_{Rb} - \epsilon & c_{b\rho} c_{a\sigma} \beta \cos \omega_{\rho\sigma} & c_{b\rho} c_{b\sigma} \beta \cos \omega_{\rho\sigma} \\ c_{a\rho} c_{a\sigma} \beta \cos \omega_{\rho\sigma} & c_{b\rho} c_{a\sigma} \beta \cos \omega_{\rho\sigma} & \epsilon_{Sa} - \epsilon & 0 \\ c_{a\rho} c_{b\sigma} \beta \cos \omega_{\rho\sigma} & c_{b\rho} c_{b\sigma} \beta \cos \omega_{\rho\sigma} & 0 & \epsilon_{Sb} - \epsilon \end{vmatrix}$$

Factorization into two second degree determinants is possible because both partial systems are alternant.

Problem 11.12:   In the following cis-configuration of cyanine dyes

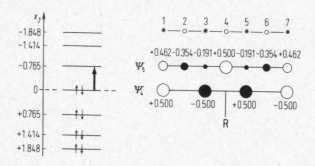

the band at $\lambda_{max} = 555$ nm is shifted by various substituents R as follows:

R	$-H$	$-CH_3$	$-CH_2CH_3$	$-CH(CH_3)_2$	$-C(CH_3)_3$
$\Delta\lambda_{max}$ [nm]	—	-17	-13	-10	$+33$

The isoconjugate alternant HMO model for the cis-cyanine chromophore has seven centers. Since one of the nitrogen atoms contributes two electrons to the π-system, the longest wavelength transition takes place from the doubly occupied nonbonding molecular orbital Ψ_4 into the lowest unoccupied antibonding molecular orbital Ψ_5.

The alkyl group is located at center 4 and, as a result of its positive inductive effect $\delta\alpha_R = -0.3\beta$ (β is negative!), raises the level ϵ_5 by

$$\delta\epsilon_5 = c_{54}^2\,\delta\alpha_R = -0.25 \cdot 0.3 \cdot \beta = -0.075\,\beta,$$

corresponding to the observed hypsochromic shift. With increasing size of the partial system R, this hypsochromic shift decreases and finally turns into a bathochromic shift in the case of the $C(CH_3)_3$ group. The reason for this switchover is a twisting of the 3−4 bond due to the bulk of the tertiary butyl group. This steric effect can be described by a perturbation $\delta\beta_{34} = -\beta(1-\cos\omega_{34})$, and for $\omega_{34} > 0$ leads, according to (11/22),

$$
\begin{aligned}
\delta\Delta E_\pi(4 \to 5) &= -2(c_{53}\cdot c_{54} - c_{43}\cdot c_{44})\beta(1-\cos\omega_{34}) \\
&= -2(-0.095 - 0)\beta(1-\cos\omega_{34}) \\
&= 0.190(1-\cos\omega_{34})\beta
\end{aligned}
$$

to a diminution of ΔE_π which overcompensates the inductive effect, so that a lowered excitation energy results.

Problem 11.13: Aromatic hydrocarbons and iodine can form donor-acceptor complexes (CT or 'charge transfer' complexes). The absorption spectrum of these solutions shows a CT band arising from the transfer of an electron from the aromatic system into the iodine molecule:

	Benzene	Naphthalene	Anthracene	Diphenyl
λ_{max} [nm]	297	360	430	340

Apart from a constant factor, the excitation energy, which determines the position of the CT band, is a linear function of the ionization potential of the aromatic hydrocarbon. Predict the wavelength of the CT band of the phenanthrene-I_2 complex.

From the spectroscopic data ($\tilde{\nu}$!) and orbital energy coefficients of the highest bonding molecular orbital x_b

$\tilde{\nu}_{max}$ [cm^{-1}]	33700	29400	27800	23200
x_b	1.000	0.705	0.618	0.414

the following regression is plotted:

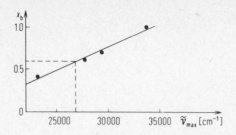

As can be seen, a band of the iodine donor-acceptor complex at $26800\ cm^{-1}$ corresponds to the orbital energy of phenanthrene $x_b = 0.605$, a result which agrees well with the experimental value $\nu_{max}^{exp} = 26500\ cm^{-1}$.

11.3. Charge Distribution and Bond Lengths in the Electronically Excited State

Problem 11.14: Use the relationship (11/32) to calculate the interatomic distances for the first excited state $(\Psi_b \to \Psi_a)$ of the following π-electron systems:

(a)   (b)   (c)   (d)

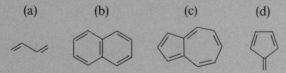

and compare them with ground state interatomic distances.

According to the following relation derived from (11/31) and (11/32)

$$\Delta R_{\mu\nu}^* = -0.1678\,(c_{a\mu}c_{a\nu} - c_{b\mu}c_{b\nu})$$

and after substitution of the appropriate HMO data, we find for the systems (a) – (d):

(a) Butadiene (cf. (11/15)):

$\mu - \nu$	$\Delta R_{\mu\nu}^*$	$R_{\mu\nu}$	$R_{\mu\nu}^*$
1–2, 3–4	+0.075	1.356 <	1.431
2–3	−0.046	1.431 >	1.385

(b) Naphthalene (cf. Problem 10.4):

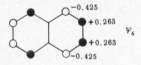

$\mu-\nu$	$\Delta R^*_{\mu\nu}$	$R_{\mu\nu}$		$R^*_{\mu\nu}$
1–2	+0.038	1.384	<	1.422
2–3	−0.023	1.405	>	1.382
1–9	– – –	1.413	=	1.413
9–10	– – –	1.419	=	1.419

(c) Azulene (cf. Problem 10.4):

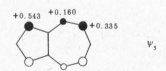

$\mu-\nu$	$\Delta R^*_{\mu\nu}$	$R_{\mu\nu}$		$R^*_{\mu\nu}$
1–2	+0.003	1.396	<	1.399
1–9	−0.003	1.406	>	1.403
4–10	+0.023	1.408	<	1.431
4–5	+0.008	1.395	<	1.403
5–6	+0.001	1.399	<	1.400
9–10	−0.014	1.439	>	1.425

(d) Fulvene:

In addition, according to

$$R_{\mu\nu} = 1.506 - 0.1678\,p_{\mu\nu} \qquad (10/12)$$

and using the bond orders

the interatomic distances $R_{\mu\nu}$ can also to be calculated.

$\mu - \nu$	$\Delta R_{\mu\nu}^*$	$R_{\mu\nu}$		$R_{\mu\nu}^*$
1–2	+0.054	1.375	<	1.429
2–3	−0.036	1.419	>	1.383
4–5	−0.011	1.431	>	1.420
5–6	+0.024	1.379	<	1.403

For the excitation $\Psi_b \rightarrow \Psi_a$ the interatomic distances in systems (a) – (d) change as follows:

(a)

(b)

(c)

(d)

Problem 11.15: Starting from the improved qualitative molecular orbitals of triafulvalene (b) (Problem 8.11), calculate the bond orders of the central bond of the dicyclopropenyl dication (a) and of triafulvalene (b) for the ground state and the first excited state.

(a)   (b)

How will a twisting of the two partial systems about the central bond affect the position of the longest wavelength absorption in each case?

The improved orbitals Ψ'_1, Ψ'_2, and Ψ'_3 of trifulvalene required for the solution of the problem are obtained from

$$\Psi'_J = N_J \left(\Psi^0_J + \sum_{K \neq J} \frac{(H_{JK} - S_{JK} x'_J)}{x'_J - x'_K} \Psi_K \right) \tag{8/74}$$

$$N_J = \frac{1}{\sqrt{\sum_\mu c^2_{J\mu}}} \tag{8/77}$$

by inserting the improved orbital energies x'_J (Problem 8.11) and the qualitative orbitals Ψ^0_J from (8/28). As in Problem 8.12, the summation can be performed most conveniently using the HMO diagrams:

$$\psi'_3 = N_3 \left(\psi^0_3 + \frac{\left[\frac{1}{6} \cdot 2 - \frac{1}{6} \cdot 2(-0.407) \right]}{-0.407 - (+2.407)} \psi^0_1 \right)$$

$$= \begin{pmatrix} \begin{array}{c} +0.355 \qquad\qquad +0.355 \\ \text{—} \quad -0.497 \quad -0.497 \quad \text{—} \\ +0.355 \qquad\qquad +0.355 \end{array} \end{pmatrix}$$

$$\psi_2' = N_2 \left(\psi_2^{\,\circ} + \frac{\left[\tfrac{1}{6}\cdot 6 - \tfrac{1}{6}\cdot 2\,(+1.741) \right]}{1.741 - (-1.667)}\ \psi_6^{\,\circ} \right)$$

$$= N_2 \left(\begin{array}{c} -0.408 \qquad\qquad +0.408 \\ \text{—} \quad -0.408 \quad +0.408 \quad \text{—} \\ -0.408 \qquad\qquad +0.408 \end{array} \quad + 0.123 \quad \begin{array}{c} -0.408 \qquad\qquad +0.408 \\ \text{—} \quad +0.408 \quad -0.408 \quad \text{—} \\ -0.408 \qquad\qquad +0.408 \end{array} \right)$$

$$= 0.955 \left(\begin{array}{c} -0.458 \qquad\qquad +0.458 \\ \text{—} \quad -0.358 \quad +0.358 \quad \text{—} \\ -0.458 \qquad\qquad +0.458 \end{array} \right)$$

$$= \begin{array}{c} -0.438 \qquad\qquad +0.438 \\ \text{—} \quad -0.342 \quad +0.342 \quad \text{—} \\ -0.438 \qquad\qquad +0.438 \end{array}$$

$$\Psi_1' = N_1 \left(\psi_1^{\,\circ} + \frac{\left[\tfrac{1}{6}\cdot 2 - \tfrac{1}{6}\cdot 2\,(+2.407) \right]}{2.407 - (-0,407)}\ \psi_3^{\,\circ} \right)$$

$$= N_1 \left(\begin{array}{c} +0.408 \qquad\qquad +0.408 \\ \text{—} \quad +0.408 \quad +0.408 \quad \text{—} \\ +0.408 \qquad\qquad +0.408 \end{array} \quad -0.167 \quad \begin{array}{c} +0.408 \qquad\qquad +0.408 \\ \text{—} \quad -0.408 \quad -0.408 \quad \text{—} \\ +0.408 \qquad\qquad +0.408 \end{array} \right)$$

$$= 1.045 \left(\begin{array}{c} +0.340 \qquad\qquad +0.340 \\ \text{—} \quad +0.476 \quad +0.476 \quad \text{—} \\ +0.340 \qquad\qquad +0.340 \end{array} \right)$$

$$= \begin{array}{c} +0.355 \qquad\qquad +0.355 \\ \text{—} \quad +0.497 \quad +0.497 \quad \text{—} \\ +0.355 \qquad\qquad +0.355 \end{array}$$

The lowest antibonding molecular orbital Ψ_4^0 remains unaltered, since here all terms H_{JK} and S_{JK} are equal to zero.

$$\psi_4^! = \psi_4^0 =$$

Starting from the qualitative molecular orbitals and then using a second order perturbation calculation leads in the present case to excellent agreement (± 0.01) with exact HMO values.

The bond orders resulting for the central double bonds are:

(a)

$$p_{34}^0 = \sum_{J=1}^{6} b_J c_{J3} c_{J4}$$

$$= 0.260$$

$$p_{34}^* = 0.624$$

(b)

$$p_{34}^0 = \sum_{J=1}^{6} b_J c_{J3} c_{J4}$$

$$= 0.754$$

$$p_{34}^* = 0.507$$

The bond order of the dication (a) thus increases on excitation ($\Psi_2 \to \Psi_3$), whereas that of the neutral trifulvalene decreases on excitation ($\Psi_3 \to \Psi_4$), because in the latter case the coefficients are $c_{43} = c_{44} = 0$. With increasing angle of twist, according to

$$\delta \Delta E_\pi = 2 (p_{\mu\nu}^* - p_{\mu\nu}) \delta \beta_{\mu\nu} \tag{11/34}$$

the longest wavelength bands will show a hypsochromic shift for (a) and a bathochromic shift for (b).

Problem 11.16: As an extension of Problem 10.14, calculate the changes in the dipole moments accompanying the longest wavelength electronic transitions for fulvene and heptafulvene.

According to the relation

$$\Delta \mu_{\pi x}^* (J \to K) = e \cdot \sum_\mu \Delta q_\mu^* x_\mu$$

$$= e \cdot \sum_\mu (c_{K\mu}^2 - c_{J\mu}^2) x_\mu$$

which follows from (11/37) and (11/39), substitution of the coordinates from Problem 10.14 and the appropriate HMO coefficients (Vol. 3) yields the following results:

(a) Fulvene:

$$\Delta\mu_{\pi x}^{*}(3 \rightarrow 4) = e \cdot a \,[2 \cdot 0 \cdot (-0.060) + 2 \cdot 0.951(-0.239) + 1.539(+0.036) + 2.539(+0.561)]$$
$$= 4.8 \cdot 1.4\,[-0.456 + 0.055 + 1.424]$$
$$= 6.72\,[1.025] = 6.889\,D$$
$$\mu_{\pi x}^{*} = \mu_{\pi x} + \Delta\mu_{\pi x}^{*} = -4.790 + 6.889 = +2.099\,D$$

The marked change in the dipole moment on excitation ($\Psi_3 \rightarrow \Psi_4$) comes about because the initial and final orbitals of the promoted electron display widely differing coefficients

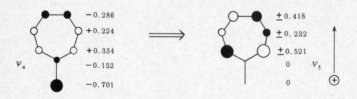

and the charge density in the side chain consequently increases during the transition.

(b) Heptafulvene:

$$\Delta\mu_{\pi x}^{*}(4 \rightarrow 5) = e \cdot a \,[2 \cdot 0 \cdot (+0.093) + 2 \cdot 0.783(+0.004) + 2 \cdot 1.758(+0.160) +$$
$$+ 2.192(-0.023) + 3.192(-0.491)]$$
$$= 4.8 \cdot 1.4\,[+0.006 + 0.563 - 0.050 - 1.567]$$
$$= 6.72\,[-1.048] = -7.044\,D$$
$$\mu_{\pi x}^{*} = +4.19 - 7.044 = -2.854\,D$$

In contrast to (a), the sign of the dipole moment in the present case changes in the opposite sense on excitation, i.e. in keeping with the molecular orbitals Ψ_4 and Ψ_5 participating in the transition:

the charge density increases at the ring centers.

Problem 11.17: The dipole moment of formaldehyde decreases from $2 \cdot 3\ D$ to $1 \cdot 5\ D$ on $n \to \pi^*$ electronic excitation. Discuss this change in terms of an HMO model.

The $n \to \pi^*$ transition of formaldehyde can be described in the HMO scheme of a C=O group as follows:

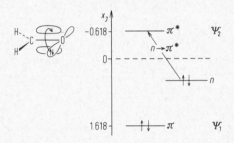

The orbitals calculated in Problem 10.7 read

$$\Psi_2 = b\Phi_C - a\Phi_O = 0.851\,\Phi_C - 0.526\,\Phi_O,$$
$$\Psi_1 = a\Phi_C - b\Phi_O = 0.526\,\Phi_C + 0.851\,\Phi_O.$$

As can be seen, $b > a$ because of the higher electron affinity of oxygen.

The dipole moment of formaldehyde in the ground state $\mu = 2.3\ D$ arises from the polarization of the σ- and π-components of the C=O bond owing to the higher electron affinity of the oxygen and also from the oxygen electron lone pairs. In the following calculation the σ-component is neglected. The electrons of the π-system and of the lone pair n on oxygen, which should be located in a pure 2p-atomic orbital are considered together. We thus obtain the charge on the carbon center $Z_C = 1$ and on the oxygen center $Z_O = 3$. The charge orders in the ground state and in the excited state are

$$q_C = 2a^2 \quad ; \quad q_C^* = 2a^2 + b^2$$
$$q_O = 2b^2 + 2 \ ; \ q_O^* = 2b^2 + a^2 + 1$$

The differences are $(a^2 + b^2 = 1)$

$$\delta q_C = 2a^2 - 1 = a^2 - b^2 \ ; \ \delta q_C^* = 2a^2 + b^2 - 1 = a^2,$$
$$\delta q_O = 2b^2 - 1 = b^2 - a^2 \ ; \ \delta q_O^* = 2b^2 + a^2 - 2 = -a^2,$$

where

$$\delta q_C = -\delta q_O \; ; \; \delta q_C^* = -\delta q_O^*$$

The π- and the n-components of the total dipole moment ($L = 1.2$ Å) are obtained from the differences

$$\mu_{\pi,n} = e \cdot L \cdot \delta q_O = e \cdot L(b^2 - a^2) = 4.8 \cdot 1.2 \cdot 0.446 = 2.6\,D \,,$$

$$\mu_{\pi,n}^* = e \cdot L \cdot \delta q_O^* = e \cdot L(-a^2) = 4.8 \cdot 1.2 \cdot (-0.277) = -1.6\,D$$

and the resulting change of the dipole moment in the excited state is

$$\Delta \mu_{\pi,n}^* = \mu_{\pi,n}^* - \mu_{\pi,n} = -1.6 - 2.6 = -4.2\,D$$

Comparison with the observed lowering of $0.8\,D$ shows that the HMO treatment again affords values which are about five times too large. Now calculation of those coefficients a and b which reproduce the observed change shows that $b < a$, in contradiction to the relative electron affinities of the C- and O-centers. Moreover, the absolute value of the two dipole moments can only be explained by an abnormally high moment of the σ-bond. Thus an approximation with interaction-free electrons clearly fails in this case if predictions going beyond a qualitative discussion are required.

Problem 11.18: Using an isoconjugate model, determine in which direction the longest wavelength absorption of phenol will shift upon replacement of a nonpolar solvent by one which can undergo hydrogen bonding.

The isoconjugate model for phenol is the benzyl anion (cf. Problem 6.15) with $Z_\pi = 8$ electrons:

The longest wavelength excitation corresponds to the transition $\Psi_4 \to \Psi_5$ and is associated with a charge transfer from the exocyclic center into the ring.

To account for a change in excitation energy due to a change of solvent, two different cases of intermolecular hydrogen bonding will now be considered:

(a)   (b)

$\delta\alpha_1$ positive $\delta\alpha_1$ negative

According to

$$\delta\Delta E_\pi = (q_1^* - q_1)\,\delta\alpha_1 \tag{11/41}$$

and (11/42), these will give rise to a hypsochromic shift of the longest wavelength phenol band (^1L_a) in the HMO scheme in case (a), and a bathochromic one in case (b).

A corresponding influence of the $\Psi_4 \to \Psi_5$ transition is confirmed by the following UV data of phenol derivatives

$\tilde{\nu}_{max}$ 47600   46100   42600   [cm^{-1}]

11.4. Absorption Intensities

Problem 11.19: Show by LCMO linkage of a six- and a seven-membered ring that the longest wavelength absorption of the phenyltropylium cation

is a band with pronounced charge transfer character.

The 'inner' molecular orbitals of the π-electron systems to be joined are presented in the following energy level scheme

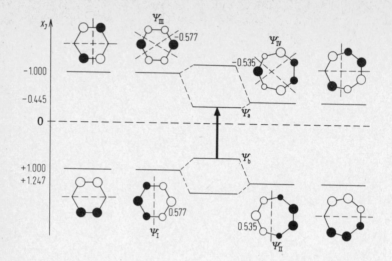

If, in a first approximation, only bonding and antibonding molecular orbitals, respectively, are to be combined, then the orbitals to be considered are Ψ_I and Ψ_{II}, Ψ_{III} and Ψ_{IV}, whose coefficients have finite values at the points of juncture. As already suggested by a qualitative approach, the electron in the molecular orbitals participating in the long wavelength transition will be located in Ψ_b to a greater extent in the benzene moiety, and in Ψ_a more in the seven-membered ring.

The calculation proceeds by first determining the orbital energy coefficients x_b and x_a by analogy with [7.9]. Substitution of the values obtained into the secular equations forming the basis of the determinants and normalization of the resulting coefficients affords the desired linear combination of molecular orbitals.

(a) Ψ_b:
$$\begin{vmatrix} 1-x & 0.577 \cdot 0.535 \\ 0.577 \cdot 0.535 & 1.247 - x \end{vmatrix} = x^2 - 2.247x + 1.152 = 0$$

$$x = +1.124 \pm 0.332$$

$$x_b = +0.792$$

$$(1 - x_b)c_1 + 0.309 c_2 = 0$$

$$c_I = c_2 = \frac{-c_1(1 - x_b)}{0.309} = -0.673 c_1 = -0.673 c_{II}$$

$$N_b = \frac{1}{\sqrt{c_1^2 + c_2^2}} = 0.830$$

$$\Psi_b = 0.830 \, \Psi_I - 0.558 \, \Psi_{II}$$

(b) Ψ_a:

$$\begin{vmatrix} -1-x & (-0.577)(-0.535) \\ (-0.577)(-0.535) & -0.445-x \end{vmatrix} = x^2 + 1.445x + 0.350 = 0$$

$$x = -0.723 \pm 0.415$$

$$x_a = -0.308$$

$$(-1 - x_a)c_1 + 0.309 c_2 = 0$$

$$c_{III} = c_2 = \frac{c_1(1+x_a)}{3} = 2.239 c_1 = 2.239 c_{IV}$$

$$N_a = \frac{1}{\sqrt{c_1^2 + c_2^2}} = 0.408$$

$$\Psi_a = 0.408 \, \Psi_{III} + 0.913 \, \Psi_{IV}$$

The electron distribution is given by the squares of the coefficients of the two linear combinations.

Ψ_a:	17 % in Ψ_{III}	83 % in Ψ_{IV}
Ψ_b:	69 % in Ψ_{I}	31 % in Ψ_{II}
$\Psi_b \rightarrow \Psi_a$:	−52 %	+52 %

Thus the overall charge transfer corresponds to about half an electron.

Problem 11.20: Use exact HMO values (Volume 3) to calculate the transition moments of 1,4-dehydrobenzene corresponding to Table (11/55).

The coordinate system is conveniently set up as follows:

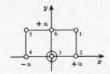

With an average C-C bondlength $a = 1.4\,\text{Å}$ (cf., e.g., [10.6]) the transition moments for the four longest wavelength electronic transitions are obtained, according to (11/48), as:

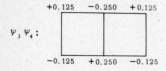

$$\Psi_3, \Psi_4:$$

$$\mu_{34,x} = e \sum_{\mu} u_{34,\mu} x_{\mu} = 0\,D$$

$$\mu_{34,y} = e \sum_{\mu} u_{34,\mu} y_{\mu} = 0\,D$$

$$\left.\begin{matrix} \Psi_3, \Psi_5 \\ \Psi_2, \Psi_4 \end{matrix}\right\}:$$

$$\mu_{35,x} = \mu_{24,x} = 4 \cdot 0.177 \cdot e \cdot a$$
$$= 0.708 \cdot 4.8 \cdot 1.4 = 4.76\,D$$
$$\mu_{35,y} = \mu_{24,y} = 0\,D$$

$$\Psi_2, \Psi_5:$$

$$\mu_{25,x} = 0\,D$$

$$\mu_{25,y} = 2 \cdot 0.25 \cdot 4.8 \cdot 1.4 = 3.36\,D$$

Hence, in contrast to [11.17], finite intensities are to be expected only for the last three transitions, the directions of polarization being:

$$\Psi_3 \rightarrow \Psi_4 : \text{forbidden}$$

$$\Psi_3 \rightarrow \Psi_5 : \text{parallel to the } x\text{-axis}$$

$$\Psi_2 \rightarrow \Psi_4 : \text{parallel to the } x\text{-axis}$$

$$\Psi_2 \rightarrow \Psi_5 : \text{parallel to the } y\text{-axis}$$

Problem 11.21: Calculate the intensity of the longest wavelength transition of chains having $2n$ carbon $2p_z$ centres as a function of their length.

According to (5/7) the highest bonding molecular orbital Ψ_b and the lowest antibonding molecular orbital Ψ_a of a linear chain with $2N$ centers read

$$\Psi_b = \sqrt{\frac{2}{n+1}} \sum_{\mu=1}^{n} \left(\sin \left(\frac{\pi \cdot \left(\frac{n}{2}\right)}{n+1} \mu \right) \right) \Phi_\mu = \sum_\mu c_{b\mu} \Phi_\mu ,$$

$$\Psi_a = \sqrt{\frac{2}{n+1}} \sum_{\mu=1}^{n} \left(\sin \left(\frac{\pi \left(\frac{n}{2}+1\right)}{n+1} \mu \right) \right) \Phi_\mu = \sum_\mu c_{a\mu} \Phi_\mu .$$

The transition order at center μ is therefore

$$c_{b\mu} c_{a\mu} = \frac{2}{n+1} \sin \left(\frac{\pi}{2} \cdot \frac{n}{n+1} \mu \right) \cdot \sin \left(\frac{\pi}{2} \cdot \frac{n+2}{n+1} \right) \mu$$

or, after rearrangement according to $\sin \alpha \sin \beta = \frac{1}{2} [\cos (\alpha - \beta) - \cos (\alpha + \beta)]$,

$$c_{b\mu} c_{a\mu} = \frac{1}{n+1} \left[\cos \left(\frac{\pi}{n+1} \mu \right) - \cos (\pi \mu) \right].$$

With respect to the center of the chain

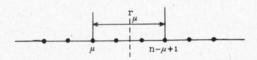

the transition orders are antisymmetric

$$c_{b\mu} c_{a\mu} = -c_{b(n-\mu+1)} c_{a(n-\mu+1)} .$$

Since the total length of the chain is $(n-1)R$, the distance r_μ between the centers μ and $n - \mu + 1$ amounts to

$$r_\mu = R (n - 2\mu + 1)$$

and the sum of the transition orders $Q_x = \sum_\mu u_{ab,\mu} r_\mu$ is

$$Q_x = \sum_{\mu=1}^{\frac{n}{2}} c_{b\mu} c_{a\mu} r_\mu = \frac{R}{n+1} \sum_{\mu=1}^{\frac{n}{2}} \left[\cos \left(\frac{\pi}{n+1} \mu \right) - \cos (\pi \mu) \right] (n - 2\mu + 1).$$

The follow numerical values result:

	n	Q_x
Ethylene	2	0.50 R
Butadiene	4	0.95 R
Hexatriene	6	1.37 R
Octatetraene	8	1.79 R

Q_x can also be given in closed form

$$Q_x = R \sum_{\mu=1}^{\frac{n}{2}} \cos\left(\frac{\pi}{n+1}\mu\right) - R \sum_{\mu=1}^{\frac{n}{2}} \cos(\pi\mu) - \frac{2R}{n+1}\sum_{\mu=1}^{\frac{n}{2}} \mu \cos\left(\frac{\pi}{n+1}\mu\right) + \frac{2R}{n+1}\sum_{\mu=1}^{\frac{n}{2}} \mu \cdot \cos(\pi\mu)$$

The individual partial sums can be rewritten with the aid of the relations

$$\sum_{k=0}^{n} \cos(kx) = \frac{\cos\left(\frac{n}{2}x\right) \cdot \sin\left(\frac{n+1}{2}x\right)}{\sin\left(\frac{x}{2}\right)}$$

$$\sum_{k=1}^{n} k \cos(kx) = \frac{(n+1)\sin\left(\frac{2n+1}{2}x\right)}{2\sin\left(\frac{x}{2}\right)} - \frac{1 - \cos((n+1)x)}{4\sin^2\left(\frac{x}{2}\right)}$$

Substitution and extensive rearrangement eventually leads to

$$Q_x = R \cdot \frac{ctg^2\left(\frac{\pi}{2n+2}\right)}{2n+2}.$$

Problem 11.22: Calculate the transition moments of the four lowest excited states of cis- and of trans-hexatriene from HMO values (Volume 3):

(a)   (b)

The values 1·4 Å and 120° are to be assumed for all bond lengths and all bond angles, respectively.

The energy level scheme of a linear chain with six centers (Vol. 3) affords the longest wavelength transitions as:

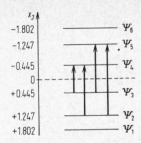

$\Psi_2 \to \Psi_4$ and $\Psi_3 \to \Psi_5$ are degenerate. By analogy with Problem 11.20, the transition moments μ_{JK} result from the transition orders $u_{JK,\mu} = c_{J\mu}c_{K\mu}$, which are introduced below in the relevant molecular diagrams:

(a) cis-Hexatriene:

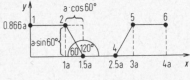

$\Psi_3\Psi_4$:
$$+0.271 \quad -0.054 \qquad +0.054 \quad -0.271$$
$$+0.175 \quad -0.175$$

$$\mu_{34,x} = e \cdot \sum_\mu u_{34,\mu} x_\mu$$
$$= e \cdot a\,[0.271(0-4) + 0.054(-1+3) + 0.175(1.5-2.5)]$$
$$= 4.8 \cdot 1.4\,[-1.084 + 0.108 - 0.175]$$
$$= 6.72(-1.151) = -7.73D$$

$$\mu_{34,y} = 6.72 \cdot 0.866[+0.271 - 0.054 + 0.054 - 0.271]$$
$$= 5.82 \cdot 0 \qquad = 0D$$

$\left.\begin{array}{l}\Psi_2\Psi_4 \\ \Psi_3\Psi_5\end{array}\right\}$:
$$+0.218 \quad -0.121 \qquad -0.121 \quad +0.218$$
$$-0.097 \quad -0.097$$

$$\mu_{24,x} = \mu_{35,x}$$
$$= 6.72[0.218(0+4) - 0.121(1+3) - 0.097(1.5+2.5)]$$
$$= 0D$$

$$\mu_{24,y} = \mu_{35,y}$$
$$= 5.82[2 \cdot 0.218 - 2 \cdot 0.121]$$
$$= 1.13\,D$$

$\Psi_2\Psi_5$:
$$+0.175 \quad -0.271 \qquad +0.271 \quad -0.175$$
$$+0.054 \quad -0.054$$

$$\mu_{25,x} = 6.72[0.175(0-4) + 0.271(-1+3) + 0.054(1.5-2.5)]$$
$$= -1.425\,D$$

$$\mu_{25,y} = 5.82[+0.175 - 0.271 + 0.271 - 0.175]$$
$$= 0\,D$$

(b) trans-Hexatriene:

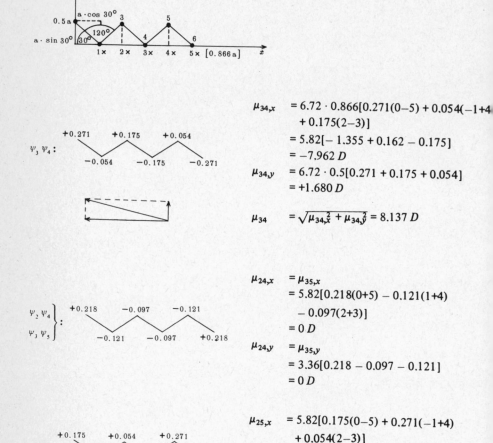

$$\mu_{34,x} = 6.72 \cdot 0.866[0.271(0-5) + 0.054(-1+4) + 0.175(2-3)]$$
$$= 5.82[-1.355 + 0.162 - 0.175]$$
$$= -7.962\,D$$

$$\mu_{34,y} = 6.72 \cdot 0.5[0.271 + 0.175 + 0.054]$$
$$= +1.680\,D$$

$$\mu_{34} = \sqrt{\mu_{34,x}^2 + \mu_{34,y}^2} = 8.137\,D$$

$$\mu_{24,x} = \mu_{35,x}$$
$$= 5.82[0.218(0+5) - 0.121(1+4) - 0.097(2+3)]$$
$$= 0\,D$$

$$\mu_{24,y} = \mu_{35,y}$$
$$= 3.36[0.218 - 0.097 - 0.121]$$
$$= 0\,D$$

$$\mu_{25,x} = 5.82[0.175(0-5) + 0.271(-1+4) + 0.054(2-3)]$$
$$= -0.675\,D$$

$$\mu_{25,y} = 3.36[0.175 + 0.054 + 0.271]$$
$$= +1.680\,D$$

$$\mu_{25} = \sqrt{\mu_{25,x}^2 + \mu_{25,y}^2} = 1.810\,D$$

Corresponding to the relative intensities (11/53), the spectra of cis- and trans-hexatriene are qualitatively predicted to have the following schematic structures:

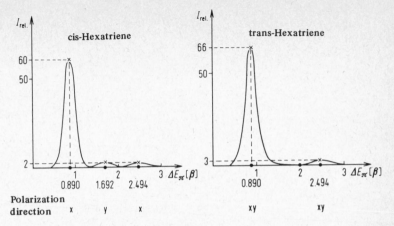

The additional low-intensity band occurring in the spectrum of cis-hexatriene as compared with that of the trans isomer arises from the allowed transitions $\Psi_2 \rightarrow \Psi_4$ and $\Psi_3 \rightarrow \Psi_5$. It is designated as the "cis-peak", and is used as a spectroscopic characterization of olefins having cis-configuration.

Problem 11.23: Starting from qualitative molecular orbitals (Problem 11.4), determine the direction of polarization of the four longest wavelength transitions of calicene.

In Problem 11.4 the qualitative orbital energies x_J^0 were corrected by a second order perturbation calculation, the four longest wavelength transitions being obtained as:

$$
\begin{array}{ll}
-1.000 & \Psi_6 \\
-0.978 & \Psi_5 \\
0 & \\
+0.500 & \Psi_4 \\
+0.789 & \Psi_3 \\
\end{array}
$$

The corresponding qualitative molecular orbitals yield the following polarization directions

$\Psi_4\ \Psi_5$

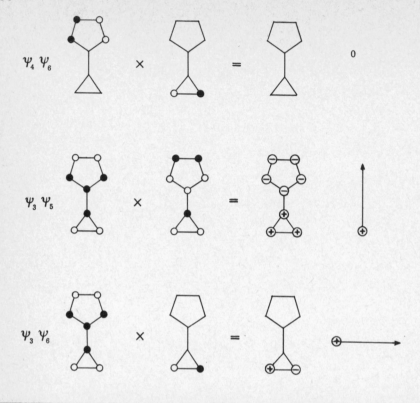

Problem 11.24: The longest wavelength electronic excitation of azulene is accompanied by an electron transfer, in which negative charge is transferred from the five- to the seven-membered ring. Calculate the orientation of the corresponding transition moment.

With the coordinates of Problem 10.15

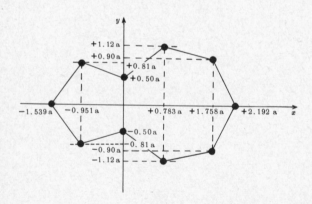

and the charge orders given below for azulene (cf. Vol. 3), we first obtain the dipole moment in the ground state:

q_μ

$$\mu_{\pi x} = e \cdot a \sum_\mu (q_\mu - 1) x_\mu \qquad (10/42)$$

Charge orders (ground state):
0.855
1.173 1.027   0.986
1.047   0.870
1.173 1.027   0.986
0.855

$$= 4.8 \cdot 1.4 [0.047(-1.539) + 2 \cdot 0.173(-0.951)$$
$$+ 2 \cdot 0 \cdot 0.027 + 2 \cdot (-0.145) \cdot 0.783$$
$$+ 2 \cdot (-0.014)1.758 + (-0.130) \cdot 2.192]$$
$$= 6.72 \cdot (-0.963)$$
$$= -6.47 D$$

With the corresponding HMO coefficients of the participating molecular orbitals, the change in dipole moment occurring on excitation $\Psi_5 \rightarrow \Psi_6$ is given by (11/39) as:

$$\Delta q_\mu = c_{6\mu}^2 - c_{5\mu}^2 \qquad\qquad \Delta\mu_{\pi x}^* = e \cdot a \sum_\mu \Delta q_\mu x_\mu \qquad (11/39)$$

Change values:
+0.195
-0.291 +0.017   -0.102
0.100   0.261
-0.291 +0.017   -0.102
+0.195

$$= 4.8 \cdot 1.4 [0.100(-1.539) + 2(-0.291)(-0.951)$$
$$+ 2 \cdot 0.017 \cdot 0 + 2 \cdot 0.195 \cdot 0.783$$
$$+ 2(-0.102)1.758 + 0.261 \cdot 2.192]$$
$$= 6.72 \cdot 0.917$$
$$= 6.16 D$$
$$\mu_{\pi x}^* = \mu_{\pi x} + \Delta\mu_{\pi x}^* = -6.47 + 6.16 = -0.31 D$$

On excitation, charge transfer thus occurs, as mentioned before, from the 5-membered ring into the 7-membered ring. To a first approximation the dipole moment of azulene thus becomes equal to zero.

The transition moment μ_{56} is obtained in analogy to Problem 11.22 from the relevant transition orders $\mu_{56,\mu}$

$$u_{56,\mu} = c_{5\mu} c_{6\mu} \qquad\qquad \mu_{56,x} = e \cdot a \sum_\mu u_{56,\mu} x_\mu$$

Transition orders:
+0.075
+0.034 +0.075   +0.034
0   0
-0.034 -0.075   -0.034
-0.075

$$= 6.72 [(+0.034 - 0.034)(-0.951) + (0.075$$
$$- 0.075)0.783 + (0.034 - 0.034)1.758]$$
$$= 0 D$$
$$\mu_{56,y} = 6.72 [2 \cdot 0.075 \cdot 0.5 + 2 \cdot 0.034 \cdot 0.81 + 2 \cdot 0.034$$
$$\cdot 0.90 + 2 \cdot 0.075 \cdot 1.12]$$
$$= 6.72 \cdot 0.359$$
$$= 2.41 D$$

The directions of the charge transfer (a) and the transition moment (b) are clearly mutually perpendicular:

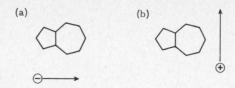

In general this is always the case when the orbitals Ψ_J and Ψ_K participating in the transition $J \to K$ display different symmetry properties with respect to a nodal plane containing the direction of transfer.

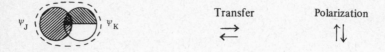

In contrast, for the same symmetry behavior

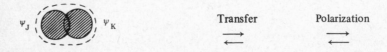

the directions of transfer and polarization coincide.

Problem 11.25: Polar structures played an important role in discussions of electronic spectra using resonance theory. In the case of anthracene, these

structures appear to indicate that the longest wavelength absorption is polarized parallel to the long axis of the molecule. Verify this apparently plausible assumption using HMO data (Volume 3).

The transition moment of the longest wavelength anthracene band $\Psi_b \to \Psi_a$, as already apparent from qualitative considerations, is oriented perpendicular to the long molecular axis, contrary to the assumptions of resonance theory.

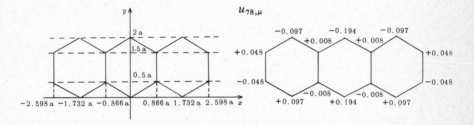

$$\Psi_7 \qquad\qquad \Psi_8 \qquad\qquad \Psi_7 \times \Psi_8$$

With the coordinates and transition orders:

the magnitude of the transition moment is given by

$$\mu_{78,x}$$
$$\mu_{78,x} = e \sum u_{78,\mu} x_\mu = 0\,D$$
$$u_{78,y} = e \sum u_{78,\mu} y_\mu$$
$$\qquad = e \cdot a[0.5 \cdot 2(-0.048 - 0.008) + 1.5 \cdot 2(+0.048 + 0.008) + 2(2 \cdot (-0.097) - 0.194)]$$
$$\qquad = 6.72(-0.056 + 0.168 - 0.776) = -4.46\,D$$

Furthermore, the cross polarization of the ^1L_a band of anthracene can also be qualitatively predicted by use of the electronic spectroscopy selection rules, which are based on the symmetry properties of the participating molecular orbitals (cf. Problem 11.26). The experimentally confirmed results show once again that resonance theory is rather unsuitable for describing electronically excited states.

11.5. Selection Rules for Electron Spectroscopy

Problem 11.26: Determine the polarization of the nine longest wavelength transitions of naphthalene, diphenylene, and anthracene from their molecular orbitals (Volume 3).

(a) Naphthalene:
According to the energy level scheme (Vol. 3), the molecular orbitals participating in the 10 longest wavelength transitions

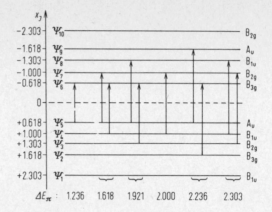

$$\Delta E_\pi : \quad 1.236 \quad 1.618 \quad 1.921 \quad 2.000 \quad 2.236 \quad 2.303$$

belong to the given irreducible representations of the symmetry group D_{2h} of naphthalene. Multiplication of the irreducible representations of the inital and final orbitals of the promoted electron gives the irreducible representations of the transition densities

D_{2h}	B_{3g}	B_{2g}	B_{1u}	A_u
A_u	B_{3u}	B_{2u}	B_{1g}	A_g
B_{1u}	B_{2u}	B_{3u}	A_g	
B_{2g}	B_{1g}	A_g		
B_{3g}	B_{1g}			

According to the Character Table (8/84), Vol. 1, p. 268, of these, only B_{2u} and B_{3u} are compatible with a finite transition moment along the y- or x-axis. The four allowed longest wavelength transitions are consequently polarized as follows:

$$\Psi_5 \to \Psi_6: \quad A_u \overset{\times}{} B_{3g} \Rightarrow B_{3u} \qquad \text{parallel to the } x\text{-axis}$$

$$\left. \begin{array}{l} \Psi_5 \to \Psi_7: \; A_u \overset{\times}{} B_{2g} \Rightarrow B_{2u} \\ \Psi_4 \to \Psi_6: \; B_{1u} \overset{\times}{} B_{3g} \Rightarrow B_{2u} \end{array} \right\} \qquad \text{parallel to the } y\text{-axis; degenerate}$$

$$\Psi_4 \to \Psi_7: \quad B_{1u} \overset{\times}{} B_{2g} \Rightarrow B_{3u} \qquad \text{parallel to the } x\text{-axis}$$

With respect to the two transitions polarized along the long axis (B_{2u}), the loss of the HMO degeneracy of 1,4-dehydrobenzene discussed in [11.18] should be remembered, which gives reason to believe that the intense band (^1L_a) is preceded by a weak band (^1L_b).

(b) Diphenylene:
From the orbital energy scheme (Vol. 3) the 10 longest wavelength transitions are

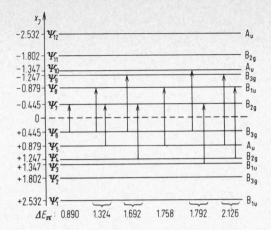

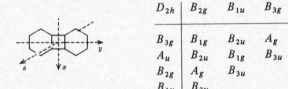

According to the irreducible representation of the transition densities (symmetry D_{2h})

D_{2h}	B_{2g}	B_{1u}	B_{3g}	A_u
B_{3g}	B_{1g}	B_{2u}	A_g	B_{3u}
A_u	B_{2u}	B_{1g}	B_{3u}	
B_{2g}	A_g	B_{3u}		
B_{1u}	B_{3u}			

only B_{2u} and B_{3u} are consistent with a finite moment parallel to the y- or the x-axis. For the allowed transitions the resulting directions of polarization are

$$\left.\begin{array}{l} \Psi_6 \to \Psi_8:\ B_{3g} \dot\times B_{1u} \Rightarrow B_{2u} \\ \Psi_5 \to \Psi_7:\ A_u \dot\times B_{2g} \Rightarrow B_{2u} \end{array}\right\} \quad y\text{-polarized; degenerate}$$

$$\left.\begin{array}{l} \Psi_6 \to \Psi_{10}:\ B_{3g} \dot\times A_u \Rightarrow B_{3u} \\ \Psi_3 \to \Psi_7\ \ B_{1u} \dot\times B_{2g} \Rightarrow B_{3u} \end{array}\right\} \quad x\text{-polarized; degenerate}$$

$$\left.\begin{array}{l} \Psi_5 \to \Psi_9:\ A_u \dot\times B_{3g} \Rightarrow B_{3u} \\ \Psi_4 \to \Psi_8:\ B_{2g} \dot\times B_{1u} \Rightarrow B_{3u} \end{array}\right\} \quad x\text{-polarized; degenerate}$$

It should be pointed out that the longest wavelength transition is forbidden.

(c) Anthracene:

Anthracene also possesses D_{2h} symmetry. The initial and final orbitals for the nine longest wavelength transitions

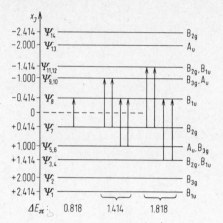

are in part accidently degenerate. The individual transition densities belong to the following irreducible representations:

D_{2h}	B_{1u}	B_{3g}	A_u	B_{2g}	B_{1u}
B_{2g}	B_{3u}	B_{1g}	B_{2u}	A_g	B_{3u}
A_u	B_{1g}				
B_{3g}	B_{2u}				
B_{2g}	B_{3u}				
B_{1u}	A_g				

In accord with the transition moments compatible with the irreducible representations B_{2u} and B_{3u}, which are finite and polarized parallel to the y- or x-axis, the five allowed transitions have the following directions of polarization:

$$\Psi_7 \to \Psi_8: B_{2g} \dot{\times} B_{1u} \Rightarrow B_{3u} \qquad \text{parallel to the } x\text{-axis}$$

$$\left.\begin{array}{l} \Psi_7 \to \Psi_{10}: B_{2g} \dot{\times} A_u \Rightarrow B_{2u} \\ \Psi_6 \to \Psi_8: B_{3g} \dot{\times} B_{1u} \Rightarrow B_{2u} \end{array}\right\} \qquad \text{parallel to the } y\text{-axis; degenerate}$$

$$\left.\begin{array}{l} \Psi_7 \to \Psi_{12}: B_{2g} \dot{\times} B_{1u} \Rightarrow B_{3u} \\ \Psi_3 \to \Psi_8: B_{2g} \dot{\times} B_{1u} \Rightarrow B_{3u} \end{array}\right\} \qquad \text{parallel to the } x\text{-axis; degenerate}$$

The above discussion confirms the result of Problem 11.24, that the ^1L_a band of anthracene is cross-polarized, in contrast to the resonance formulation.

Problem 11.27: Between which molecular orbitals of triphenylmethyl cation (Volume 3) can electronic transitions be induced by absorption of light, and how are these transitions polarized?

The energy level scheme (Vol. 3) shows that occupied and unoccupied molecular orbitals belonging to the irreducible representations A_1'', A_2'' and E'' of symmetry group D_{3h} are present. Multiplication leads to the following irreducible representations of the transition densities:

D_{3h}	A_1''	A_2''	E''
A_1''	A_1'		
A_2''	A_2'	A_1'	
E''	E'	E'	$A_1' + A_2' + E'$

Of these, only E'' is associated with finite transition moments in the x,y-plane, so that the resulting allowed transitions are

$$A_1'' \rightarrow E''$$
$$A_2'' \rightarrow E''$$
$$E'' \rightarrow E''$$
$$E'' \rightarrow A_1''$$
$$E'' \rightarrow A_2''$$

In the energy level scheme a total of eight transitions appear, several of which are degenerate.

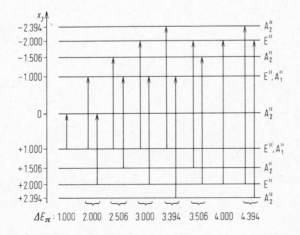

ΔE_π: 1.000 2.000 2.506 3.000 3.394 3.506 4.000 4.394

12. Reacting Molecules

12.1. Use of HMO Theory for Equilibria

Problem 12.1: Calculate the changes ΔH^0_{298} (X, gas phase) for the following *Diels–Alder* reactions:

(a)

(b)

(a) The reaction involves disappearance of two $C=C$ double bonds and formation of four $C-C$ single bonds. Hence neglecting the delocalization energies, the enthalpy change occurring during reaction is

$$\Delta H^0_{298}((a), \text{gas phase}) = -2\,\Delta Hb^0_{298}(C=C) + 4\,\Delta Hb^0_{298}(C-C)$$
$$= -2(-147) + 4(-83.1) = -38.4\ \text{kcal/mol}$$

(b) In this case, three $C-C$ single bonds are formed while one $C\equiv C$ triple bond is lost in the reaction.

$$\Delta H^0_{298}((b), \text{gas phase}) = -\Delta Hb^0_{298}(C\equiv C) + 3\,\Delta Hb^0_{298}(C-C)$$
$$= -(-194) + 3(-83.1) = -55.3\ \text{kcal/mol}$$

Correcting the result for the delocalization energies of benzene (10/72) and anthracene (Problem 10.31) yields

$$\Delta H^0_{298}((b), \text{gas phase}) = \Delta H^0_{298}((b), \text{gas phase}) - 2\,DE\,(\text{Anthracene}) + 2\,DE\,(\text{Ben}$$
$$= -55.3 - (-106.3) + 2(-39.9) = -28.8\ \text{kcal/mol}$$

At $25°C$ both reactions are accordingly exothermic.

Problem 12.2: Starting from the enthalpy and entropy values given below, calculate the position of the following hypothetical gas phase equilibrium:

$$2 \left[\text{C}_6\text{H}_5\text{CH}_3 \right] \underset{}{\overset{K}{\rightleftharpoons}} \left[\text{C}_6\text{H}_6 \right] + \left[\text{H}_3\text{C—C}_6\text{H}_4—\text{CH}_3 \right]$$

ΔHf^0_{298}	11·95	19·82	4·29 [kcal/mol]
S^0_{298}	76·42	64·34	84·23 [cal/deg. mol]
ΔG^0_{298}	29·23	30·99	28·95 [kcal/mol]

From the values tabulated here (taken from Vol. 3, p. 259, German edition)

Compound	ΔHf^0_{298} [kcal/mol]	S^0_{298} [Clausius]	ΔG^0_{298} [kcal/mol]
Toluene (g)	11.95	76.42	29.228
Benzene (g)	19.82	64.34	30.989
p-Xylene (g)	4.29	84.23	28.952

we find:

$$\Delta H^0_{298} = -2 \cdot 11.95 + (19.82 + 4.29) = +0.21 \text{ kcal/mol}$$
$$\Delta S^0_{298} = -2 \cdot 76.42 + (64.34 + 84.23) = -4.27 \text{ cal/deg mol}$$
$$\Delta G^0_{298} = -2 \cdot 29.228 + (30.989 + 28.952) = +1.485 \text{ kcal/mol}$$

Substituting into

$$\log K = \frac{[\text{Benzene}]\,[p\text{-Xylene}]}{[\text{Toluene}]^2} = -\frac{\Delta G^0}{RT}$$

$$= -\frac{1.485}{1.987 \cdot 10^{-3} \cdot 298 \cdot 2.303} = -1.09$$

gives the equilibrium constant $K = 1/12$: i.e. the equilibrium is shifted predominantly in favor of toluene due mainly to the entropy term.

$$\Delta G^0 = \Delta H^0 - T\,\Delta S^0 \tag{12/6}$$
$$= 0.21 - 298(-4.27)10^{-3} = 0.21 + 1.27 = 1.48 \text{ kcal/mol.}$$

12.2. Redox Potentials

Problem 12.3: With what precision can the half-wave potential of an aromatic hydrocarbon be predicted from the values of (12/15)?

The starting point for the discussion consists in calculating the regression lines in [12.3] from the values of Table (12/15). According to the formulas (9/4) − (9/13), with the independent variables $x = E_{1/2}$ and the dependent variables $y = x_a$ one obtains

$$T_x = -42.18$$
$$T_y = -9.458$$
$$\bar{x} = -2.109$$
$$\bar{y} = -0.4729 \qquad \frac{T_x^2}{N} = 88.95762$$
$$\Sigma x_i^2 = 90.9276$$
$$\Sigma y_i^2 = 4.863468 \qquad \frac{T_y^2}{N} = 4.472688$$
$$\Sigma x_i y_i = 20.81509$$

$$\frac{T_x T_y}{N} = 19.946922$$

$$S_{xx} = 1.96998$$
$$S_{yy} = 0.390780$$
$$S_{xy} = 0.868168$$

$$\left. \begin{array}{l} \dfrac{S_{xy}}{S_{xx}} = b = 0.440699 \\[2mm] a = \bar{y} - b\bar{x} = 0.456534 \end{array} \right\} \qquad y = 0.457 + 0.441\,x$$

The line cuts the abscissa at $x = -1.034$. It should be pointed out once more that, by definition, the measured values are to be taken as independent variables x, and the theoretical data as the dependent ones y. A variance analysis according to (9/22) yields:

Source	SQ	Φ	DQ	SE(y)
Due to regr.	0.38260	1		
About regr.	0.00818	18	0.00045	⇒ 0.0213
Total	0.39078	19		

The standard deviation $SE(y)$ obtained according to (9/24) is substituted together with the other numerical values in the relation (9/36):

$$x_{u,l} = \left(\frac{Y_g - \bar{y}}{b} + \bar{x} \right) \pm t_{P,\Phi} \cdot \frac{SE(y)}{b} \sqrt{1 + \frac{1}{N} + \frac{(Y_g - \bar{y})^2}{b^2 S_{xx}}} \qquad (9/36)$$

$$E_{1/2} = \left(\frac{x_a + 0.473}{0.441} + (-2.109) \right) + t_{P,\Phi} \cdot \frac{0.0213}{0.441} \sqrt{1 + \frac{1}{20} + \frac{(x_a + 0.473)^2}{(0.441)^2 \cdot 1.970}}$$

The confidence limits for the half-wave potential $E_{1/2}$ are seen to depend not only on the desired confidence level (*Students' t*, (9/56) Vol. 1, p. 291):

$$\Phi = N - 2 = 18; \text{ Confidence level } 80\%: P = 0.2; \quad t_1 = 1.330$$
$$90\%: P = 0.1; \quad t_2 = 1.734$$
$$95\%: P = 0.05; t_3 = 2.101$$

but also on the size of the expected values, i.e. the orbital energy coefficients x_a. In this context, the following four cases will be discussed:

(A) $x_a = \bar{y}$ $t_1 \Rightarrow 0.0658$

$$E_{1/2} = -2.109 \pm t_{P,\Phi} \cdot 0.0495 \quad t_2 \Rightarrow 0.0858 \; [V]$$

$t_3 \Rightarrow 0.1040$

(B) $x_a - \bar{y} = -0.3$ $t_1 \Rightarrow 0.0728$

$$E_{1/2} = -2.789 \pm t_{P,\Phi} \cdot 0.0547 \quad t_2 \Rightarrow 0.0948 \; [V]$$

$t_3 \Rightarrow 0.1149$

(C) $x_a = -1$ $t_1 \Rightarrow 0.0855$

$$E_{1/2} = -3.304 \pm t_{P,\Phi} \cdot 0.0643 \quad t_2 \Rightarrow 0.1115 \; [V]$$

$t_3 \Rightarrow \text{o.}1351$

(D) $x_a = 0$ $t_1 \Rightarrow 0.0821$

$$E_{1/2} = -1.036 \pm t_{P,\Phi} \cdot 0.0617 \quad t_2 \Rightarrow 0.1070 \; [V]$$

$t_3 \Rightarrow 0.1296$

The narrowest limits of confidence are of course found in the middle of the parameter range (A), where the deviations to be expected for a 90 % confidence level amount to less than ± 0.1 V. At the boundary of the parameter range (B) the accuracy is less, mainly because of the uncertainty in the slope of the regression line. For extreme values such as (C) (benzene) or (D) (nonbonding molecular orbitals) the resulting error is 25 % greater than in the case of (A).

Problem 12.4: Calculate the reduction potential of the following neutral π-electron system as a function of the angle of twist ω between the two partial systems:

The π-electron system of the radial is alternant and, because of the odd number of centers, has a singly occupied nonbonding level $x_{nb} = 0$.

$$N^* - N^0 = 13 - 12 = 1$$

The entering electron on reduction to the anion goes into the nonbonding level. Since the coefficient $c_{nb,0}$ of the phenyl moiety has the value zero at the juncture position 0, twisting through an angle ω has no effect on x_{nb} and hence no effect on the reduction potential. Since $x_a = x_{nb} = 0$, the value for the angularly independent reduction potential follows from Problem 12.3 on a 90 % confidence level as

$$E_{1/2} = -1.04 \pm 0.11 \ V.$$

On the other hand, it should be borne in mind that the coefficients of the nonbonding molecular orbitals change as a function of ω; thus for the extreme cases $\omega = 0°$ and $\omega = 90°$, calculation after the manner of (5/29) through (5/36) (cf. Problem 5.11) affords:

$$\xi^2 \left(3 \cdot 1 + 2 \cdot \frac{1}{4} + 4 \cdot \frac{9}{4} + 4 + 3\right) = 1$$

$$\xi = \frac{1}{\sqrt{\dfrac{39}{2}}}$$

$$\xi^2 \left(3 \cdot 1 + 2 \cdot \frac{1}{4} + 4 \cdot \frac{9}{4} + 4\right) = 1$$

$$\xi = \frac{1}{\sqrt{\dfrac{33}{2}}}$$

In the intermediate range $0° < \omega < 90°$ the coefficients in the ortho and para positions of the phenyl group amount to $|\xi \cdot \cos \omega|$ so that the normalization coeficient is

$$\xi = \frac{1}{\sqrt{\dfrac{33 + 6 \cos^2 \omega}{2}}}$$

Problem 12.5: From the nonbonding molecular orbitals of the partial systems R and S involved, calculate the LCMO approximate orbital energy coefficients x_a of the lowest antibonding levels in α,ω-diphenylalkenes with an odd number of double bonds

$$\bigcirc\!\!\!\!-\text{(CH=CH)}_n\!\!-\!\!\bigcirc\,; \quad n = 2r + 1 \quad (r = 0, 1, 2).$$

Compare the values resulting from the relationship $x_a = f(r)$ for $r = 0, 1, 2$ and formally for $r = \frac{1}{2}, \frac{3}{2}, \frac{5}{2}$ with the experimental half-wave potentials (12/15) and discuss the deviations.

The counting rules (5/29) through (5/33) yield the nonbonding molecular orbitals of the alternant partial systems R and S

with the coefficients $2\,\xi\,(-1)^r$ at the juncture points ρ and σ and the normalization condition

$$\xi^2 = \frac{1}{3 + 4\,(r + 1)} = \frac{1}{7 + 4r}\,.$$

After linkage, the two "inner" orbitals are obtained (cf. Section 7.5) with the energies

$$\epsilon_{a,b} = \alpha \pm x_a\,\beta = \alpha \pm c_\rho c_\sigma \beta$$

Hence for the highest unoccupied level one finds

$$x_a = -c_\rho c_\sigma = -4\,\xi^2 = -\frac{4}{7 + 4r}$$

and the values so calculated are compared below with the experimental half-wave potentials (12/15).

r	0	0.5	1	1.5	2	2.5
x_a	−0.571	−0.444	−0.364	−0.308	−0.267	−0.235
$E_{1/2}$	−2.15	−1.98	−1.79	−1.64	−1.54	−1.46 [V]

A graphic representation reveals that, except for $r = 0$, all points (x) are relatively well placed on the straight line shown.

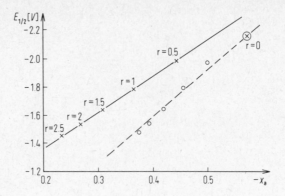

The correlation can be improved corresponding to the dashed line $(- - -)$ if the bond length alternancy in the side chains of the partial systems R and S is taken into consideration. With this in mind, we introduce an increased resonance integral $m\beta$ with $m > 1$ for bonds with high double bond character:

Generalization of the derivation leading to the formula

$$\sum_{\mu} B_{\mu\nu} c_{nb,\mu}^* = 0 \tag{5/29}$$

to include the general case that the bonds attached to the unstarred center ν^o do not all have the same resonance integral

leads to the condition

$$\sum_{\mu} B_{\mu\nu} m_{\mu} c_{nb,\mu}^* = 0$$

For the partial systems R and S the coefficients at the centers of juncture always amount to $2 \, \xi \, (-m)^r$ and the normalization condition reads

$$\xi^2 = \frac{1}{3 + 4 + 4m^2 + 4m^4 \, ... + 4m^{2r}}$$

$$= \frac{1}{3 + 4 \sum\limits_{S=0}^{r} (m^2)^S} = \frac{1}{3 + 4 \left(\dfrac{m^{2(r+1)} - 1}{m^2 - 1} \right)}$$

According to

$$x_a = -4 \, \xi^2 m^{2r} = -\frac{4 \, m^{2r}}{3 + 4 \left(\dfrac{m^{2(r+1)} - 1}{m^2 - 1} \right)}$$

with $m = 1.2$, the orbital energy coefficients x_a are

r	0	0.5	1	1.5	2	2.5
x_a	−0.571	−0.499	−0.451	−0.418	−0.394	−0.376

These have already been entered in the regression as the value pairs (o).

Problem 12.6: Derive a relationship between the position of the ^1L_a band and the half-wave potential of an alternant aromatic hydrocarbon, and verify it using the data in (11/19) and (12/15). What half-wave potential would consequently be expected for benzene, which cannot be reduced polarographically under normal conditions?

The half-wave potential $E_{1/2}$ and the orbital energy coefficients x_a of the lowest unoccupied molecular orbital are related according

$$E_{1/2} = A + B x_a. \tag{12/14}$$

From Problem 12.3 we obtained the regression line

$$x_a = 0.457 + 0.441 \, E_{1/2}$$

and, to a first approximation,

$$E_{1/2} = -1.036 + 2.269\, x_a\, [V].$$

On the other hand, we have

$$\tilde{\nu}^{\text{exp.}} = 8200 + 22000\,(-2x_a)\,[\text{cm}^{-1}].\tag{11/18}$$

Since both $E_{1/2}$ and $\tilde{\nu}^{\text{exp.}}$ are linearly dependent upon x_a in the HMO model, we expect the following relationship to apply to alternant systems:

$$\tilde{\nu}^{\text{exp.}} = -11900 - 19400\, E_{1/2}$$

$$E_{1/2} = -0.613 - 5.16 \cdot 10^{-5}\, \tilde{\nu}^{\text{exp.}}$$

This relationship is plotted with the values from (11/19) and (12/15) below. The following pairs of values (↓) are seen to correspond

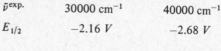

$\tilde{\nu}^{\text{exp.}}$	30000 cm^{-1}	40000 cm^{-1}
$E_{1/2}$	−2.16 V	−2.68 V

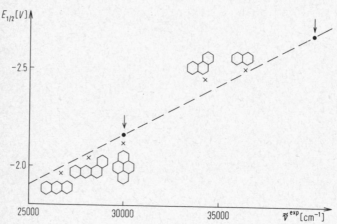

For benzene, whose ^1L_a band lies at 50 000 cm^{-1}, the half-wave reduction pontential is thus

$$E_{1/2} = -0.613 - 5.16 \cdot 10^{-5} \cdot 50000 = -3.19\ V.$$

This quantity is inaccessible to direct measurement, since the supporting electrolyte (tetrabutylammonium iodide in dioxane/water), already liberates hydrogen at more positive values.

Problem 12.7: Discuss the inductive effect of an alkyl group at centre μ on the half-wave potential of aromatic π-electron systems, using first order perturbation calculations. Apply the derived formula to azulene, and compare the results with the following experimental values $\Delta E_{1/2} = E_{1/2}$ (methylazulene) $- E_{1/2}$ (azulene):

μ	1	2	4	5	6
$-\Delta E_{1/2}$	0·06	0·12	0·08	0·01	0·08 [V]

Replacement of the hydrogen atom at center μ of a π-electron-system by a methyl group changes the energy of the lowest unoccupied *Hückel* molecular orbital by the amount

$$\delta\epsilon_a = c_{a\mu}^2 \cdot \delta\alpha_\mu \tag{6/12}$$

The perturbation

$$\delta\alpha_\mu = h \cdot \beta$$

is positive (β negative!) and is generally set equal for all centers μ. Using the normal perturbation parameter for the methyl group $h = -1/3$ (cf. Problem 10.25), we obtain

$$\delta x_a = -\frac{1}{3} c_{a\mu}^2 .$$

From the relation derived in Problem 12.3

$$E_{1/2} = -1.036 + 2.269 \, x_a$$

it follows that

$$\Delta E_{1/2} = 2.269 \, \delta x_a = -0.756 \, c_{a\mu}^2 .$$

Thus polarographic reduction is seen to become more difficult on alkyl substitution at center μ. The potential should be more negative the greater the coefficient $c_{a\mu}$ of the lowest unoccupied molecular orbital at position μ.

With the aid of the HMO Table (5)(7) (Vol. 3) the following comparison is obtained for the five isomeric methylazulenes:

μ	1	2	4	5	6
$c_{a\mu}^2$	0.004	0.100	0.221	0.010	0.261
$-\Delta E_{1/2}^{exp.}$	0.06	0.12	0.08	0.01	0.08

The relevant graphic representation

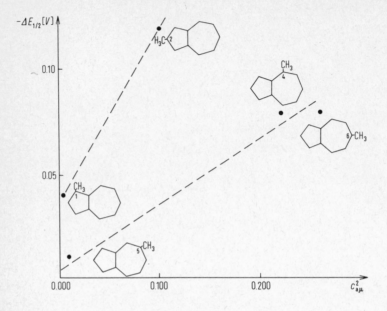

shows that some important factors must have been overlooked. A methyl group apparently has a greater perturbing effect in a five-membered ring than in a seven-membered ring. This situation can be partly explained as follows: the inductive effect of an alkyl group at a π-center results from the polarity of the C_{sp3}/C_{sp2} σ-bond. If the angle CCC in an unsaturated system deviates from $120°$, a greater or smaller s-character results for the radial atomic orbital.

The inductive effect of an alkyl group at center μ increases, however, with increasing s-character of the radial atomic orbital. For this reason, a more pronounced perturbation is to be expected on substitution in the five-membered ring.

Problem 12.8: The following half-wave potentials are measured on polarographic reduction of pyrene:

$E_{1/2} = -2.10; -2.46; -2.67$ [V].

What are the reduction intermediates, and what will be the final product?

The given reduction potentials indicate that two intermediates are involved and that the end product must therefore be a hexahydro derivative, which is not reduced futher under the experimental conditions. The π-systems of the intermediates have lowest unoccupied molecular orbitals of energy ϵ_a which correspond to the measured potentials -2.46 and -2.67 V.

For the dihydro derivative of pyrene the following structures can be discussed:

(a)   (b)

Of these, the unsaturated system (a) should be more easily reduced than pyrene itself, which would correspond to a first step involving four electrons. For (b), however, a first two-electron step is expected to be followed by a second one at the half wave potential of phenanthrene (cf. (12/15) : $E_{1/2} = -2.45$ V). Further reduction leads from (b) to the diphenyl derivative (c) and finally as in (12/18) to the hexahydro derivative (d):

(c)   (d)

Accordingly the measured reduction potential (c) → (d) corresponds to that of diphenyl (cf. (12/15) : $E_{1/2} = -2.70$ V). Further reduction to an octahydro derivative — analogous to (F) in (12/18) — does not occur here, since the potential is shifted into the range of hydrogen evolution owing to the five-fold alkyl substitution of the styrene skeleton.

Problem 12.9: Use (12/22) to calculate the ΔE_π values of the o-quinones given below, whose half-wave potentials were determined under the same experimental conditions as those of the p-quinones in (12/23):

$E_{1/2}$: 0·79   0·62   0·58   0·46 [V]

Compare the relation between the theoretical and experimental values with those for p-quinones. Hint: Use the approximation formula (10/74) for the systems not listed in the HMO Tables (Volume 3).

An extension of the approximation treatment according to (12/21) and (12/22)

$$\Delta E_\pi = A + E_\pi(T) - E_\pi(R)$$

yields after insertion of the corresponding HMO data (Vol. 3) and the approximation for 2-vinylnaphthalene not given in the table

$$\Delta X_\pi(\text{2-Vinylnaphthalene}) = 0.062 + 0.811 \sqrt{\pi_{\rho\rho} \cdot \pi_{\sigma\sigma}} \qquad (10/74)$$
$$= 0.062 + 0.811 \sqrt{0.500 \cdot 0.405} = 0.427$$
$$X_\pi(\text{2-Vinylnaphthalene}) = 0.427 + 13.683 + 2.000 \qquad = 16.110$$

the following ΔE_π-values:

$E_\pi = 4\alpha + 4.472\,\beta$ $E_\pi = 6\alpha + 8.000\,\beta$ $\Delta E_\pi - 2\alpha = 3.528\,\beta$

$E_\pi = 12\alpha + 16.110\,\beta$ $E_\pi = 14\alpha + 19.448\,\beta$ $\Delta E_\pi - 2\alpha = 3.338\,\beta$

$E_\pi = 8\,\alpha + 10.424\,\beta$

$E_\pi = 10\,\alpha + 13.683$

$\Delta E_\pi - 2\,\alpha = 3.259\,\beta$

$E_\pi = 12\,\alpha + 16.383\,\beta$

$E_\pi = 14\,\alpha + 19.448\,\beta$

$\Delta E_\pi - 2\,\alpha = 3.065\,\beta$

The graphic representation below shows the straight line for the *o*-quinones to run almost parallel to that for the *p*-quinones [12.4].

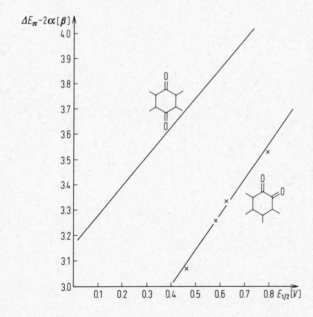

The almost constant difference arises because, in the crude approximation used here, the quinone π-electron systems are divided into different numbers of partial systems: 4 for *p*-quinone and only 2 for *o*-quinone.

Moreover, further effects should also have been taken into consideration, such as an additional stabilization by hydrogen bonding in the *o*-dihydroxy compounds.

Problem 12.10: Two steps are observed upon polarographic reduction of aryl aldehydes: a pH-dependent one which corresponds to the reduction process (a), and a pH-independent one at more negative potential which is attributed to the direct introduction of an electron into the π-electron system (b):

Interpret the values given in the following table in terms of an LCMO approximation using relation (10/74).

Compound	$E_{1/2}^{(a)}$ [V]	$E_{1/2}^{(b)}$ [V]
Benzaldehyde	-0.911	-1.553
Cinnamaldehyde	-0.591	-1.296
1-Naphthaldehyde	-0.765	-1.437
2-Naphthaldehyde	-0.806	-1.466
9-Anthracenaldehyde	-0.506	-1.168
9-Phenanthrene aldehyde	-0.758	-1.410

(a) *pH*-dependent polarographic reduction step:
In analogy to the treatment of the quinones (12/20), the potential-determining
equilibrium (a) can be described with the aid of the following model system in which
the isoconjugate π-electron systems are used both for the aldehyde and for the radical
formed:

(A)   (B)

The value to be correlated with the half-wave potential $E_{1/2}^{(a)}$ is the difference between the total π-electron energies

$$\Delta E_{\pi}^{(a)} = E_{\pi}(B) - E_{\pi}(A) \ .$$

Other energy contributions should be independent of the type of aldehyde. The
quantity $\Delta E_{\pi}^{(a)}$ can be calculated in the LCMO approximation by way of the formula
(10/74) as follows:

$$E_{\pi}(A) = E_{\pi}(R) + E_{\pi}(S) + 0.811\,\beta\,\sqrt{\pi_{\rho\rho}\,\pi_{\sigma\sigma}} + 0.062\,\beta$$
$$E_{\pi}(B) = E_{\pi}(R) + E_{\pi}(T) + 0.811\,\beta\,\sqrt{\pi_{\rho\rho}\,\pi_{\tau\tau}} + 0.062\,\beta$$
$$\overline{\Delta E_{\pi}^{(a)} = E_{\pi}(T) - E_{\pi}(S) + 0.811\,\beta\,(\sqrt{\pi_{\tau\tau}} - \sqrt{\pi_{\sigma\sigma}})\,\sqrt{\pi_{\rho\rho}}}$$

Thus the required energy difference $\Delta E_{\pi}^{(a)}$ should to a first approximation be a linear
function of the square root of the atom-atom polarizability $\pi_{\rho\rho}$ at the linkage site ρ

$$\Delta E_{\pi}^{(a)} = a + b\,\sqrt{\pi_{\rho\rho}} \ .$$

With the values of the atom-atom polarizability from the HMO Tables (Vol. 3),
we obtain the following representation:

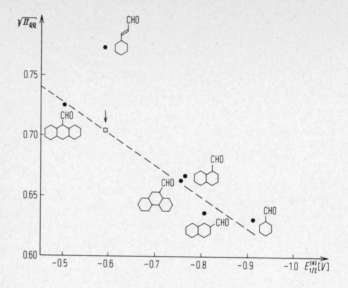

As can be seen, the relationship derived is satisfactorily confirmed for all aromatic aldehydes with the CHO group attached to the ring system. On the other hand, the atom-atom polarizability at position ρ of the styrene system is substantially overestimated, which can be attributed to neglect of the pronounced bond alternation. Assuming the extreme case of no conjugation between the double bond and the phenyl ring, the atom-atom polarizability of ethylene $\pi_{\rho\rho} = 0.500$ would apply at position ρ.

$$\sqrt{0.599} = 0.774 \qquad \sqrt{0.500} = 0.707$$

The resulting point ($\square$) is also induded in the graphic representation.

(b) pH-independent polarographic reduction steps:

In the potential-determining step of pH-independent polarographic reduction, an electron occupies the lowest unoccupied molecular orbital in complete analogy to the reduction of aromatic hydrocarbons [12.2]. The energy of this molecular orbital can be calculated in the LCMO approximation by linear combination of the lowest unoccupied molecular orbitals Ψ_{Ra} and Ψ_{Sa} of the partial systems R and S

$$\Psi_{RSa} = r\,\Psi_{Ra} + s\,\Psi_{Sa}\,.$$

This approach leads to the secular determinant

$$\begin{Vmatrix} x_{Ra} - x & c_{Ra\rho}\,c_{Sa\sigma}\,k \\ c_{Ra\rho}\,c_{Sa\sigma}\,k & x_{Sa} - x \end{Vmatrix} = 0\,,$$

in which the perturbation parameter k determines the value of the resonance integral $\beta_{\rho\sigma} = k\beta$ between the linkage sites ρ and σ. A second order perturbation according to (7/11) through (7/14) is not recommended in the present case since the difference $x_{Ra} - x_{Sa}$ is small compared to the cross terms and is even equal to zero for the isoconjugate model of benzaldehyde. From the secular determinant, the orbital energy of the lowest linear combination Ψ_{RSa} is

$$x_{RSa} = \frac{x_{Ra} + x_{Sa}}{2} + \frac{1}{2}\sqrt{(x_{Ra} - x_{Sa})^2 + 4\,(c_{Ra\rho}\,c_{Sa\sigma}\,k)^2}$$

Since in our isoconjugate model, the system S always corresponds to a double bond ($x_{Sa} = -1.000$, $c_{Sa} = 1/\sqrt{2}$), we find, for complete π-bonding between the partial systems R and S ($k = 1$),

$$x_{RSa} = \frac{x_{Ra} - 1}{2} + \frac{1}{2}\sqrt{(x_{Ra} + 1)^2 + 2\,c_{Ra\rho}^2}$$

The resulting orbital energy coefficients x_{RSa} are

Compound	x_{Ra}	$c_{Ra\rho}$	x_{RSa}
Benzaldehyde	−1.000	0.577	−0.59
Cinnamaldehyde	−0.662	0.595	−0.38
1-Naphthaldehyde	−0.618	0.425	−0.45
2-Naphthaldehyde	−0.618	0.263	−0.54
9-Anthracene-aldehyde	−0.414	0.440	−0.28
9-Phenanthrene-aldehyde	−0.605	0.415	−0.45

Excellent correlation is obtained with the measured half-wave reduction potentials $E_{1/2}^{(b)}$, as can be seen in the following graphic representation:

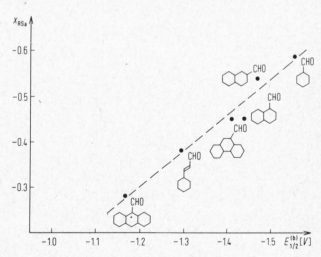

Problem 12.11: Plot the polarographically determined oxidation and reduction potentials of the following hydrocarbons against each other:

Compound	$E_{1/2}^{Ox}$ [V]	$E_{-1/2}^{Red}$ [V]
Tetracene	0·54	−1·14
1,2-Benzopyrene	0·76	−1·36
Anthracene	0·84	−1·46
Pyrene	0·86	−1·61
1,2-Benzoanthracene	0·92	−1·53
1,2:5,6-Dibenzoanthracene	1·00	−1·56
Phenanthrene	1·23	−1·90
Fluoranthene	1·18	−1·35
Naphthalene	1·31	−1·98
Diphenyl	1·48	−2·08

Discuss the reason for the excellent regression and explain the deviation observed in one case.

A plot of the oxidation versus the reduction potentials has the following appearance

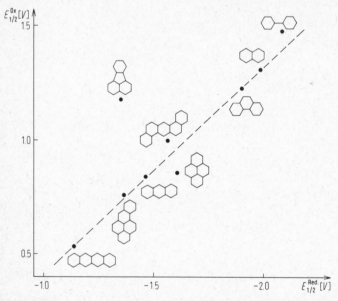

The alternant π-electron systems are seen to give a satisfactory correlation, while only the nonalternant fluoranthrene shows a marked deviation. The result obtained for the

alternant π-electron systems was to be expected. As repeatedly mentioned, their reduction potentials are a linear function of the orbital energy coefficient x_a of the lowest unoccupied molecular orbital.

$$E_{1/2}^{Red} = a + bx_a .$$

Their oxidation potentials are likewise a linear function of the orbital energy coefficient x_b of the highest occupied molecular orbital.

$$E_{1/2}^{Ox} = c + dx_b .$$

Since $x_a = -x_b$ in an alternant π-electron system, a linear relationship exists between the reduction- and oxidation potentials:

$$E_{1/2}^{Red} = e + f E_{1/2}^{Ox} .$$

On the other hand, in a nonalternant π-electron system $x_a \neq -x_b$. The orbital energy coefficients for fluoranthene read

$$x_a = -0.371 \qquad ; \qquad x_b = 0.618 .$$

Based on the reduction potential of fluoranthrene $E_{1/2}^{Red} = -1.35$ V, an oxidation potential $E_{1/2}^{Ox}$ (regression) $= 0.73$ V would be expected from the regression, whereas a value of $E_{1/2}^{Ox} = 1.18$ V is actually found. This agrees with the orbital energy coefficient x_b which lies below 0.371. Comparison with phenanthrene, which has a similar oxidation potential, and whose orbital energy coefficient amounts to $x_b = 0.605$, shows that HMO theory not only explains the deviation, but also correctly predicts its direction and magnitude.

12.3. pK Values

Problem 12.12: Examine whether a second order perturbation calculation may explain the deviations of the pK values for the benzologous pyridines (12/37).

Expanding the relation

$$\delta \Delta E_\pi = q_\mu (h_{\ddot{N}} - h_{\overset{\oplus}{N}}) \beta \tag{12/36}$$

by including the second order perturbation term affords

$$\delta \Delta E_\pi = q_\mu (h_{\ddot{N}} - h_{\overset{\oplus}{N}}) \beta + \frac{\pi_{\mu\mu}}{2} (h_{\ddot{N}} - h_{\overset{\oplus}{N}})^2 \beta$$

386

In this expression, $\pi_{\mu\mu}$ is the atom-atom polarizability (7/66) defined as a dimensionless quantity. Because the first term of the sum is constant — in alternant systems the charge orders amount to $q_\mu = 1$ (5/27) — the relative deviations of the pK values of benzologs of pyridine (12/37) should consequently run parallel to the atom-atom polarizabilities. However, as shown by the graphic representation below, this is not the case.

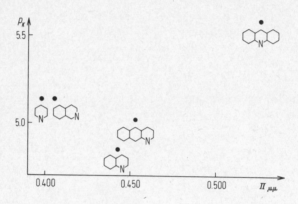

Hence it may be concluded that the deviations are attributable less to differential changes in the total π-electron energies than to other factors not included in our model, such as different kinds of solvation.

It should be possible to account for changes in the resonance integrals β_{CN} on protonation via the free valences F_μ at those centers μ which correspond in the isoconjugate model to the nitrogen positions. The relative deviations in the pK values should then be correlatable with the F_μ values. However, comparison of the HMO Tables (Vol. 3) shows that the latter are practically equal to the atom-atom polarizabilities, and thus also fail to explain the differences in the pK values of benzologous pyridines.

Problem 12.13: What prediction does a first order perturbation calculation allow for the pK value of benzologous phenols and for benzologous carboxylic acids?

With benzologous phenols, in analogy with the benzologous carboxylic acids, loss of a proton leads to anions whose π-electron systems can be described with the same isoconjugate model as that of the conjugate acid. Consequently, the relation

$$\delta \Delta E_\pi = q_\mu (h_{\ddot{N}} - h_N^\oplus)\beta \qquad (12/36)$$

is also directly applicable to these systems provided that the perturbation parameters h are varied accordingly. In contrast to the benzologous pyridines, the charge order q_μ is no longer constant, however, since the alternant isoconjugate model extends over an odd number N of centers occupied by $N + 1$ electrons.

(a) Benzologous phenols:

The charge order q_O can be estimated in principle by the frequently used treatment (5/29)–(5/33). For instance, if a reduced resonance integral $\beta_{CO} = \beta/2$ is assigned to the CO bond in the phenols then — as shown for β-naphthol — the charge order q_O is obtained in the following way:

With respect to the center ν

$$\xi + 2\xi + \frac{1}{2}\eta = 0; \quad \eta = -6\xi.$$

Normalization yields

$$\xi^2(1 + 1 + 1 + 1 + 4 + 36) = 1; \quad \xi = \frac{1}{\sqrt{44}}.$$

The charge order is

$$q_O = 1 + \frac{36}{44} = 1.818.$$

The charge orders q_O thus obtained are compared with pK values (taken from the German edition, Vol. 3, 3.3.6) and retabulated here:

Compound	pK	q_O
Phenol	9.96	1.842
2-Naphthol	9.93	1.818
2-Anthrol	9.92	1.780
1-Naphthol	9.85	1.766
1-Anthrol	9.82	1.711

The charge orders on the oxygen centers are obviously very similar to each other. The extreme values differ by only about 7 %. Moreover, the difference between the perturbation parameters $h_{\ddot{O}} - h_{O\ominus}$ (6/80) must be smaller than 0.5 because of the pronounced hydrogen bonding in aqueous solution. We can therefore conclude that the pK values of the benzologs of phenol should differ only insignificantly, as is confirmed by the tabulated experimental values.

(b) Benzologous carboxylic acids:

As can be readily demonstrated, the nonbonding molecular orbital of the isoconjugate models is limited in these cases exclusively to the three centers corresponding to the COOH and the $COO^{\ominus}$ group, respectively. This situation will now be illustrated for naphthalene-2-carboxylic acid as an example:

$$\xi = \frac{1}{\sqrt{2}}; \quad q_O = 1 + \frac{1}{2} = 1.500$$

Thus, the charge orders q_O are identical for all benzologous carboxylic acids within the framework of this model and almost equal pK values can again be expected, as confirmed by the experimental values which are tabulated here:

Compound	pK
Benzoic acid	4.20
Naphthalene-2-carboxylic acid	4.17
Anthracene-2-carboxylic acid	4.18
Naphthalene-1-carboxylic acid	3.69
Anthracene-1-carboxylic acid	3.69

Problem 12.14: What does the HMO theory predict regarding the basicity of 1-azaazulene relative to the benzologous pyridines?

The basicity of the unknown 1-azaazulene relative to the benzologous pyridine can be estimated starting from the relation

$$\delta \Delta E_\pi = q_N (h_{\ddot{N}} - h_N^\oplus) \beta \qquad (12/36)$$

In contrast to alternant π-electron systems, however, the charge orders q_μ are not equal to 1 in the nonalternant isoconjugate azulene model.

$$q_1 = 1.173$$

Since in (12/36) both the difference $h_N - h_{N^\oplus}$ and also the resonance integral β are negative quantities, the difference $\delta \Delta E_\pi$ is always positive. A larger $\delta \Delta E_\pi$ value is obtained for 1-azaazulene with $q_1 > 1$ relative to the benzologous pyridines. This means that the equilibrium of type (12/31) lies further on the side of the conjugate acid, and 1-azaazulene should consequently be a stronger base than the benzologous pyridines. The size of the pK value, cannot be predicted, however, since a suitable regression is not available.

Problem 12.15: Examine whether the regression [12.8] can be improved by a more favourable value for the *Coulomb* potential of the nitrogen atom.

The regression [12.8] depicts the relationship between the pK values of aromatic amines and the HMO quantities $\Delta E_\pi - 2\alpha$ for the corresponding isoconjugate models. A change in the *Coulomb* potential at the nitrogen center of the base can be obtained with the aid of a perturbation calculation:

$$\delta E_\pi(\text{Base}) = q_N \delta \alpha_N + \frac{\pi_{NN}}{2\beta} (\delta \alpha_N)^2$$

This difference $\delta E_\pi(\text{base})$ contributes to the ΔE_π value. A corresponding correction of the total π-electron energy of the acid does not occur, since the nitrogen center is not present in the isoconjugate model. The pK value of the aromatic amine is consequently a function of three variables:

$$p_K^{\text{calc.}} = a + b_1 x_1 + b_2 x_2 + b_3 x_3$$

$$b_1 = \beta \qquad b_2 = \delta\alpha_N \qquad b_3 = \frac{(\delta\alpha_N)^2}{2\beta}$$

$$x_1 = \frac{\Delta E_\pi - 2\alpha}{\beta} \qquad x_2 = q_N \qquad x_3 = \pi_{NN}$$

Inclusion of the variable $x_3 = \pi_{NN}$ leads to a problem which can only be solved by iteration, because b_3 is a higher power of b_2. For this reason we shall merely examine the dependency of x_1 and x_2, which corresponds to a first order perturbation.

The starting point for the regression calculation is the following table of data:

Compound	$y_i = p_K^{\text{exp.}}$	$x_{1i} = \dfrac{\Delta E_\pi - 2\alpha}{\beta}$	$x_{2i} = q_N$
Aniline	4.19	0.721	1.571
p-Aminodiphenyl	3.81	0.756	1.516
β-Naphthylamine	3.77	0.744	1.529
α-Naphthylamine	3.40	0.812	1.450
2-Aminoanthracene	3.40	0.769	1.471
1-Aminoanthracene	3.22	0.848	1.381
9-Aminoanthracene	2.70	0.951	1.286

To begin with the regression of y_i on the x_{1i} values is calculated according to the procedure given in (9/3) through (9/13), the experimental quantity being chosen as the dependent variable since its dependence upon two independent variables is to be investigated.

$$T_y = 24.49 \qquad\qquad T_{x_1} = 5.601$$

$$\bar{y} = 3.498571 \qquad\qquad \bar{x}_1 = 0.800143$$

$$\sum_i y_i^2 = 87.0635 \qquad\qquad \sum_i x_i^2 = 4.519123$$

$$S_{yy} = 1.383486 \qquad\qquad S_{x_1 x_1} = 0.037523$$

$$\sum_i x_{1i} y_i = 19.37989$$

$$S_{x_1 y} = -0.215609$$

$$b_1 = \frac{S_{x_1 y}}{S_{x_1 x_1}} = -5.746$$

$$a = \bar{y} - b_1\bar{x}_1 = -1.099$$

$$p_K^{\text{calc.}} = -1.099 - 5.746 \frac{(\Delta E_\pi - 2\alpha)}{\beta}$$

The associated variational analyses (9/22) accordingly reads:

Source	SQ	Φ	DQ
Due to About	1.238900 0.144586	1 5	0.028917
Total	1.383486	6	

$$SE\ (pK^{\text{calc.}}) = \sqrt{DQ_{\text{About}}} = 0.170$$

In view of the question to be answered one can first investigate whether the independent variable q_N, which introduces the change in the *Coulomb* integral α_N, gives a significant regression when considered by itself. The analogous calculation gives

$$T_y = 24.49 \qquad\qquad T_{x_2} = 3.204$$

$$\bar{y} = 3.498571 \qquad\qquad \bar{x}_2 = 0.457714$$

$$\sum_i y_i^2 = 87.0635 \qquad\qquad \sum_i x_{2i}^2 = 1.523436$$

$$S_{yy} = 1.383486 \qquad\qquad S_{x_2 x_2} = 0.056920$$

$$\sum_i x_{2i}\, y_i = 11.4832$$

$$S_{x_2 y} = 0.273777$$

$$b = \frac{S_{x_2 y}}{S_{x_2 x_2}} = 4.810$$

$$a = \bar{y} - b_2\bar{x}_2 = -3.513$$

$$p_K^{\text{calc.}} = -3.513 + 4.810\, q_N$$

The associated variational analysis reads

Source	SQ	Φ	DQ
Due to About	1.316827 0.066659	1 5	0.013332
Total	1.383486	6	

$$SE\ (pK^{\text{calc.}}) = \sqrt{DQ_{\text{About}}} = 0.115$$

Surprisingly, the variation about the regression on the charge orders q_N is found to be smaller than that based on changes in the total π-electron energy. A statistical test would show that the reduction on a confidence level of 80 % is scarcely significant. Thus it can already be concluded that taking account of the differing *Coulomb* integrals of the nitrogen centers must lead to an improvement in the agreement between the calculated and experimental pK values.

Starting from the expression

$$p_K^{calc.} = a + b_1 x_1 + b_2 x_2$$

an attempt to implement this improvement by means of a double regression runs into an unexpected but very instructive difficulty. As shown by the table of data introduced initially, a highly satisfactory linear relation exists between x_1 and x_2, i.e. between $(\Delta E_\pi - 2\alpha)/\beta$ and q_N. Consequently, a double regression, proceeding as shown in standard works on statistics, leads to two equations in the unknowns b_1 and b_2:

$$a_{11} b_1 + a_{12} b_2 = k_1$$
$$a_{21} b_1 + a_{22} b_2 = k_2$$

The associated determinant has a very small value:

$$\begin{Vmatrix} a_{11} & a_{12} \\ a_{21} & a_{22} \end{Vmatrix} \approx 0.00005$$

Thus while an equation of the desired type which minimizes the scatter about the regression can certainly be found, the errors for the coefficients b_1 and b_2 will be extraordinarily large. The latter can assume a wide range of arbitrary values as long as a restrictive condition

$$A_1 b_1 + A_2 b_2 = k$$

given by the regression between x_1 and x_2 is retained.

Problem 12.16: Use the regression of the pK values versus the charge order q_N for the compounds in Table (12/42) to predict the pK value of 1-aminopyrene:

The isoconjugate model for 1-aminopyrene is an odd alternant π-electron system whose nonbonding molecular orbital follows from (5/36):

$$\Psi_{nb} = \frac{1}{\sqrt{11}} \left(-\phi_2 - \phi_5 + \phi_6 - \phi_8 + \phi_9 - \phi_{11} + \phi_{12} + 2\,\phi_{17}\right)$$

According to (5/43) the charge order at the exocyclic center is

$$q^{\bullet}_{17} = q^{\bullet}_{17} + (c_{nb,17})^2 = 1 + \frac{4}{11} = 1.364$$

The regression calculated in Problem 12.15

$$pK = -3.513 + 4.810\, q_N$$

for the pK values of the standard compounds (12/42) yields the following predictions:

Compound	q_N	pK calc.	pK calc.
Aniline	1.571	4.04	4.19
p-Aminodiphenyl	1.516	3.78	3.81
β-Naphthylamine	1.529	3.84	3.77
α-Naphthylamine	1.450	3.46	3.40
2-Aminoanthracene	1.471	3.56	3.40
1-Aminoanthracene	1.381	3.13	3.22
9-Aminoanthracene	1.286	2.67	2.70

The good agreement between calculated and experimental pK values is especially obvious from the following graphic presentation:

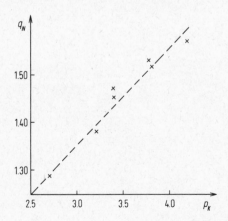

For 1-aminopyrene a value of $q_N = 1.364$ affords a $pK^{calc.}$ value of 3.05, which also agrees well with the experimental pK value of 2.9.

Problem 12.17: Use the two last-mentioned procedures to calculate the pK value of *ortho*-aminodiphenyl. The experimental value is 3·0; estimate the twist angle from the difference.

(a) In the isoconjugate approximation (12/41) the pK value can be estimated by way of the charge order $q_{13}^{\ominus}$ and the regression given in Problems 12.15 and 12.16 as follows:

$$\Psi_{nb} = \frac{1}{\sqrt{31}}(\phi_1 - \phi_3 + \phi_5 - 2\,\phi_7 + 2\,\phi_9 - 2\,\phi_{11} + 4\,\phi_{13})$$

$$q_{13}^{\ominus} = q_{13} + c_{nb,13}^2 = 1.000 + \frac{16}{31} = 1.516$$

$$pK^{calc.} = -3.513 + 4.810\,q_{13}^{\ominus} = 3.78$$

(b) According to the approximate formula (12/44) and the regression [12.9], and using the atom-atom polarizability $\pi_{1,1} = 0.424$ from the HMO Table ⑥–⑥ (Vol. 3), the pK value for *ortho*-aminodiphenyl is

$$\sqrt{\pi_{12,12}} = \sqrt{\pi_{1,1}} = 0.651 \Rightarrow 3.65$$

The value obtained according to both (a) and (b) lies above the experimental pK value of 3.0. This means that the strength of the conjugate acid has been predicted to be too small, and that either the free base is more stable or the acid less stable than would be expected from the planar model.

If an attempt is made to take account of the twist of the free base in the framework of the q_N approximation, an even larger discrepancy results between the calculated and the experimental value. A pK value of 4.04 would be expected for two mutually perpendicular phenyl rings with the value $q_N = 1.571$ calculated for aniline.

In conclusion, it will be shown how q_N values for intermediate twist angles ω can be calculated. Using the resonance integral $\beta \cos \omega$ for the central bond, the calculation proceeds analogously to Problem 12.13.

The relation with respect to center ν is

$$-\xi - \xi + \eta \cos \omega = 0 \quad ; \quad \xi = \eta\,\frac{\cos \omega}{2}$$

Normalization affords

$$1 = 3\,\xi^2 + 7\,\eta^2 = \eta^2\left(7 + \frac{3}{4}\cos^2\omega\right)$$

The resulting charge order is

$$q_N = 1 + \frac{16}{28 + 3 \cos^2 \omega}$$

Substitution of the cos values gives, e.g.

$$\omega = 0 \qquad q_N = 1.516$$
$$\omega = 45° \qquad q_N = 1.542$$
$$\omega = 90° \qquad q_N = 1.571$$

and hence — as already noted — higher values of pK calc. on twisting of the phenyl rings in the free base, according to regression (a).

The lower experimental pK value is apparently only to be understood within our model if the twisting of the conjugate acid is also taken into consideration. This can be achieved most simply by way of the ΔE_π values. For both extreme conformations $\omega = 0$ and $\omega = 90°$, the following data may be taken from the HMO Table ⑥–⑥ (Vol. 3) and from Table (12/42):

ω	E_π (Base)	E_π (Acid)
0°	$14\,\alpha + 17.151\,\beta$	$12\,\alpha + 16.383\,\beta$
90°	$14\,\alpha + 16.721\,\beta$	$12\,\alpha + 16.000\,\beta$

A larger value of the difference

$$\Delta E_\pi - 2\,\alpha = (17.151 - 16.383)\,\beta = 0.768\,\beta$$

is to be expected if the conjugate acid is more strongly twisted than the free base. This could be explained by the fact that a hydrated $NH_3^\oplus$ group is bulkier than a hydrated NH_2 group. However, it is known that bulky groups ortho to an amino group also exert a strong acidifying influence, even in the absence of conjugation effects, since quaternization $NH_2 \to NH_3^\oplus$ is then sterically hindered. Such an effect is probably operative in the case at hand.

Problem 12.18: Calculate the atom localization energy for the equilibrium:

starting from the HMO data given in Volume 3.

From the HMO Tables (Vol. 3) we obtain the data

$$E_\pi \text{ (Diphenyl)} \qquad = E_\pi(\;⑥\!-\!⑥\;) \qquad = 12\,\alpha + 16.383\,\beta$$
$$E_\pi \text{ (Fluorenyl cation)} = E_\pi(\;⑥⑤⑥\;) \quad = 12\,\alpha + 17.544\,\beta$$

The resulting atom localization energy is

$$A_9^\ominus = E_\pi \text{(Diphenyl)} - E_\pi \text{(Fluorenyl cation)} = -1.161\,\beta$$
$$q_9^\ominus = 1.161$$

Comparison with the values of Table (12/50) shows that the 'pK' value of the fluorenyl cation should be strongly negative. The experimental 'pK' value amounts to -7.5.

Problem 12.19: Calculate the atom localization energies $A_\mu^\oplus$ for the conjugate acids of the alcohols shown below, and compare the calculated quantities with the experimentally determined 'pK' values:

| 'pK' | -22 to 27 | -13 | -7 |

Compare the resulting regression with that of the benzologous tropylium cations [12.10] and discuss the difference.

Using the values from the HMO Tables (Vol. 3), the atom localization energies are calculated as follows:

Benzyl cation:

$$A_1^\oplus = E_\pi \text{(Benzene)} - E_\pi \text{(Benzyl cation)}$$
$$= (6\,\alpha + 8.000\,\beta) - (6\,\alpha + 8.721\,\beta) = -0.721\,\beta$$
$$a_1^\oplus = 0.721$$

Diphenylmethyl cation:

$$A_1^\oplus = 2 \cdot E_\pi \text{(Benzene)} - E_\pi \text{(Diphenylmethyl cation)}$$
$$= 2(6\,\alpha + 8.000\,\beta) - (12\,\alpha + 17.301\,\beta) = -1.301\,\beta$$
$$a_1^\oplus = 1.301$$

Triphenylmethyl cation:

$$A_1^\oplus = 3 \cdot E_\pi \text{(Benzene)} - E_\pi \text{(Triphenylmethyl cation)}$$
$$= 3(6\,\alpha + 8.000\,\beta) - (18\,\alpha + 25.800\,\beta) = -1.800\,\beta$$
$$a_1^\oplus = 1.800$$

A graphic representation, which also shows the regression for the benzologous tropylium cations [12.10], indicated by the dashed line, has the following appearance:

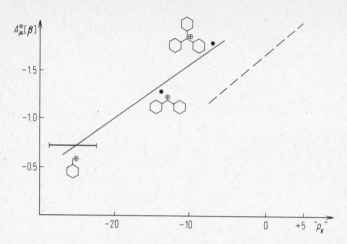

The points corresponding to the three phenylmethyl carbonium ions lie on a line which is displaced by about 0.5 β units along the ordinate relative to that for the benzologous tropylium cations. This is because the HMO model overemphasizes the electron delocalization in the phenylmethyl carbonium ions, while the cyclic electron delocalization in the benzologous tropylium cations is rendered approximately correctly. As can easily be demonstrated, a reduction of the resonance integral between the methyl carbon and the phenyl ring would markedly reduce the atom localization energies.

Problem 12.20: The very low basicity of benzene is not amenable to direct measurement. Starting with regression [12.12], calculate the ΔpK value of benzene relative to that of naphthalene.

The data in Table (12/53) lead to the following relation for the regression line in [12.12]:

$$a_\mu^\ominus = a + b\,\Delta p_K$$
$$y = a + b\,x$$

$T_x = 27.6$	$T_y = 12.841$
$\bar{x} = 4.6$	$\bar{y} = 2.140167$
$\sum_i x_i^2 = 212.22$	
$S_{xx} = 85.26$	
$\sum_i x_i y_i = 55.7448$	
$S_{xy} = -3.3238$	

$$b = \frac{S_{xy}}{S_{xx}} = -0.03898$$

$$a = \bar{y} - b\bar{x} = 2.3195$$

$$a_{\mu}^{\circ} = 2.3195 - 0.03898\,\Delta pK$$

The atom localization energy of benzene is

$$a_{\mu}^{\circ}\,(\text{Benzene}) = X_{\pi}\,(\text{Benzene}) - X_{\pi}\,(\text{Pentadienyl cation})$$
$$= 8.000 - 5.464 = 2.536$$

Substitution in the regression leads to the following ΔpK value of benzene relative to naphthalene:

$$2.536 = 2.3195 - 0.03898\,\Delta pK \quad ; \quad \Delta pK = -5.6$$

Problem 12.21: Which of the isomeric conjugate acids of azulene exists in equilibrium with the neutral hydrocarbon in an acid solution? How high is the basicity of azulene relative to that of the isomeric naphthalene?

The data of the HMO Tables (Vol. 3) afford the atom localization energies for protonation of azulene as:

$X_{\pi} = 13.364$

Coefficient of atom localization energies	Cations of residual system	X_{π}
$a_1^{\oplus} = 1.925$	⑦$-K_2^{\oplus}$	11.439
$a_2^{\oplus} = 2.362$	⑦$\big\langle^{\oplus}$	11.002
$a_4^{\oplus} = 2.552$	⑤$-K_4^{\oplus}$	10.812
$a_5^{\oplus} = 2.341$	⑤$-K_3^{\oplus}$	11.023
$a_6^{\oplus} = 2.730$	⑤$\big\langle^{K_2^{\oplus}}_{K_2}$	10.634

The azulenium cation with the methylene group in position 1

is clearly the most stable of the five isomeric conjugate acids.

Based on the regression from Problem 12.20

$$a_\mu^\circ = 2.3195 - 0.03898\,\Delta pK$$

the basicity of azulene, relative to that of naphthalene, is given by the value $\Delta pK = +10.1$. Hence azulene is an extremely basic hydrocarbon, which is known to exist as the 1-azulenium cation in dilute mineral acids.

The second most stable conjugate acid with the methylene group in position 5 would display a value of $\Delta pK = -0.5$ relative to naphthalene and therefore does not participate in an acid-base equilibrium.

Problem 12.22:   Calculate the relative 'pK' value of cycloheptatriene:

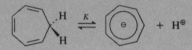

While discussing the *Hückel* rules [5.5] it was shown that the bonding molecular orbitals of the stable cycloheptatrienylium cation are occupied by a total of six electrons. The cycloheptatrienylium anion consequently contains two electrons in the degenerate lowest antibonding molecular orbitals.

$$Z_\pi = 6 \qquad\qquad Z_\pi = 8$$

On deprotonation of cycloheptatriene two electrons must therefore be promoted into the antibonding molecular orbitals of the 7-perimeter, leading to the qualitative prediction that cycloheptatriene must be a relatively weak acid. The atom localization energy is calculated according to (12/52) as:

$$A_\mu^\ominus \left(\bigcirc_\ominus\right) = E_\pi\left(\wedge\wedge\wedge\right) + 2a - E_\pi\left(\bigcirc_\ominus\right)$$

$$= (6a + 6.988\beta) + 2a - (8a + 5.604\beta) = 1.384\beta$$

The atom localization energy of the cycloheptatrienylium anion cannot be compared with the corresponding atom localization energy for the protonation of neutral hydrocarbons, since the *Coulomb* interaction between the anion and an entering proton is neglected. Based on the regression [12.13] for acidic hydrocarbons a "pK" value of 27 would result for cycloheptatriene.

In conclusion, it should also be noted that seven equivalent resonance structures can be drawn for both the cation and the anion. It would be erroneous, however, to attribute a high resonance energy and consequent special stability to the cycloheptatrienylium anion on this basis.

Problem 12.23: Which side of the prototropic equilibria (a) and (b) is favoured?

The two prototropic equilibria formally proceed via an anionic intermediate.

Neglecting changes in the σ-bonds and strain energies, the equilibria between the hydrocarbons are determined solely by changes in the total π-electron energies. These are calculated from the E_π values of the residual systems as follows:

$$E_\pi = 4\,\alpha + 4.000\,\beta \qquad E_\pi = 4\,\alpha + 4.962\,\beta$$

$$\Delta E_\pi = 0.962\,\beta$$

(b)

$$E_\pi = 8\alpha + \underbrace{10.000\,\beta \qquad\qquad E_\pi = 8\alpha + 10.424\,\beta}_{\Delta E_\pi = 0.424\,\beta}$$

Both equilibria − of which (a) is of course hypothetical − thus lie on the right-hand side.

12.5. Reduction of Aromatic Hydrocarbons

Problem 12.24: Calculate the free valences F_μ of the naphthalene radical anion, and compare them with those of naphthalene.

The bond orders $p_{\mu\nu}^\ominus$ of the naphthalene radical anion are calculated according to

$$p_{\mu\nu}^\ominus = \sum_J b_J c_{J\mu} c_{J\nu}$$

with the occupation numbers

$$b_1 = \text{........} = b_5 = 2 \; ; \; b_6 = 1 \; ; \; b_7 = \text{........} = b_{10} = 0 \, .$$

Based on the bond orders of the neutral molecule we obtain the relation

$$p_{\mu\nu}^\ominus = p_{\mu\nu} + c_{6\mu} c_{6\nu}$$

Starting from the data of the HMO Table ⑥⑥ (Vol. 3), we get

$$
\begin{aligned}
p_{12} &= p_{34} = p_{56} = p_{78} &&= 0.614 \\
p_{23} &= p_{67} &&= 0.672 \\
p_{19} &= p_{4,10} = p_{5,10} = p_{89} &&= 0.555 \\
p_{9,10} & &&= 0.518
\end{aligned}
$$

The free valences of the radical anion are calculated from

$$F_\mu^\ominus = \sqrt{3} - \sum_\rho p_{\mu\rho}^\ominus$$

in which summation is to be performed only over those centers ρ which are linked to center μ. We find:

$$F_1^\ominus = F_4^\ominus = F_5^\ominus = F_8^\ominus = 0.563$$
$$F_2^\ominus = F_3^\ominus = F_6^\ominus = F_7^\ominus = 0.446$$
$$F_9^\ominus = F_{10}^\ominus = 0.104$$

The values for the neutral molecule are taken from the HMO Tables (Vol. 3):

$$F_1 = F_4 = F_5 = F_8 = 0.453$$
$$F_2 = F_3 = F_6 = F_7 = 0.404$$
$$F_9 = F_{10} = 0.104$$

Comparison of $F_\mu^\ominus$ and F_μ indicates that the discrimination between centers 1 and 2 is greater in the radical anion than in the neutral molecule, so that reactions of type (12/61) occur exclusively at position 1. Furthermore, this center also has a higher charge order in the radical anion since $|c_{61}| > |c_{62}|$. The free valences at positions 9 and 10 remain unchanged, since the coefficients c_{69} and $c_{6,10}$ are equal to zero.

Problem 12.25: Which radical is preferentially formed in the second step of the polarographic reduction of anthracene and of phenanthrene?

$$R \underset{}{\overset{e^\ominus}{\rightleftarrows}} \cdot R^\ominus \overset{H^\oplus}{\rightarrow} \cdot RH$$

To answer the question posed, we calculate the charge orders and the free valences (cf. Problem 12.24) of the radical anions of anthracene and phenanthrene formed in the potential-determining step.

$$q_1^\ominus = 1.096 \qquad F_1^\ominus = 0.499$$
$$q_2^\ominus = 1.048 \qquad F_2^\ominus = 0.429$$
$$q_9^\ominus = 1.193 \qquad F_9^\ominus = 0.600$$

$$q_1^\ominus = 1.115 \qquad F_1^\ominus = 0.520$$
$$q_2^\ominus = 1.001 \qquad F_2^\ominus = 0.403$$
$$q_3^\ominus = 1.099 \qquad F_3^\ominus = 0.468$$
$$q_4^\ominus = 1.054 \qquad F_4^\ominus = 0.417$$
$$q_{10}^\ominus = 1.172 \qquad F_{10}^\ominus = 0.691$$

Both the $q_\mu^\ominus$ and the $F_\mu^\ominus$ values clearly show that the radical anions of phenanthrene and anthracene accept the proton at position 9 and 10, respectively. In this way the following radicals RH are formed:

Problem 12.26: Which dihydro derivatives will be formed on polarographic reduction of anthracene and of phenanthrene?

In the preceding problem 12.25 it was shown that polarographic reduction of anthracene and of phenanthrene initially generates radicals with methylene groups in positions 9 or 10. The π-electron system of these radicals is alternant and extends over an odd number of centers, so that a nonbonding molecular orbital results in each case. Under the potential prevailing during the first step, another electron is immediately taken up:

The question of which position of the anion formed undergoes electrophilic attack by water, i.e. which dihydro derivative is formed, can be decided with the aid of the charge orders $q_\mu^\ominus$ and free valences $F_\mu^\ominus$. These values can be obtained from the HMO Tables ⑥——⑥ and ⑥——⑥ (Vol. 3). In the case of phenanthrene (localization 10), the charge orders have to be corrected for the additional occupation of the nonbonding molecular orbital by a further electron. On the other hand, the free valences $F_\mu^\ominus$ are independent of the number of electrons in the nonbonding molecular orbital, since the coefficients of the unstarred set always have the value zero. It should also be noted that the numbering of the ⑥——⑥ system in the HMO Table (Vol. 3) differs from that chosen here. The resulting values

$$q_1^\ominus = 1.000 \qquad F_1^\ominus = 0.393$$
$$q_2^\ominus = 1.100 \qquad F_2^\ominus = 0.445$$
$$q_3^\ominus = 1.000 \qquad F_3^\ominus = 0.393$$
$$q_4^\ominus = 1.100 \qquad F_4^\ominus = 0.480$$
$$q_{10}^\ominus = 1.400 \qquad F_{10}^\ominus = 0.664$$

$$q_1^\ominus = 1.032 \qquad F_1^\ominus = 0.395$$
$$q_2^\ominus = 1.000 \qquad F_2^\ominus = 0.422$$
$$q_3^\ominus = 1.032 \qquad F_3^\ominus = 0.395$$
$$q_4^\ominus = 1.000 \qquad F_4^\ominus = 0.449$$
$$q_5^\ominus = 1.000 \qquad F_5^\ominus = 0.433$$
$$q_6^\ominus = 1.129 \qquad F_6^\ominus = 0.452$$
$$q_7^\ominus = 1.000 \qquad F_7^\ominus = 0.402$$
$$q_8^\ominus = 1.129 \qquad F_8^\ominus = 0.500$$
$$q_9^\ominus = 1.516 \qquad F_9^\ominus = 1.068$$

show that, according to both the $q_\mu^\ominus$ and the $F_\mu^\ominus$ values, electrophilic attack by water is clearly favored in position 10 of anthracene and in position 9 of phenanthrene. Consequently, the following dihydro derivatives must be formed:

The prediction agrees with experimental findings.

12.6. Substitution Reactions Involving Aromatic Hydrocarbons

Problem 12.27: Which centres will be attacked preferentially on electrophilic substitution of anthracene, phenanthrene, and azulene?

Calculation of the coefficients $a_\mu^\ominus$ of the atom localization energies $A_\mu^\ominus$ proceeds by analogy with (12/72) according to

$$a_\mu^\ominus = |\, X_\pi\,(Wheland\text{-transition state}) - X_\pi(\text{educt})\,|.$$

The following values result:

(a) Anthracene:

$$a_1^\ominus = X_\pi \left(\text{⑥⑥⑥} \right) - X_\pi \left(\text{⑥⑥}_{K_3} \right) = 19.314 - 17.083 = 2.231$$

$$a_2^\ominus = X_\pi \left(\text{⑥⑥⑥} \right) - X_\pi \left(\text{⑥⑥}_{K_2} \right) = 19.314 - 16.891 = 2.423$$

$$a_9^\ominus = X_\pi \left(\text{⑥⑥⑥} \right) - X_\pi \left(\text{⑥—⑥} \right) = 19.314 - 17.301 = 2.013$$

The electrophilic substitution proceeds preferentially at centers 9 or 10, corresponding to the lowest $a_\mu^\ominus$ value.

(b) Phenanthrene:

$$a_1^\ominus = X_\pi \left(\bigcirc \bigcirc \bigcirc \right) - X_\pi \left(\bigcirc \bigcirc K_3 \right) = 19.448 - 17.131 = 2.317$$

$$a_2^\ominus = X_\pi \left(\bigcirc \bigcirc \bigcirc \right) - X_\pi \left(\bigcirc \bigcirc K_2 \right) = 19.448 - 16.951 = 2.497$$

$$a_3^\ominus = X_\pi \left(\bigcirc \bigcirc \bigcirc \right) - X_\pi \left(\bigcirc \bigcirc^{K_2} \right) = 19.448 - 16.995 = 2.453$$

$$a_4^\ominus = X_\pi \left(\bigcirc \bigcirc \bigcirc \right) - X_\pi \left(\bigcirc \bigcirc^{K_3} \right) = 19.448 - 17.083 = 2.365$$

$$a_9^\ominus = X_\pi \left(\bigcirc \bigcirc \bigcirc \right) - X_\pi \left(\bigcirc \!-\! \bigcirc \right) = 19.448 - 17.151 = 2.297$$

As in the case of anthracene, the electrophilic substitution again proceeds preferentially at centers 9 or 10, corresponding to the lowest $a_\mu^\ominus$ value.

(c) Azulene:

$$a_1^\ominus = X_\pi \left(\text{⑤⑦} \right) - X_\pi \left(K_2\text{-⑦} \right) = 13.364 - 11.439 = 1.925$$

$$a_2^\ominus = X_\pi \left(\text{⑤⑦} \right) - X_\pi \left(\text{⑦} \right) = 13.364 - 11.002 = 2.362$$

$$a_4^\ominus = X_\pi \left(\text{⑤⑦} \right) - X_\pi \left(\text{⑤-}K_4 \right) = 13.364 - 10.812 = 2.552$$

$$a_5^\ominus = X_\pi \left(\text{⑤⑦} \right) - X_\pi \left(\text{⑤}K_3 \right) = 13.364 - 11.023 = 2.341$$

$$a_6^\ominus = X_\pi \left(\text{⑤⑦} \right) - X_\pi \left(\text{⑤}^{K_2}_{K_2} \right) = 13.364 - 10.634 = 2.730$$

In the nonalternant π-electron system of azulene, the lowest $a_\mu^\ominus$ value is found for centers 1 or 3, and consequently electrophilic substitution occurs preferentially at these centers.

Problem 12.28: Which centre is preferred in electrophilic, radical, and nucleophilic substitutions in azulene?

The atom localization energies $A_\mu^\ominus$, $A_\mu^\bullet$, and $A_\mu^\oplus$ or their coefficients $a_\mu^\ominus$, $a_\mu^\bullet$, and $a_\mu^\oplus$ are calculated according to the relations (12/72) through (12/76) from the difference of the total π-electron energies (cf. e.g., Problem 12.27). For azulene as a nonalternant π-system, the equation

$$a_\mu^\ominus = a_\mu^\bullet = a_\mu^\oplus \tag{12/77}$$

is no longer valid, since the residual system — as may be seen from the HMO Tables (Vol. 3) — does not always exhibit a nonbonding molecular orbital. For this reason, it should be pointed out that corresponding to the occupation numbers

Substitution type	Partial system	Z_π	Occupation number
electrophilic $(a_\mu^\ominus)$		8	$b_1 = b_2 = b_3 = b_4 \quad = 2$ $b_5 = b_6 = b_7 = b_8 = b_9 = 0$
radical $\quad(a_\mu^\bullet)$		9	$b_1 = b_2 = b_3 = b_4 \quad = 2$ $b_5 \qquad\qquad = 1$ $b_6 = b_7 = b_8 = b_9 \quad = 0$
nucleophilic $(a_\mu^\oplus)$		10	$b_1 = b_2 = b_3 = b_4 = b_5 = 2$ $b_6 = b_7 = b_8 = b_9 \quad = 0$

the residual systems can also contain electrons in antibonding molecular orbitals. The coefficients X_π of the total π-electron energy given in the HMO Tables of the partial systems (Vol. 3) refer in each case to the π-electron number $Z_\pi = 9$, and thus correspond to the X_π values of the partial system formed on radical substitution. Taking account of the above statements, we obtain the following coefficients a_μ of the atom localization energies:

μ	1	2	4	5	6
$a_\mu^\ominus$	1.925	2.362	2.552	2.341	2.730
$a_\mu^\bullet$	2.262	2.362	2.241	2.341	2.359
$a_\mu^\oplus$	2.600	2.362	1.930	2.341	1.988

The table shows that electrophilic attack should proceed preferentially at center 1 of azulene, but radical and nucleophilic attack are favored at center 4. This prediction is confirmed by experiment.

Problem 12.29: On the basis of qualitative molecular orbitals, discuss at which centres of pentalene electrophilic, radical, and nucleophilic substitution will occur.

Centers 1 and 2 are potential substitution sites in pentalene. The resulting partial systems R_1 and R_2 are

R_1 R_2

We require approximation values of the total π-electron energies which should be derived from qualitative molecular orbitals. The latter have already been given for pentalene in Problem 8.3 (cf. also Problem 8.7). From the coefficients x_j^0 of the qualitative orbital energies we obtain, for occupation of the molecular orbitals Ψ_1^0 to Ψ_4^0, the coefficients of the total π-electron energy as:

$$X_\pi^0 = \sum_j b_j x_j^0 = 9.8 .$$

This value is not relevant to an assessment of the relative reactivities, since it enters as a constant into all calculated atom localization energies.

The qualitative molecular orbitals for the partial systems R_1 and R_2 are to be derived according to the rules given in (8/1)–(8/6) and (8/21)–(8/23).

Ψ_J^0		N_J	Z_b	Z_a	x_J^0
Ψ_7^0		$\dfrac{1}{\sqrt{4}}$	0	3	$-1\frac{1}{2}$
Ψ_6^0		$\dfrac{1}{\sqrt{7}}$	1	6	$-1\frac{3}{7}$
Ψ_5^0		$\dfrac{1}{\sqrt{7}}$	2	5	$-\frac{6}{7}$
Ψ_4^0		$\dfrac{1}{\sqrt{7}}$	4	3	$+\frac{2}{7}$
Ψ_3^0		$\dfrac{1}{\sqrt{4}}$	2	1	$+\frac{1}{2}$
Ψ_2^0		$\dfrac{1}{\sqrt{5}}$	3	0	$+1\frac{1}{5}$
Ψ_1^0		$\dfrac{1}{\sqrt{7}}$	7	0	$+2$

Ψ_J^0		N_J	Z_b	Z_a	x_J^0
Ψ_7^0		$\dfrac{1}{\sqrt{6}}$	0	5	$-1\dfrac{2}{3}$
Ψ_6^0		$\dfrac{1}{\sqrt{7}}$	1	6	$-1\dfrac{3}{7}$
Ψ_5^0		$\dfrac{1}{\sqrt{5}}$	1	2	$-\dfrac{2}{5}$
Ψ_4^0		$\dfrac{1}{\sqrt{4}}$	0	0	0
Ψ_3^0		$\dfrac{1}{\sqrt{7}}$	5	2	$+\dfrac{6}{7}$
Ψ_2^0		$\dfrac{1}{\sqrt{6}}$	4	1	$+1$
Ψ_1^0		$\dfrac{1}{\sqrt{7}}$	7	0	$+2$

Solution of the problem proceeds analogously to that of Problem 12.28. The desired coefficients a_μ of the atom localization energies are obtained via the X_π values, which are calculated approximately from the above qualitative orbital energy coefficients x_j^0. Depending upon the type of substitution reaction, the following occupation numbers result for the partial systems:

Electrophilic attack: $b_1 = b_2 = b_3 = 2$; $b_4 = b_5 = b_6 = b_7 = 0$
Radical attack: $b_1 = b_2 = b_3 = 2$; $b_4 = 1$; $b_5 = b_6 = b_7 = 0$
Nucleophilic attack: $b_1 = b_2 = b_3 = b_4 = 2$; $b_5 = b_6 = b_7 = 0$

From the resulting qualitative X_π values

$$X_\pi^\ominus = 7.4$$
$$X_\pi^\bullet = 7.7$$
$$X_\pi^\oplus = 8.0$$

R_1

$$X_\pi^\ominus = 7.7$$
$$X_\pi^\bullet = 7.7$$
$$X_\pi^\oplus = 7.7$$

R_2

the qualitative coefficients of the atom localization energies are calculated as:

$$a_1^\ominus = 2.4 \qquad a_2^\ominus = 2.1$$
$$a_1^\bullet = 2.1 \qquad a_2^\bullet = 2.1$$
$$a_1^\oplus = 1.8 \qquad a_2^\oplus = 2.1$$

These show that electrophilic substitution preferentially occurs at position 2, whereas nucleophilic attack should proceed at position 1. Both centers appear to be equivalent with respect to radical attack.

The exact HMO coefficients of the atom localization energies are given for comparison:

$$a_1^\ominus = 2.380 \qquad a_2^\ominus = 2.027$$
$$a_1^\bullet = 1.959 \qquad a_2^\bullet = 2.027$$
$$a_1^\oplus = 1.538 \qquad a_2^\oplus = 2.027$$

These are seen to agree well with the approximate values.

Problem 12.30: Calculate the reactivity numbers N_μ for benzene, anthracene, and phenanthrene, and compare them with the localization energies. A relationship exists between the coefficients a_μ of the atom localization energies A_μ and the reactivity numbers N_μ which is described by the regression line

$$a_\mu = k_1 + k_2 N_2.$$

Calculate the value of the parameters k_1 and k_2 which allow optimal prediction of the values a_μ starting from the N_μ values.

The reactivity numbers are calculated according to

$$N_\mu = 2 \sum_\rho c_{nb,\rho}. \qquad (12/80)$$

It is necessary to first determine the coefficients of the nonbonding molecular orbitals of the partial systems according to (5/29)–(5/33):

$$N_1 = \frac{4}{\sqrt{3}} = 2.309$$

$$N_1 = \frac{8}{\sqrt{26}} = 1.569$$

$$N_2 = \frac{8}{\sqrt{18}} = 1.886$$

$$N_3 = \frac{4}{\sqrt{10}} = 1.265$$

$$N_1 = \frac{10}{\sqrt{29}} = 1.857$$

$$N_2 = \frac{10}{\sqrt{21}} = 2.182$$

$$N_3 = \frac{10}{\sqrt{24}} = 2.041$$

$$N_4 = \frac{10}{\sqrt{26}} = 1.961$$

$$N_{10} = \frac{10}{\sqrt{31}} = 1.796$$

In the following table, the reactivity numbers thus determined are compared with the coefficients a_μ of the atom localization energies obtained (cf. Problem 12.27) from the differences of the total π-electron energies of the hydrocarbons and the corresponding partial systems (HMO Tables: Vol. 3). Because of the alternance of the system

$$a_\mu = a_\mu^\oplus = a_\mu^\bullet = a_\mu^\ominus \qquad (12/77)$$

Compound	μ	$a_\mu \equiv y_i$	$N_\mu \equiv x_i$
Benzene	1	2.536	2.309
Anthracene	1	2.231	1.569
	2	2.423	1.886
	9	2.013	1.265
Phenanthrene	1	2.317	1.857
	2	2.497	2.182
	3	2.453	2.041
	4	2.365	1.961
	10	2.297	1.796

The parameters of the regression

$$y = a + bx$$
$$a_\mu = K_1 + K_2 N_\mu$$

are calculated as follows according to (9/4)–(9/13):

$$T_x = 16.866 \qquad\qquad T_y = 21.132$$

$$\bar{x} = 1.874 \qquad\qquad \bar{y} = 2.348$$

$$\sum_i x_i^2 = 32.396854$$

$$S_{xx} = 0.789970$$

$$\sum_i x_i y_i = 39.993159$$

$$S_{xy} = 0.391791$$

$$b = 0.495957$$

$$a = 1.418577$$

$$a_\mu = 1.419 + 0.496\, N_\mu$$

Problem 12.31: What directing effect would be expected for an alkyl group in position 1 and in position 2 of naphthalene?

The differing reactivities of the α and β positions of naphthalene are reflected in the HMO model by the differing atom localization energies $a_\alpha = 2.299 < a_\beta = 2.480$. The preference for the α position by 0.181 β-units does not disappear on alkyl substitution, provided that steric effects can be excluded.

In order to describe α-attack of an electrophilic, radical, or nucleophilic reagent in the framework of the HMO approximation, we require the charge orders in the *Wheland* transition state under consideration. The corresponding values have been calculated in Problem 5.3 and amount to:

electrophilic attack   radical attack   nucleophilic attack

The corresponding atom localization energies are displaced to more positive values by alkylation as a result of the positive perturbation $\delta\alpha_\mu$

$$\delta A_\mu = q_\mu \cdot \delta\alpha_\mu$$
$$\delta a_\mu = q_\mu \cdot h_\mu \; ; \; (\delta\alpha_\mu = h_\mu \beta)$$

Thus the preferred *Wheland* transition state is that which exhibits the smallest perturbation δa_μ, i.e. that which carries the alkyl group at the position of lowest charge order q_μ.

Accordingly, in the case of electrophilic attack the following sequence is obtained for 1-alkylnaphthalene:

$$\text{(structure, position 4)} \quad < \quad \text{(structure, position 5)} \quad < \quad \text{(structure, position 8)}$$

It follows that the preferential site of attack will be position 4. The following sequence is obtained for 2-alkylnaphthalene

$$\text{(structure, position 1)} \quad < \quad \text{(structure, position 8)} \quad < \quad \text{(structure, position 4)} \quad \approx \quad \text{(structure, position 5)}$$

with preference for position 1.

All charge orders q_μ are the same in the *Wheland* transition state of radical substitution and no discrimination would therefore be expected between the different α-positions. It should be noted, however, that many radical reactions (e.g. with $^\cdot CCl_3$) assume electrophilic or nucleophilic character in their final phase, owing to formation of a polar σ-bond. For this reason alkyl groups are found experimentally to exert a directing influence in such cases.

Nucleophilic substitution becomes difficult in the absence of suitable leaving groups, especially in alkyl-substituted naphthalenes. Nevertheless, the sequence of *Wheland* transition states, which would result according to the above treatment, is given for the sake of illustration;

$$\text{(structure, position 8)} \quad < \quad \text{(structure, position 5)} \quad < \quad \text{(structure, position 4)}$$

$$\text{(structure, position 4)} \quad \approx \quad \text{(structure, position 5)} \quad < \quad \text{(structure, position 8)} \quad < \quad \text{(structure, position 1)}$$

As expected, the predictions for nucleophilic attack within the framework of the model chosen are in opposite sequence to those for electrophilic substitution.

Problem 12.32: How will the electrophilic substitution of benzene be influenced by a substituent Y which introduces a negative perturbation $\delta \alpha_\rho$?

Introduction of a negative perturbation $\delta\alpha_\rho$ into the formula for electrophilic attack on benzene

$$\delta A_\rho^\circ = (q_\rho^T - q_\rho^E)\,\delta\alpha_\rho \qquad (12/86)$$

changes the sign of the terms $\delta A_\rho^\ominus$ given in (12/87):

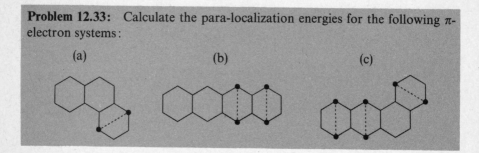

$$\delta A_\rho^\circ = 0.333\,\delta\alpha_\rho \qquad\qquad \delta A_\rho^\circ = 0 \qquad (12/87)$$

The *Wheland* transition state for the attack in the ortho- or para-position to the acceptor substituent A then lies above that for attack in the meta position. Substitution in the meta position is therefore preferred. In conclusion, it can be shown that donor substituents such as alkyl groups enhance the rate of electrophilic substitution in the ortho and para-positions relative to that in substituted benzene because the transition state is lowered. In contrast, acceptor substituents lower the rate of electrophilic substitution.

12.7. *Diels/Alder* Additions

Problem 12.33: Calculate the para-localization energies for the following π-electron systems:

(a)   (b)   (c)

The paralocalization energies of the π-electron systems (a), (b), and (c) are calculated by analogy with (12/89) as follows:

(a) Phenanthrene:

$$P_{1,4} = E_\pi\left(\;\bigcirc\bigcirc\; + \; \| \;\right) + 2\alpha - E_\pi\left(\;\text{phenanthrene}\;\right) = -3.765\beta$$

Comparison of the value found with the paralocalization energy $P_{9,10} = -3.114\,\beta$ of anthracene shows that, in agreement with experiment, the *Diels/Alder* reaction proceeds more readily with anthracene.

(b) Tetracene:

$$P_{1.4} = E_\pi\left(+ \| \right) + 2\alpha - E_\pi\left(\right)$$

$$= 18\alpha + 21.314\beta - E_\pi\left(\right)$$

$$P_{5.12} = E_\pi\left(+ \right) + 2\alpha - E_\pi\left(\right)$$

$$= 18\alpha + 21.683\beta - E_\pi\left(\right)$$

(c) 1,2-Benzanthracene:

$$P_{1.4} = E_\pi\left(+ \| \right) + 2\alpha - E_\pi\left(\right)$$

$$= 18\alpha + 21.314\beta - E_\pi\left(\right)$$

$$P_{7.12} = E_\pi \left(\bigcirc + \bigcirc\bigcirc \right) + 2\alpha - E_\pi \left(\text{[polycyclic structure]} \right)$$

$$= 18\alpha + 21.683\beta - E_\pi \left(\text{[polycyclic structure]} \right)$$

$$P_{8.11} = E_\pi \left(\| + \text{[polycyclic structure]} \right) + 2\alpha - E_\pi \left(\text{[polycyclic structure]} \right)$$

$$= 18\alpha + 21.448\beta \; E_\pi \left(\text{[polycyclic structure]} \right)$$

Even if the total π-electron energies of systems (b) and (c) are unknow, it may still be concluded from the calculated values that the *Diels/Alder* reaction occurs preferentially at positions 5/12 of tetracene and at positions 7/12 of 1,2-benzanthracene.

The total π-electron energies of tetracene and 1,2-benzanthracene are

$$E_\pi \left(\text{[tetracene structure]} \right) = 18\alpha + 24.930\beta$$

$$E_\pi \left(\text{[1,2-benzanthracene structure]} \right) = 18\alpha + 25.101\beta$$

from which the paralocalization energies are found to be

$$P_{1,4} = -3.616\,\beta \qquad P_{1,4} = -3.787\,\beta$$
$$P_{5,12} = -3.247\,\beta \qquad P_{7,12} = -3.418\,\beta$$
$$P_{8,11} = -3.653\,\beta$$

Thus it is seen that the *Diels/Alder* reaction should proceed more readily with tetracene than with 1,2-benzanthracene.

12.8. Reactions with σ/π-Conversion

Problem 12.34: Use a correlation diagram to explain why the methyl cation $CH_3^\oplus$ is (almost) planar, and the methyl anion $CH_3^\ominus$ is pyramidal.

In order to set up a qualitative correlation diagram we consider the two extreme cases:

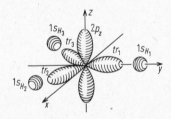

D_{3h} C_{3v}

One of the simplest ways of deriving qualitative correlation diagrams is the following:

Starting from the system of symmetry D_{3h} we hybridize the $2s$-, $2p_x$-, and $2p_y$-atomic orbitals of the carbon according to (2/30) to give the trigonal molecular orbitals tr_1, tr_2, and tr_3:

Combination with the $1s$-atomic orbitals of the hydrogen atoms furnishes the three CH-σ-bond orbitals:

$$\sigma_1 = \lambda\, tr_1 + \eta\, 1s_{H1} \approx \frac{1}{\sqrt{2}}\,(tr_1 + 1s_{H1})$$

$$\sigma_2 = \lambda\, tr_2 + \eta\, 1s_{H2} \approx \frac{1}{\sqrt{2}}\,(tr_2 + 1s_{H2})$$

$$\sigma_3 = \lambda\, tr_3 + \eta\, 1s_{H3} \approx \frac{1}{\sqrt{2}}\,(tr_3 + 1s_{H3})$$

The carbon $2p_z$ atomic orbital is left over as the fourth orbital. For symmetry reasons, the three σ-bond orbitals always have the same nergy E_σ, which lies lower than that of the carbon $2p_z$ atomic orbital. On introduction of an interaction B between the σ-bond orbitals according to (10/62) through (10/68), then starting from the linear combination

$$\Psi = c_1\,\sigma_1 + c_2\,\sigma_2 + c_3\,\sigma_3$$

the resulting secular determinant is

$$\left\| \begin{array}{ccc} E_\sigma - E & B & B \\ B & E_\sigma - E & B \\ B & B & E_\sigma - E \end{array} \right\| = 0,$$

whose solutions

$$E_1 = E_\sigma + 2B \quad ; \quad \Psi_1 = \frac{1}{\sqrt{3}}\,(\sigma_1 + \sigma_2 + \sigma_3)$$

$$E_2 = E_\sigma - B \quad ; \quad \Psi_2 = \frac{1}{\sqrt{2}}\,(\sigma_1 - \sigma_2)$$

$$E_3 = E_\sigma - B \quad ; \quad \Psi_3 = \frac{1}{\sqrt{6}}\,(\sigma_1 + \sigma_2 - 2\sigma_3)$$

lead to the following energy level scheme:

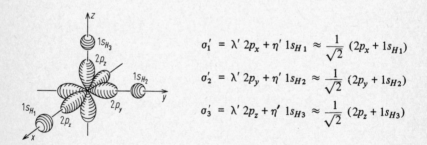

For the pyramidal arrangement of C_{3v} symmetry, we start from the $2p_x$-, $2p_y$-, and $2p_z$-atomic orbitals of the nonhybridized carbon and obtain

$$\sigma_1' = \lambda'\,2p_x + \eta'\,1s_{H1} \approx \frac{1}{\sqrt{2}}\,(2p_x + 1s_{H1})$$

$$\sigma_2' = \lambda'\,2p_y + \eta'\,1s_{H2} \approx \frac{1}{\sqrt{2}}\,(2p_y + 1s_{H2})$$

$$\sigma_3' = \lambda'\,2p_z + \eta'\,1s_{H3} \approx \frac{1}{\sqrt{2}}\,(2p_z + 1s_{H3})$$

In this case the fourth orbital is the carbon $2s$-atomic orbital, which lies lower than the $2p_z$-atomic orbital of the D_{3h} arrangement. Introduction of an interaction B' between the σ-bond orbitals would again lead to an analogous splitting.

$$E_1' = E_\sigma' + 2B' \quad ; \quad \Psi_1' = \frac{1}{\sqrt{3}}\,(\sigma_1' + \sigma_2' + \sigma_3')$$

$$E_2' = E_\sigma' - B' \quad ; \quad \Psi_2' = \frac{1}{\sqrt{2}}\,(\sigma_1' - \sigma_2')$$

$$E_3' = E_\sigma' - B' \quad ; \quad \Psi_3' = \frac{1}{\sqrt{6}}\,(\sigma_1' + \sigma_2' - 2\sigma_3')$$

A σ-bond between a trigonal carbon atomic orbital and a $1s$-hydrogen atomic orbital is "better" than a σ-bond of type $C(2p)/H(1s)$ (cf. [2.18]). For this reason, E_σ' is lower-lying than E_σ. On the other hand, the interaction B' is greater in magnitude than B because of the closer proximity of the σ'-bond orbitals. In the following approach this is immaterial, since all three molecular orbitals are occupied by two electrons in both the methyl anion and the methyl cation. Thus, in analogy to [10.16], the energetic mean (*) of the three molecular orbitals remains the same in each case.

Hence the correlation diagram is:

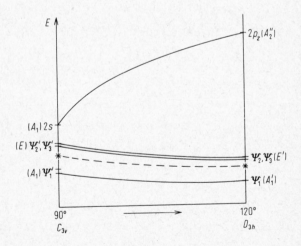

The correlation diagram reveals that, for occupation with six electrons, the D_{3h} arrangement is favored and the methyl cation should thus be planar. With the same geometry the two additional electrons in the methyl anion must occupy the $2p_z$-atomic orbital. As the diagram shows, however, it is more advantageous for the system to assume a pyramidal arrangement (C_{3v}), since the lone pair can then drop into the energetically lower-lying $2s$-atomic orbital, until the resulting gain in energy is compensated by the raising of the σ-molecular orbitals.

Problem 12.35: Construct the molecular orbital correlation diagram for the disrotatory and the conrotatory ring opening of cyclohexadiene to cis-hexatriene:

The solution of this problem proceeds in complete analogy to the treatment of the ring opening of cyclobutene [12.28] through [12.30]. The only difference lies in the fact that the number of molecular orbitals to be considered is increased by two.

The geometry of cyclohexadiene and that of the associated hexatriene is idealized as belonging to group C_{2v}. According to the relevant character tables (Vol. 1, p.268) the individual molecular orbitals behave as follows with respect to C_2 or C_s:

Molecular orbital	$C_2(z)$	C_2 irreducible representation	σ_{xz}	C_s irreducible representation
σ^*	as	B	as	A''
π_2^*	s	A	as	A''
π_1^*	as	B	s	A'
π_1	s	A	as	A''
π_2	as	B	s	A'
σ	s	A	s	A'

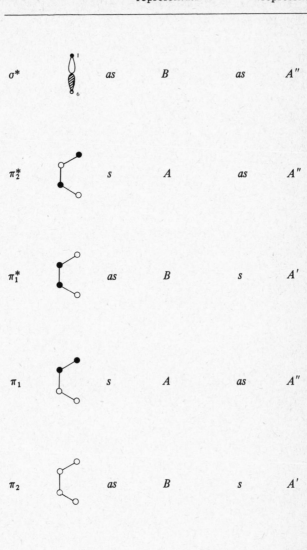

Molecular orbital		$C_2(z)$	C_2 irreducible representation	σ_{xz}	C_s irreducible representation
Ψ_6		s	A	as	A"
Ψ_5		as	B	s	A'
Ψ_4		s	A	as	A"
Ψ_3		as	B	s	A'
Ψ_2		s	A	as	A"
Ψ_1		as	B	s	A'

Observing the non-crossing rule, the following qualitative molecular orbital correlation diagrams for con- and disrotatory ring opening of cyclohexadiene can be drawn with the aid of the above tables. In these diagrams, it is assumed that the σ-orbital in cyclohexadiene lies below the π-orbitals, and that the σ^*-orbital lies above the π^*-orbitals.

Conrotatory ring opening (C_2):

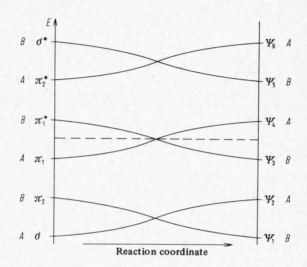

Disrotatory ring opening (C_s):

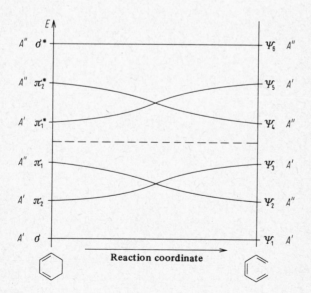

424

Starting from the molecular orbital correlation diagrams of Problem 12.35, the associated configuration correlation diagrams are obtained in the following way: the ground state configurations and the necessary excited state configurations are formed by analogy with (12/100)–(12/101) by occupation of the relevant molecular orbitals with electrons. The specific irreducible representations to which the individual configurations belong are obtained by "multiplication" of the irreducible representations of the occupied molecular orbitals.

In the present case we consider, for the educt cyclohexadiene and the product hexatriene, the ground state configuration Γ and the three singly excited configurations I, II, and III, which we assume to be the most favorable energetically:

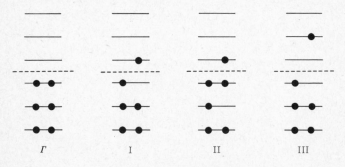

Γ I   II   III

On conrotatory (C_2) and disrotatory (C_s) rearrangement, these configurations transform into the following configurations of the corresponding compound

$$\bigcirc \quad \longrightarrow \quad \mathsf{C}$$

C_2

III	$(\sigma)^2 (\pi_2)^2 (\pi_1)^1 (\pi_2^*)^1$	$\xrightarrow{A}$	$(\Psi_1)^2 (\Psi_2)^2 (\Psi_4)^1 (\Psi_6)^1$		
II	$(\sigma)^2 (\pi_2)^1 (\pi_1)^2 (\pi_1^*)^1$	$\xrightarrow{A}$	$(\Psi_1)^1 (\Psi_2)^2 (\Psi_3)^1 (\Psi_4)^2$		
I	$(\sigma)^2 (\pi_2)^2 (\pi_1)^1 (\pi_1^*)^1$	$\xrightarrow{B}$	$(\Psi_1)^2 (\Psi_2)^2 (\Psi_3)^1 (\Psi_4)^1$	I
Γ	$(\sigma)^2 (\pi_2)^2 (\pi_1)^2$	$\xrightarrow{A}$	$(\Psi_1)^2 (\Psi_2)^2 (\Psi_4)^2$	
	$(\sigma)^2 (\pi_2)^2 (\pi_1^*)^1 (\sigma^*)^1$	$\xleftarrow{A}$	$(\Psi_1)^2 (\Psi_2)^2 (\Psi_3)^1 (\Psi_5)^1$	III
	$(\sigma)^1 (\pi_2)^2 (\pi_1)^1 (\pi_1^*)^2$	$\xleftarrow{A}$	$(\Psi_1)^2 (\Psi_2)^1 (\Psi_3)^2 (\Psi_4)^1$	II
	$(\sigma)^2 (\pi_2)^2 (\pi_1^*)^2$	$\xleftarrow{A}$	$(\Psi_1)^2 (\Psi_2)^2 (\Psi_3)^2$	Γ

		C_s		
III	$(\sigma)^2 (\pi_2)^2 (\pi_1)^1 (\pi_2^*)^1$	$\xrightarrow{A'}$	$(\Psi_1)^2 (\Psi_2)^1 (\Psi_3)^2 (\Psi_4)^1$	II
II	$(\sigma)^2 (\pi_2)^1 (\pi_1)^2 (\pi_1^*)^1$	$\xrightarrow{A'}$	$(\Psi_1)^2 (\Psi_2)^2 (\Psi_3)^1 (\Psi_5)^1$	III
I	$(\sigma)^2 (\pi_2)^2 (\pi_1)^1 (\pi_1^*)^1$	$\xrightarrow{A''}$	$(\Psi_1)^2 (\Psi_2)^1 (\Psi_3)^2 (\Psi_5)^1$	
Γ	$(\sigma)^2 (\pi_2)^2 (\pi_1)^2$	$\xrightarrow{A'}$	$(\Psi_1)^2 (\Psi_2)^2 (\Psi_3)^2$	Γ
	$(\sigma)^2 (\pi_2)^1 (\pi_1)^2 (\pi_2^*)^1$	$\xleftarrow{A''}$	$(\Psi_1)^2 (\Psi_2)^2 (\Psi_3)^1 (\Psi_4)^1$	I

The configurations of cyclohexadiene and hexatriene assumed to have the lowest energies are seen to transform into very high energy configurations of the other extreme. Observing the non-crossing rule, we thus obtain the qualitative configuration correlation diagram for conrotatory and disrotatory ring opening of cyclohexadiene:

Conrotatory ring opening (C_2):

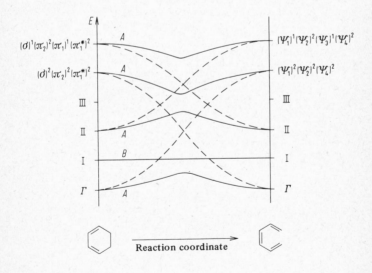

Disrotatory ring opening (C_s):

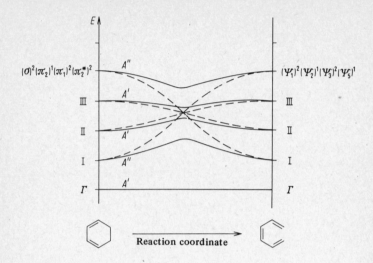

Thermal ring opening of cyclohexadiene is therefore disrotatory, and photochemical ring opening is conrotatory.

Index

430